PU

Edi

COI

VOLUME I

It is just half a century since *Come Hither* first appeared – yet it still holds its place as, surely, the most magically haunting anthology of poetry ever made in the English language. Imagine a romantic path winding without a break through some very wild landscape, from our oldest ballads and nursery rhymes to the works of C. S. Lewis and Tolkien and even later storytellers of our own time. There *is* such a path, and *Come Hither* tracks its poetry. It passes through forests, mountains, whirlwinds, chasms of ice, gardens and summer meadows, and the uncharted 'land of Luthany and the region Elenore'. Along its way are phantoms, dreams, monsters, changelings, elves and angels, animals rare or homely, children of all kinds, and Prince Lucifer himself.

But *Come Hither* is more than a collection of poems. No sooner do you reach the last than a new door opens. Here, in the disguise of Notes, de la Mare adds hundreds of other verses, legends, riddles and other gossipy items. You can find, for instance, how to call up a fairy ('you may command thys fayrie to the utmost'), or why the boy Nelson chanced to the Navy, or which of the angels sings 'most wildly well', and any number of useful spells and charms. But possibly best of all is the marvellous tale which opens the book, and which is meant as guide and key to the rest. It is about a child exploring an old stone house. Some parts are easy enough: THRAE – that means Earth, and NAHUM – that's Human, for sure. But you could read this story once a year for most of your life and still not come to the end of its real mysteries or of the pathways that it offers into the poems that follow. You can enter this country anywhere yourself by opening *Come Hither*. Whatever you find will stay with you though – long after the covers are closed.

Cover design by Erik Blegvad

COME HITHER

VOLUME I

*

A COLLECTION OF
RHYMES AND POEMS
FOR THE YOUNG
OF ALL AGES

*

MADE BY
WALTER DE LA MARE

*

WOOD-ENGRAVINGS BY
DIANA BLOOMFIELD

PUFFIN BOOKS
in association with Longman Young Books

Puffin Books: a Division of Penguin Books Ltd,
Harmondsworth, Middlesex, England
Penguin Books Australia Ltd, Ringwood, Victoria, Australia

—

First published by Constable 1923
Published in Puffin Books 1973

—

This edition copyright © Alfred A. Knopf, Inc., 1957

—

Made and printed in Great Britain
by Richard Clay (The Chaucer Press), Ltd,
Bungay, Suffolk
Set in Monotype Fournier

Contents

Acknowledgements   iiv

The Story of This Book   1

Morning and May   25

Mother, Home, and Sweetheart   43

Feasts: Fairs: Beggars: Gipsies   91

Beasts of the Field: Fowls of the Air   115

Elphin, Ouph, and Fay   147

Summer: Greenwood: Solitude   167

War   199

Dance, Music, and Bells   231

Autumn Leaves: Winter Snow   255

About and Roundabout   289

Acknowledgements

FOR the use of copyright poems in this volume I have to thank – and most gratefully I do so – the following authors and publishers: Mr Martin Armstrong (and Mr Martin Secker); Mr Lascelles Abercrombie (and Mr John Lane); Mr Edmund Blunden (and Mr Richard Cobden-Sanderson); Mr H. H. Bashford (Messrs Harrap & Company and Messrs Houghton, Mifflin & Company); Mrs Bunston de Bary; Mr Laurence Binyon (and Messrs. Elkin Mathews); Mr Hilaire Belloc (and Messrs Duckworth & Company); Mr Robert Bridges (and Mr John Murray); Mr Gordon Bottomley; Mr Padraic Colum (Messrs Maunsell & Roberts Ltd, and Messrs the Macmillan Company); Mr William H. Davies (Mr Jonathan Cape and Mr Alfred A. Knopf); the executors of the late Lord de Tabley; Mr C. M. Doughty; Mr Edward L. Davison (and Messrs G. Bell & Sons); Mr Charles Dalmon (and Messrs Methuen & Company); Mr John Drinkwater (Messrs Sidgwick & Jackson, and Messrs Houghton, Mifflin & Company); Mr Vivian Locke Ellis; Mr Robert Frost (and Messrs Harcourt, Brace & Company); Mr John Freeman; Miss Eleanor Farjeon (Messrs Selwyn & Blount, Messrs J. M. Dent & Sons, and Messrs E. P. Dutton & Company); Mrs Furse (and Messrs Constable & Company); Mr Robert Graves; the Viscountess Grey; Mr Edmund Gosse; Mr Wilfrid Gibson (Messrs Elkin Mathews, and Messrs Macmillan & Company); Mr Crosbie Garstin (and Messrs Sidgwick & Jackson); Mr Thomas Hardy (and Messrs Macmillan & Company); Mr Ralph Hodgson (and Messrs Macmillan & Company); Miss Gwen John; Mr Rudyard Kipling (Messrs Macmillan & Company, and Messrs Doubleday, Page & Company); Mr Sidney Royse Lysaght (and Messrs Macmillan & Company); Mr Harold Monro; Mr John Masefield; Mrs Manning-Sanders (and Messrs the Hogarth Press); Mr T. Sturge Moore (and Mr Grant Richards); Miss Charlotte Mew (Mr Harold Monro and Messrs the Macmillan Company); Miss Viola Meynell; Sir Henry Newbolt; Mr Alfred Noyes (and Messrs William Blackwood & Sons); Mr Seumas O'Sullivan (Messrs Maunsell & Roberts); Mr Conal O'Riordan; Mr F. J. Patmore; Miss Madeleine Caron Rock; Miss Lizette Woodworth Reese (and Mr Thomas B. Mosher); Mr James Stephens (Messrs Maunsell & Roberts and Messrs the Macmillan Company); Mr Siegfried Sassoon; Miss Edith Sitwell (and Mr B. H. Blackwell); Mr Edward Shanks (and Messrs Collins,

ACKNOWLEDGEMENTS

Sons & Company); Mr J. C. Squire (and Messrs Hodder & Stoughton); Mrs Katharine Tynan Hinkson; Mr Herbert Trench; Mr Walter J. Turner (and Messrs Sidgwick & Jackson); Miss Elinor Wylie (and Messrs Harcourt, Brace & Company); Mr Francis Brett Young (and Messrs W. Collins, Sons & Company); Mr W. B. Yeats (Messrs T. Fisher Unwin and Messrs the Macmillan Company).

It is, too, a happy privilege to have been permitted to include poems by Mrs Webb, Mr Eric Batterham, Mr Gilbert Sheldon, Mr Bernard Sleigh, Miss Elizabeth Ramal, and Mr Colin Francis which have not hitherto appeared in any other published collection.

My most grateful thanks are due also to Mr Edward Marsh (Messrs Sidgwick & Jackson and Messrs Dodd, Mead & Company) for two poems by Rupert Brooke; to Mr Clement Shorter for six poems by Emily Brontë, and a poem by Dora Sigerson Shorter; to Sir Henry Newbolt for seven poems by Mary Coleridge; to Mr Richard Cobden-Sanderson for three poems by John Clare; to Mr John Murray and to the executors of Canon Dixon for two poems; to Mrs Flecker (and Mr Martin Secker) for two poems by James Elroy Flecker; to Lady Gomme for rhymes from *Traditional Games*; to the Viscountess Grey for poems from *The White Wallet*; to Miss Antonie Meyer (and Messrs Constable & Company) for six translations by Kuno Meyer; to Mrs Meynell and to Mr Wilfrid Meynell (and Messrs Burns & Oates) for three poems; to Mr William Meredith and to Messrs Constable & Company for two poems by George Meredith; to Mrs Sharp for a poem by 'Fiona Macleod' (William Sharp); to Miss Morris, Mr S. C. Cockerell (and Messrs Longmans, Green & Company) for two poems by William Morris; to Mrs Owen for a poem by Wilfrid Owen; to Mrs C. Patmore (and Messrs G. Bell & Sons, Ltd) for two poems by Coventry Patmore; to Messrs Macmillan & Company for eight poems by Christina Rossetti; to Mr Lloyd Osbourne (Messrs Chatto & Windus and Messrs Charles Scribner's Sons) for four poems by Robert Louis Stevenson; to Mr William Heinemann for a poem by Algernon Charles Swinburne; to Miss E. Margaret Courtney Boyd for a poem by William Bell Scott; to Mrs Thomas (and Messrs Selwyn & Blount) for seven poems by Edward Thomas; to Mr Wilfrid Meynell (and Messrs Burns & Oates) for three poems by Francis Thompson; and to Messrs P. J. and A. E. Dobell for quotations from the writings of Thomas Traherne.

For permission to use extracts in prose and verse, references to the sources of which have for the most part appeared in previous pages, I am much indebted to Dr Blackman for his translation on page 757; to

Mr Basil Blackwell for my first acquaintance with Bunyan's *Book for Boys and Girls*; to Mrs Child Sargent, and Mr George Lyman Kittredge (and to Messrs George G. Harrap & Company) for selection from *English and Scottish Popular Ballads*; to Mr G. G. Coulton; to Dr Courtenay Dunn (and to Messrs Sampson Low, Marston & Company); to Messrs J. M. Dent & Sons for a quotation from *A Hind in Richmond Park* by W. H. Hudson; to Mr Tickner Edwardes (and Messrs Methuen & Company); to Lady Gomme; to Messrs Longmans, Green & Co. for a quotation from *The Diary of Master William Silence*; to Miss Emma Phipson (and Messrs Kegan, Paul, Trench, Trubner & Company); to Mr H. M. Tomlinson; to Professor J. Arthur Thompson (and Messrs George Newnes); to Mrs Wright; to Mr W. B. Yeats; to Mr Filson Young; to the Clarendon Press, and to the Hakluyt Society.

For generous help, counsel and kindness in the preparation of this book, it is a happiness to express my gratitude to many friends – to Miss Naomi Royde Smith, Mr Martin Freeman, Mr J. W. Haines, Mr Gilbert Sheldon, Mr Frank Morley, Mr Forrest Reid, and to Mr James MacLehose; and, last, to my niece, Miss Lucy Rowley, to whom it owes more than words can say.

As regards material which appears for the first time in this new edition [1928], my sincere thanks are due to Mr Claud Colleer Abbott for his translation of an old song from the French; to the Medici Society and to Mr Leigh Aston for extracts from *Samplers*; to the Oxford University Press for a translation from the Greek; to Mrs Frances Cornford (and to Mr Harold Monro) for 'Autumn Evening'; to Mr Havelock Ellis for an extract from *The Dance of Life*; to Mr Robert Frost (and to the *London Mercury* and the *Yale Review*) for 'The Minor Bird'; to Messrs Longmans, Green & Co. for extracts from *Samplers and Tapestry Embroidery*; to Miss M. M. Johnson for two poems, 'The Horse' and 'The Children's Orchestra'; to Mr E. V. Lucas (and to Messrs Methuen & Co. and the George H. Doran Co.) for 'The Ploughman'; to Mr John Masefield (and to Messrs Methuen & Co. and Messrs the Macmillan Company) for an extract from *A Sailor's Garland*; to Professor R. B. Morgan (and to the Cambridge University Press, Messrs Chatto & Windus and the Selden Society) for extracts from *Readings in English Social History*; to Mr William Ogilvie for 'There's Nane of My Ain to Care'; to Mrs Joseph Plunkett for a poem by Mr Joseph Plunkett; to Mr Forrest Reid (and to Messrs Constable & Co.) for an extract from *Demophon*;

to Mr Edward Shanks (and to Messrs Collins & Co.) for 'This Is the Sea'; to the Oxford University Press for an extract from W. W. Skeat's *A Student's Pastime*; to G. G. and D. M. Stuart for an extract from a translation from the French; to Miss Dorothy Wooldridge for three traditional poems included in her anthology, *The Poetry of Toil*; to my sister, Mrs Roger Ingpen, for extracts from *Women as Letter Writers*; to Mrs Bell, Mr J. H Clapham, Miss Molly Lyal, Mr Sidney Smith, Mr P. Taylor, and Mrs Amy Wallis for valuable help and suggestions, and last, to my friend, Mr Leonard Rice-Oxley, for his kindness in reading my proofs.

If by any inadvertence, copyright material has been included in these pages for the use of which permission has not been granted, or if I have failed to return thanks where thanks are due, I hope my sincere apologies will be accepted.

Many of the poets who gave their personal permission for the inclusion of poems in *Come Hither* when it was first compiled, are no longer living, and within reach of my gratitude. But in recognition of this particular and treasured kindness, and of incalculably more besides, I cannot forbear taking this opportunity of once more recording their names: Alice Meynell, Charlotte Mew, Mary Webb, Thomas Hardy, W. H. Hudson, Herbert Trench, Edmund Gosse, and Charles M. Doughty.

The Story of This Book

IN my rovings and ramblings as a boy I had often skirted the old stone house in the hollow. But my first clear remembrance of it is of a hot summer's day. I had climbed to the crest of a hill till then unknown to me, and stood there, hot and breathless in the bright slippery grass, looking down on its grey walls and chimneys as if out of a dream. And as if out of a dream already familiar to me.

My real intention in setting out from home that morning had been to get to a place called East Dene. My mother had often spoken to me of East Dene – of its trees and waters and green pastures, and the rare birds and flowers to be found there. Ages ago, she had told me, an ancestor of our family had dwelt in this place. But she smiled a little strangely when I asked her to take me there. 'All in good time, my dear,' she whispered into my ear, 'all in very good time! Just follow your small nose.' What kind of time, I wondered, was *very good time.* And *follow my nose* – how far? Such reflections indeed only made me the more anxious to be gone.

Early that morning, then, I had started out when the dew was still sparkling, and the night mists had but just lifted. But my young legs soon tired of the steep, boulder-strown hills, the chalky ravines, and burning sun, and having, as I say, come into view of the house in the valley, I went no further. Instead, I sat down on the hot turf – the sweet smell of thyme in the air, a few harebells nodding around me – and stared, down and down.

After that first visit, scarcely a week passed but that I found myself on this hill again. The remembrance of the house stayed in my mind; would keep returning to me, like a bird to its nest. Sometimes even in the middle of the night I would wake up and lie unable to sleep again for thinking of it – seeing it in my head; solemn, secret, strange.

There is a little flickering lizard called the Chameleon which, they say, changes its colour according to the place where it happens to be. So with this house. It was never the same for two hours together. I have seen it gathered close up in its hollow in the livid

1

and coppery gloom of storm; crouched like a hare in winter under a mask of snow; dark and silent beneath the changing sparkle of the stars; and like a palace out of an Arabian tale in the milky radiance of the moon. THRAE was the name inscribed on its gateway, but in letters so faint and faded as to be almost illegible.

In a sense I was, I suppose, a trespasser in this Thrae; until at least I became acquainted with Miss Taroone, the lady who lived in it. For I made pretty free with her valley, paddled and fished in its stream, and now and then helped myself to a windfall in her green bird-haunted orchards, where grew a particularly sharp and bright-rinded apple of which I have never heard the name. As custom gave me confidence, I ventured nearer and nearer to the house and would sometimes take a rest squatting on a manger in the big empty barn, looking out into the sunshine. The wings of the flies shone like glass in its shafts of light, and the robins whistled under its timber roof so shrill as almost to deafen one's ears.

Few strangers passed that way. Now and then I saw in the distance what might have been a beggar. To judge from his bundle he must have done pretty well at the house. Once, as I turned out of a little wood of birches, I met a dreadful-faced man in the lane who lifted up his hand at sight of me, and with white glaring eyes, uttered a horrible imprecation. He was chewing some fruit stolen out of the orchard, and at the very sight of him I ran like Wat himself.

Once, too, as my head looked over the hill-crest, there stood an old carriage and a drowsy horse drawn up beside the porch – with its slender wooden pillars and a kind of tray above, on which rambled winter jasmine, tufts of self-sown weeds and Traveller's Joy. I edged near enough to see there was a crown emblazoned on the panel of the carriage door. Nobody sat inside, and the coachman asleep on the box made me feel more solitary and inquisitive than ever.

Yet in its time the old house must have seen plenty of company. Friends of later years have spoken to me of it. Indeed, not far distant from Thrae as the crow flies, there was a crossing of high roads, so that any traveller from elsewhere not in haste could turn aside and examine the place if he cared for its looks and was in need of a night's lodging. Yet I do not think many such travellers – if they were men merely of the Town – can have *chosen* to lift that knocker or to set ringing that bell. To any one already lost and benighted its looks must have been forbidding.

Well, as I say, again and again, my lessons done, morning or evening would find me either on the grass slopes above Thrae, or actually in its valley. If I was tired, I would watch from a good distance off its small dark windows in their stone embrasures, and up above them the round greenish tower or turret over which a winged weather-vane twirled with the wind. I might watch: but the only person that I ever actually observed at the windows was an old maid with flaps to her cap, who would sometimes shake a duster out into the air as if for a signal to someone up in the hills.

Apart from her, I had occasionally seen Miss Taroone herself in the overgrown garden, with her immense shears, or with her trencher of bread-crumbs and other provender, feeding the birds. And I once stole near enough under a hedge to watch this sight. They hopped and pecked in a multitude beneath her hands, tits and robins, starlings and blackbirds, and other much wilder and rarer birds, as if they had no need here for wings, or were under an enchantment more powerful than that of mere crumbs of bread. The meal done, the platter empty, Miss Taroone would clap her hands, and off they would fly with a skirring of wings, with shrill cries and snatches of song to their haunts.

She seemed to mind no weather; standing bareheaded in heavy rain or scorching sunlight. And I confess the sight of her never failed to alarm me. But I made up my mind always to keep my wits about me and my eyes open; and never to be *caught* trespassing.

Then one day, as I slid down from the roof of the barn from amid the branches of a chestnut tree, green with its spiky balls of fruit, I found Miss Taroone standing there in the entry, looking out on me as if out of a frame, or like a stone figure in the niche of a church. She made no stir herself, but her eyes did. Clear cold eyes of the colour of pebbly water, in which I seemed to be of no more importance than a boat floating on the sea. I could neither speak nor run away. I could only gawk at her, my pockets bulging with the

3

unripe chestnuts I had pilfered, and a handsome slit in one leg of my breeches.

She asked me what I did there; my name; why I was not at school; where I lived; and did I eat the chestnuts? It appeared she had more often seen me — I suppose from her windows — than I had seen her. She made no movement, never even smiled while I stammered out answers to her questions, but merely kept her eyes steadily fixed on me, while her own lips just opened enough to let the words out of her mouth. She listened to me with a severe face, and said, 'Well, if you are happy to be here with the rest, so much the better.'

It was a relief when she turned away, bidding me follow her — and a foolish figure I must have cut as I clattered after her across the cobbled yard under the old red-brick arch and so through the porch and into the house.

When I was sat down in one of the shaded rooms within the house, she summoned the tall gaunt old maid with the cap-flaps I had seen at the windows, and bade her bring me some fruit and a dish of cream. Miss Taroone watched me while I ate it. And uncommonly good it was, though I would rather have been enjoying it alone. From the way she looked at me it might have been supposed it was a bird or a small animal that was sitting up at her table. The last spoonful finished, she asked me yet more questions and appeared to be not displeased with my rambling answers, for she invited me to come again and watched me take up my cap and retire.

This was the first time I was ever in Miss Taroone's house — within its solid walls I mean; and what a multitude of rooms, with their coffers and presses and cabinets, containing I knew not what treasures and wonders! But Thrae was not Miss Taroone's only house, for more than once she spoke of another — named SURE VINE, as if of a family mansion and estate, very ancient and magnificent. When, thinking of my mother, I myself ventured a question about East Dene, her green-grey eyes oddly settled on mine a moment, but she made no answer. I noticed this particularly.

Soon I was almost as free and familiar in Miss Taroone's old house as in my own father's. Yet I cannot say that she was ever anything else than curt with me in her manner. It was a long time before I became accustomed to the still, secret way she had of looking at me. I liked best being in her company when she appeared, as was usually so, not to be aware that she was not alone. She had again asked me my name 'for a sign' as she said, 'to know you by'; though she always afterwards addressed me as Simon. Certainly in those days I was 'simple' enough.

My next friend was the woman whom I had seen shaking her duster out of the upper windows. She, I discovered, was called Linnet Sara Queek or Quek or Cuec or Cueque, I don't know how to spell it. She was an exceedingly curious woman and looked as if she had never been any different, though, of course, she must once have been young and have grown up. She was bony, awkward, and angular, and when you spoke to her, she turned on you with a look that was at the same time vacant and piercing. At first she greeted me sourly, but soon became friendlier, and would allow me to sit in her huge kitchen with her parrot, her sleek tabby cat, and perhaps a dainty or two out of her larder.

She was continually muttering — though I could never quite catch what she said; never idle; and though slow and awkward in her movements, she did a vast deal of work. With small short-sighted eyes fixed on her mortar she would stand pounding and pounding; or stewing and seething things in pots — strange-looking roots and fruit and fungi. Her pantry was crammed with pans, jars, bottles, and phials, all labelled in her queer handwriting. An extraordinary place — especially when the sunbeams of evening struck into it from a high window in its whitewashed wall.

Linnet she might be called, but her voice was no bird's, unless the crow's; and you would have guessed at once, at sight of her standing in front of the vast open hearth, stooping a little, her long gaunt arms beside her, that her other name was Sara. But she could tell curious and rambling stories (as true as she could make them); and many of them were about the old days in Thrae, older days in Sure Vine, and about Miss Taroone, in whose service she had been since she was a small child.

She told me, too, some especially good tales — as good as Grimm — about some villages she knew of called the Ten Laps; and gave me a custard when I asked for more. I once mentioned East Dene to her, too, and she said there was a short cut to it (though it seemed to me a long way about) through the quarry, by the pits, and that way round. 'And then you come to a Wall,' she said, staring at me. 'And you climb over.'

'Did *you*?' said I, laughing; and at that she was huffed.

Boy though I was, it occurred to me that in this immense house there must be a great deal more work than Sara could manage unaided. Something gave me the fancy that other hands must lend their help; but if any maids actually came in to Thrae from East Dene, or from elsewhere, they must have come and gone very late, or early. It seemed bad manners to be too curious. On the other hand, I rarely saw much of the back parts of the house.

I have sometimes wondered if Thrae had not once in fact lain within the borders of East Dene, and that being so, if Miss Taroone, like myself, was unaware of it. It may have been merely pride that closed her lips, for one day, she showed me, with a curious smile, how Thrae's architect, centuries before, had planned its site. She herself led me from room to room; and she talked as she had never talked before.

Its southernmost window looked on a valley, beyond which on clear days was visible the sea, and perhaps a brig or a schooner on its surface – placid blue as turquoise. Sheer against its easternmost window the sun mounted to his summer solstice from in between a cleft of the hills – like a large topaz between the forks of a catapult. One one side of this cleft valley was a windmill, its sails lanking up into the sky, and sometimes spinning in the wind with an audible clatter. Who owned the mill and what he ground I never heard.

Northwards, through a round bull's-eye window you could see, past a maze of coppices and hills, and in the distance, the cock of a cathedral spire. And to the west stood a wood of yew, its pool partially greened over, grey with willows, and the haunt of rare birds. On the one side of this pool spread exceedingly calm meadows; and on the other, in a hollow, the graveyard lay. The stones and bones in it were all apparently of Miss Taroone's kinsfolk. At least Linnet Sara told me so. Nor was she mournful about it. She seemed to have nobody to care for but her mistress; working for love, whatever her wages might be.

It is an odd thing to say, but though I usually tried to avoid meeting Miss Taroone, and was a little afraid of her, there was a most curious happiness at times in being in her company. She never once asked me about my character, never warned me of anything, never said 'You must'; and yet I knew well that if in stupidity or carelessness I did anything in her house which she did not approve of, my punishment would come.

She once told me, 'Simon, you have, I see, the beginnings of a bad feverish cold. It is because you were stupid enough yesterday to stand with the sweat on your face talking to me in a draught. It will probably be severe.' And so it was.

She never said anything affectionate; she never lost her temper. I never saw her show any pity or meanness or revenge. 'Well, Simon,' she would say, 'Good morning'; or 'Good evening' (as the case might be); 'you are always welcome. Have a good look about you. Don't waste your time here. Even when all is said, you will not see too much of me and mine. But don't believe *everything* you may hear in the kitchen. Linnet Sara is a good servant, but still a groper.'

Not the least notion of what she meant occurred to me. But I peacocked about for a while as if she had paid me a compliment. An evening or two afterwards, and soon after sunset, I found her sitting in her westward window. Perhaps because rain was coming, the crouching headstones under the hill looked to be furlongs nearer. 'Sleeping, waking; waking, sleeping, Simon'; she said, 'sing while you can.' Like a little owl I fixed sober eyes on the yew-wood, but again I hadn't any inkling of what she meant.

She would sit patiently listening to me as long as I cared to unbosom myself to her. Her calm, severe, and yet, I think, beautiful face is clear in my memory. It resembles a little the figure in Albrecht Dürer's picture of a woman sitting beneath the wall of a house, with a hound crouched beside her, an inclined ladder, the rainbowed sea in the distance, and a bat – a tablet of magic numbers and a penthoused bell over her head.

Sometimes I would be questioned at home about my solitary

wanderings, but I never mentioned Miss Taroone's name, and spoke of her house a little deceitfully, since I did not confess how much I loved being in it.

One evening – and it was already growing late – Miss Taroone, after steadily gazing into my eyes for a few moments, asked me if I liked pictures. I professed that I did, though I had never spent much time in looking at the queer portraits and charts and mementoes that hung thick and closely on her own walls. 'Well,' she replied, 'if you like pictures I must first tell you about Nahum.'

I could not at first make head or tail of Mr Nahum. Even now I am uncertain whether he was Miss Taroone's brother or her nephew or a cousin many times removed; or whether perhaps she was really and truly Mrs Taroone and he her only son; or she still Miss Taroone and he an adopted one. I am not sure even whether or not she had much love for him, though she appeared to speak of him with pride. What I do know is that Miss Taroone had nurtured him from his cradle and had taught him all the knowledge that was not already his by right of birth.

Before he was come even to be my own age, she told me, Nahum Taroone had loved 'exploring'. As a boy he had ranged over the countryside for miles around. I never dared ask her if he had sat on Linnet Sara's 'Wall'! He had scrawled plans and charts and maps, marking on them all his wanderings. And not only the roads, paths, chaces, and tracks, the springs and streams, but the rare-birds' nesting-places and the rarer wild flowers, the eatable or poisonous fruits, trees, animal lairs, withies for whips, clay for modelling, elder shoots for pitch pipes, pebbles for his catapult, flint arrows, and everything of that kind. He was a nightboy too; could guide himself by the stars, was a walking almanac of the moon; and could decoy owls and nightjars, and find any fox's or badger's earth he was after, even in a dense mist.

I came to know Mr Nahum pretty well – so far at any rate as one can know anybody from hearsay – before Miss Taroone referred to the pictures again. And I became curious about him, and hoped to see this strange traveller, and frequently hung around Thrae in mere chance of that.

Strangely enough, by the looks on her face and the tones of her voice, Miss Taroone was inclined to mock a little at Mr Nahum because of his restlessness. She didn't seem to approve of his leaving her so much – though she herself had come from Sure Vine. Her keys would jangle at her chatelaine as if they said, 'Ours secrets enough.' And she would stand listening, and mute, as if in expectation of voices or a footfall. Then as secretly as I could, I would get away.

All old memories resemble a dream. And so too do these of Miss Taroone and Thrae. When I was most busy and happy and engrossed in it, it seemed to be a house which might at any moment vanish before your eyes, showing itself to be but the outer shell or hiding place of an abode still more enchanting.

This sound nonsensical. But if you have ever sat and watched a Transformation Scene in a pantomime, did you suppose, just before the harlequin slapped with his wand on what looked like a plain brick-and-mortar wall, that it would instantly after dissolve into a radiant coloured scene of trees and fountains and hidden beings – growing lovelier in their own showing as the splendour spread and their haunts were revealed? Well, so at times I used to feel in Thrae.

At last, one late evening in early summer, beckoning me with her finger, Miss Taroone lit a candle in an old brass stick and bade me follow her down a long narrow corridor and up a steep winding stone staircase. 'You have heard, Simon, of Mr Nahum's round room; now you shall see it.'

On the wider step at the top, before a squat oak door, she stayed, lifted her candle, and looked at me. 'You will remember,' she said, 'that what I am about to admit you into is Mr Nahum's room; not mine. You may look at the pictures, you may examine anything that interests you, you may compose yourself to the view. But replace what you look at, have a care in your handling, do nothing out of *idle* curiosity, and come away when you are tired. Remember that Mr Nahum may be returning at any hour. He would be pleased to find you here. But hasten away out of his room the very instant you feel you have no right, lot or pleasure to be in it. Hasten away, I mean, so that you may return to it with a better mind and courage.'

She laid two fingers on my shoulder, cast another look into my face under her candle, turned the key in the lock, gently thrust me beyond the door, shut it: and left me to my own devices.

What first I noticed, being for awhile a little alarmed at this strange proceeding, was the evening light that poured in on the room from the encircling windows. Below, by walking some little distance from room to room, corridor to corridor, you could get (as I have said) a single narrow view out north, south, east, or west. Here, you could stand in the middle, and turning slowly like a top on your heels, could watch float by one after the other, hill and windmill, ocean, distant city, dark yew-wood.

The crooning of doves was audible on the roof, swallows were coursing in the placid and rosy air, the whole world seemed to be turning softly out of the day's sunshine, stretching long dark shadows across hill and valley as if in delight to be on the verge of rest and slumber again, now that the heats of full summer were so near.

But I believe my first *thought* was – What a boiling hot and glaring place to sit in in the middle of the morning. And then I noticed that heavy curtains hung on either side each rounded window, for shade, concealment and solitude. As soon, however, as my eyes were accustomed to the dazzle, I spent little time upon the great view, but immediately peered about me at what was in this curious chamber.

Never have I seen in any room – and this was none so large – such a hugger-mugger of strange objects – odd-shaped coloured shells, fragments of quartz, thunderbolts and fossils; skins of brilliant birds; outlandish shoes; heads, faces, masks of stone, wood, glass, wax, and metal; pots, images, glass shapes, and what not; lanterns and bells; bits of harness and ornament and weapons. There were, besides, two or three ships of different rigs in glass cases, and one in a green bottle; peculiar tools, little machines; silent clocks, instruments of music, skulls and bones of beasts, frowsy bunches of linen or silk queerly marked, and a mummied cat (I think). And partly concealed, as I twisted my head, there, dangling in an alcove, I caught sight of a full-length skeleton, one hollow eye-hole concealed by a curtain looped to the floor from the ceiling.

I just cast my glance round on all these objects without of course seeing them one by one. The air was clear as water in the evening light, a little dust had fallen; all was in order, though at that first hasty glance there seemed none. Last, but not least, there was row on row of painted pictures. Wherever there was space on the walls free of books, this round tower room was hung with them as close as their frames and nails allowed. There I stood, hearing faintly the birds, conscious of the pouring sunlight, the only live creature amidst this departed traveller's treasures and possessions.

I was so much taken aback by it all, so mystified by Miss Taroone's ways, so cold at sight of the harmless bones above me, and felt so suddenly out of my familiars, that without a moment's hesitation I turned about, flung open the door and went helter skelter clattering down the stairs – out of the glare into the gloom.

There was no sign of Miss Taroone as I crossed through the house and sneaked off hastily through the garden. And not until the barn had shut me out from the lower windows behind me did I look back at the upper ones of Mr Nahum's tower. Until that moment I did not know how frightened I had been. Yet why, or at what, I cannot even now decide.

But I soon overcame this folly. Miss Taroone made no inquiry how I had fared on this first visit to Mr Nahum's fortress. As I have said, she seldom asked questions – except with her eyes, expressions, and hands. But some time afterwards, and after two or three spells of exploration, I myself began to talk to her of the strange things up there.

'I have looked at a good many, Miss Taroone. But the pictures! Some of them are of places I *believe* I know. I wish I could be a traveller and see what the others are of. Did Mr Nahum paint them all himself?'

Miss Taroone was sitting bolt upright in a high-backed chair, her eyes and face very intent, as always happened when Mr Nahum's name was mentioned.

'I know very little about them, Simon. When Nahum was younger he used to make pictures of Thrae, and of the woods and valleys hereabouts. There are boxfulls put away. Others are pictures brought back from foreign parts, but many of them, as

I believe,' she turned her face and looked into a shadowy corner of the room, 'are pictures of nothing on earth. He has his two worlds. Take your time. Some day you too, I dare say, will go off on your travels. Remember that, like Nahum, you are as old as the hills which neither spend nor waste time, but dwell in it for ages, as if it were light or sunshine. Some day perhaps Nahum will shake himself free of Thrae altogether. I don't *know*, myself, Simon. This house is enough for me, and what I remember of Sure Vine, compared with which Thrae is but the smallest of bubbles in a large glass.'

I do not profess to have understood one half of what Miss Taroone meant in these remarks. It was in English and yet in a hidden tongue.

But by this time I had grown to be bolder in her company, and pounced on this: 'What, please Miss Taroone, do you mean by the "two worlds"? Or shall I ask downstairs?' I added the latter question because now and then in the past Miss Taroone had bidden me go down to Linnet Sara for my answers. She now appeared at first not to have heard it.

'Now I must say to you, Simon,' she replied at last, folding her hands on her knee, 'wherever you may be in that body of yours, you feel you look out of it, do you not?'

I nodded. 'Yes, Miss Taroone.'

'Now think, then, of Mr Nahum's round room; where is that?'

'Up there,' said I, pointing up a rambling finger.

'Ah!' cried Miss Taroone, 'so it may be. But even if tomorrow you are thousands of miles distant from here on the other side of this great Ball, or in its bowels, or flying free – you will still carry a picture of it, will you not? And that will be within you?'

'Yes, in my mind, Miss Taroone?' I answered rather sheepishly.

'In your mind,' she echoed me, but not as if she were particularly pleased at the fact. 'Well, many of the pictures I take it in Mr Nahum's round tower are of *that* world. His MIND. I have never examined them. My duties are elsewhere. Your duty is to keep your senses, heart and courage and to go where you are called. And in black strange places you will at times lose yourself and find yourself, Simon. Now Mr Nahum is calling. Don't think of me too much. I have great faith in him. Sit up there with him then. Share your eyes with his pictures. And having seen them, compare them if you will. Say, This is this, and that is that. And make of all that he has exactly what use you can.'

With this counsel in my head I once more groped my way up the corkscrew stone staircase, and once more passed on from picture to picture; in my engrossment actually knocking my head against the dangling footbones of Mr Nahum's treasured and now un-alarming skeleton.

The pictures were of all kinds and sizes – in water colour, in chalks, and in oil. Some I liked for their vivid colours and deep shadows, and some I did not like at all. Nor could I always be sure even what they were intended to represent. Many of them completely perplexed me. A few of them seemed to me to be absurd; some made me stupidly ashamed; and one or two of them terrified me. But I went on examining them when I felt inclined, and a week or so after, as I was lifting out one of them into the sunshine, by chance it twisted on its cord and disclosed its wooden back.

And there, pasted on to it, was a scrap of yellowing paper with the letters BLAKE, followed by a number – CXLVII, in Roman figures. As with this one, so with the others. Each had its name and a number.

And even as I stood pondering what this might mean, my eyes rested on a lower shelf of one of Mr Nahum's cases of books – book-cases which I have forgotten to say stood all round the lower part of the room. I had already discovered that many of these books were the writings of travellers in every part of the globe. One whole book-case consisted of what Mr Nahum appeared to call Kitchen Work. But the one on a lower shelf which had now taken my attention was new to me – an enormous, thick, home-made-looking volume covered in a greenish shagreen or shark-skin.

Scrawled in ungainly capitals on the strip of vellum pasted to the back of this book was its title: THEOTHERWORLDE. Would you believe it? – at first I was stupid enough to suppose this title was one word, a word in a strange tongue, which I pronounced to myself as best I could, THEEOTHAWORLDIE – saying the

TH as in *thimble*. And that is what, merely for old sake's sake, I have continued to call the book in my mind to this day!

I glanced out of the window. The upper boughs of the yew-wood and the stones this side of it among the bright green grasses were impurpled by the reflected sunlight. Nothing there but motionless shadows. I stood looking vacantly out for a moment or two; then stooped and lugged out the ponderous fusty old volume on to the floor and raised its clumsy cover.

To my surprise and pleasure, I found, that attached within was the drawing of a boy of about my own age, but dressed like a traveller, whose face faintly resembled a portrait I had noticed on the walls downstairs, though this child had wings painted to his shoulders and there was a half circle of stars around his head. Beneath this portrait in the book, in small letters, was scrawled in a faded handwriting, NAHUM TARUNE. This, then, was Mr Nahum when he was a boy. It pleased me to find that he was no better a speller than myself. He had not even got his own name right! I liked his face. He looked out from under his stars at me, full in the eyes.

Next – after I had searched his looks and clothes and what he carried pretty closely– I turned over a few of the stiff leaves and found more of his writing with a big VII scrawled on the top. I should have been a stupider boy even than I was if I had not at once turned over the pictures till I came to that with VII on the label on the back of it. This picture was of a Maze outlined in gaudy colours which faded towards the middle – a sort of oasis in which grew a tree. Fabulous looking animals and creatures with wings sprawled around its margins. After repeated attempts I found to my disappointment that your only way out of the oasis and the maze was, after long groping, by the way you went in. Underneath it was written ' *This is the key*'. And above it in green letters stood this: Behold upon the mountains the feet of him that bringeth good tidings, that publisheth peace!

It was unfortunate that so little more of daylight was now left dying in the sky that evening; for as yet I had not the confidence to kindle the wax candles that stood in their brass sticks in the round tower. It was high time for me to be getting home. In my haste to be off I nearly collided with Miss Taroone, who happened to be standing in the dusklight looking out from under her porch. Too much excited even to beg her pardon, I blurted out: 'Miss Taroone, I have found out what the pictures are of. It's a Book. *Theeothaworldie*. Mr Nahum's portrait's in it, but they've put wings to him; and it's all in his writing – rhymes.'

She looked down at me, though I could not quite see her face.

'Then, good-night to you, Simon; and happy dreams,' she said, in her unfriendly voice.

'I like the round room better and better,' I replied as heartily as I could. 'That picture of Mr Nahum – and there are lots more, I think – is a *little* bit like an uncle of mine who died in Russia; my Uncle John.'

'John's as good a name, I suppose, as any other, Simon,' said Miss Taroone. She stood looking out on the dusky country scene. 'There's a heavy dew tonight, and the owls are busy.'

They were indeed. Their screechings sounded on all sides of me as I ran off homewards, chanting over to myself the words that had somehow stuck in my memory.

Well, at last I began to read in Mr Nahum's book – I won't say page by page, but as the fancy took me. It consisted chiefly of rhymes and poems, and some of them had pictured capitals and were decorated in clear bright colours like the pages of the old books illuminated by monks centuries ago. Apart from the poems were here and there pieces of prose. These, I found, always had some bearing on the poems, and, like them, many of them were queerly spelt. Occasionally Mr Nahum had jotted down his own thoughts in the margin. But the pictures were my first concern.

Sometimes I went off to them from the book in order to find the particular one I wanted. And sometimes the other way round: I would have a good long stare at a picture, then single out the proper rhyme in the book. Often, either in one way or the other, I failed. For there were far fewer pictures than there were pages in the book, and for scores of pages I found no picture at all. It seemed Mr Nahum had made paintings only of those he liked best.

The book itself, I found, was the first of three, the other two being similar to itself but much thicker and heavier. Into these I dipped occasionally, but found that the rhymes in them interested me less or were less easily understandable. Even some of those in the first book were a little beyond my wits at the time. But experience seems to be like the shining of a bright lantern. It suddenly makes clear in the mind what was already there perhaps, but dim. And often though I immediately liked what I read, long years were to go by before I really understood it, made it my own. There would come a moment, something would happen; and I would say to myself: 'Oh, that, then, is what *that* meant!'

Before going any further I must confess that I was exceedingly slow over Mr Nahum's writings. Even over Volume I. When first I opened its pages I had had a poor liking for poetry because of a sort of contempt for it. 'Poetry!' I would scoff to myself, and would shut up the covers of any such book with a kind of yawn inside me. Some of it had come my way in lesson books. This I could gabble off like a parrot, and with as much understanding; and I had just begun to grind out a little Latin verse for my father.

But I had never troubled to think about it; to share my Self with it; to examine it in order to see whether or not it was true; or to ask why it was written in this one way and in no other way. But apart from this, there were many old rhymes in Mr Nahum's book – nursery things – which I had known since I knew anything. And I still have an old childish love for rhymes and jingles like them.

But what about the others? I began to ponder. After being so many hours alone in Mr Nahum's room, among his secret belongings, I almost felt his presence there. When your mind is sunk in study, it is as if you were in a dream. But you cannot tell where, or in whose company, you may wake out of a dream. I remember one sultry afternoon being started out of my wits by a sudden clap of thunder. I looked up, to find the whole room black, zigzag, and strange, and for a moment I fancied Mr Nahum was actually there behind me; and not a friendly Mr Nahum.

That is mere fancy; though in other ways he became so real to me at last that I would do things as if he had asked me to do them. For this reason, I think, I persevered with his book, swallowing some of the poems as if they were physic, simply because he had written them there. But the more I read, the more I came to enjoy them for their own sakes. Not all of them, of course. But I did see this, that like a carpenter who makes a table, a man who has written a poem has written it like that *on purpose*.

With this thought in my head I tried one day to alter the words of one or two of the simple and easy poems; or to put the words in a different order. And I found by so doing that you not only altered the sound of the poem, but that even the slightest alteration in the sound a little changed the sense. Either you lost something of the tune and runningness; or the words did not clash right; or you blurred the picture the words gave you; or some half-hidden meaning vanished away. I don't mean that every poem is perfect; but only that when I changed them it was almost always very much for the worse. I was very slow in all this; but, still, I went on. No. III, I remember, was the old jingle, 'Old King Cole':

> Old King Cole was a merry old soul,
> And a merry old soul was he;
>   He called for his pipe,
>   And he called for his bowl,
> And he called for his fiddlers three . . .

Now, suppose, instead of these four lines of the rhyme you put:

> Old King Cole was a jolly old man,
> The jolliest old man alive;
> He called for his cup, and he called for a pipe
> And he called for his fiddlers five.

By so doing you have actually added two extra fiddlers; and yet somehow you have taken away some of the old three's music. Or you may put:

'Cole the First was now a monarch advanced in age, and of a convivial temperament. On any festive occasion he would bid his retainers bring him his goblet and smoking materials, and would command his musicians to entertain him on their violins: which they did.'

Well, all the *facts* are there and many more words, but scarcely

17

a trace of *my* old King Cole, and not a single tweedle-eedle of the fiddling. Would anyone trouble to learn that by heart?

Now underneath this rhyme Mr Nahum had written a sort of historical account of King Cole, a good deal of it in German and other languages. All I could make out of it was this: if ever a King Cole inhabited the world, he probably had another name; that he lived too far back in history for anyone to make sure when he had lived or that he had lived at all; and that his 'pipe' and 'bowl' probably stand for objects much more mysterious and far less common.

Having the rhyme quite free to myself, I didn't mind reading this; but if ever I have to give up either, I shall keep the rhyme.

Having discovered, then, that every poem must have been written as it was written, on purpose, I took a little more pains with those I cared for least. In some even then I could not piece out the meaning; in others I could not easily catch the beat and rhythm and tune. But I learned to read them very slowly, so as fully and quietly to fill up the time allowed for each line and to listen to its music, and to see and hear all that the words were saying.

Then, too, what Miss Taroone had said came back to my mind. Even when Mr Nahum's poems were about real things and places and people, they were still only of places and people the words made for me in my *mind*. I must, that is, myself imagine all they told. And I found that the mention in a poem even of quite common and familiar things – such as a star, or a buttercup, or a beetle – did not bring into the mind quite the same kind of images of them as the things and creatures themselves do in the naked eye.

> Now the day is over,
> Night is drawing nigh;
> Shadows of the evening
> Steal across the sky . . .

This was one of the earliest poems in Mr Nahum's book. I had often, of course, seen the shadows of evening – every grass-blade or pebble casts its own; but these words not only called them vividly into my mind, but set shadows there (shadows across the sky) that I had never really seen at all – with my own eyes I mean. I discovered afterwards, also, that shadows are only the absence of light, though light is needed to make them visible. Just the same, again, with the sailors in the same poem:

> Guard the sailors tossing
> On the deep blue sea . . .

They are plain and common words, but their *order* here is the poem's only, and the effect they had on me, and still have, is different from the effect of any other words on the same subject. Though, too, like Mr Nahum, I have now seen something of the world (have been seasick and nearly drowned) I have never forgotten those imaginary sailors, or that imaginary sea; can still hear the waves lapping against that (unmentioned) ship's thin wooden walls, as if I myself were sleeping there, down below.

So what I then read has remained a clear and single remembrance, as if I myself had seen it in a world made different, or in a kind of vision or dream. And I think Mr Nahum had chosen such poems in Volume I as carried away the imagination like that; either into the past, or into another mind, or into the all-but-forgotten; at times as if into another world. And this kind has been my choice in this book.

Not that his picture to a particular poem was always the picture I should have made of it. Take for example another nursery jingle in his book:

> 'How many miles to Babylon?'
> 'Three score and ten.'
> 'Can I get there by candle-light?'
> 'Ay, and back again.'

Mr Nahum's corresponding picture was not of Babylon or of a candle, or of a traveller at all, but of a stone tomb. On its thick upper slab he had drawn-in an old earthen lamp, with a serpent for handle – its wick alight, and shining up on a small owl perched in the lower branches of the thick tree above.

That is one of the pleasures of reading – you may make any picture out of the words you can and will; and a poem may have as many different meanings as there are different minds.

There I would sit, then, and Mr Nahum's book made of 'one

little room an everywhere'. And though I was naturally rather stupid and dense, I did in time realize that 'rare poems ask rare friends', and that even the simplest ones may have secrets which will need a pretty close searching out.

Of course I could not copy out all of the poems even in THEEOTHAWORLDIE, Volume I, and I took very few from Volumes II and III. I chose what I liked best – those that, when I read them, never failed to carry me away, as if on a Magic Carpet, or in Seven League Boots, into a region of their own. When the nightingale sings, other birds, it is said, will sit and listen to him: and I remember very well hearing a nightingale so singing on a spray in a dewy hedge, and there were many small birds perched mute and quiet near. The cock crows at midnight; and for miles around his kinsmen answer. The fowler whistles his decoy for the wild duck to come. So certain rhymes and poems affected my mind when I was young, and continue to do so now that I am old.

To these (and the few bits of prose) which I chose from Mr Nahum, I added others afterwards, and they are in this book too. All of them are in English; a few from over the ocean: but how very few they all are by comparison with the multitudes even of their own kind. And there are the whole world's languages besides! Even of my own favourites not all have found a place. There was not room enough. I have left out others also that may be found easily elsewhere. I am afraid, too, there may be many mistakes in my copying, though I have tried to be careful.

Miss Taroone knew that I was making use of Mr Nahum's book; though she never questioned me about it. I came and went in her house at last like a rabbit in a warren, a mouse in a mousery. The hours I spent in those far-gone days in Mr Nahum's round room! At times I wearied of it, and hated his books, and even wished I had never so much as set eyes on Thrae at all.

But after such sour moments, a gossip and an apple with Linnet Sara in her kitchen, or a scamper home, or a bathe under the hazels in the stream whose source, I believe, is in the hills beyond East Dene, would set me to rights again. For sheer joy of return I could scarcely breathe for a while after remounting the stone staircase, re-entering Mr Nahum's room, and closing the door behind me.

From above his broad scrawled pages I would lift my eyes to his windows and stare as if out of one dream into another. How strange from across the sky was the gentle scented breeze blowing in on my cheek, softly stirring the dried kingfisher skin that hung from its beam; how near understanding then the tongues of the wild birds; how close the painted scene – as though I were but a picture too, and this my frame.

But there came a day that was to remove me out of the neighbourhood of Miss Taroone's Thrae into a different kind of living altogether. I was to be sent to school. After a hot debate with myself, and why I scarcely know, I asked my father's permission to spend the night at Miss Taroone's. He gave me a steady look and said, Yes.

I found Miss Taroone seated on the steps of her porch, and now that I look back at her then, she curiously reminds me – though she was ages older – of a picture you will find in the second stanza of poem No. 233 in this book. Standing before her – it was already getting towards dark – I said I was come to bid her goodbye; and might I spend the night in Mr Nahum's round room. She raised her eyes on me, luminous and mysterious as the sky itself, even though in the dusk.

'You may *say* good-bye, Simon,' she replied; 'but unless I myself am much mistaken in you, your feet will not carry you out of all thought of me; and some day they will return to me whether you will or not.'

Inside I was already in a flutter at thought of the hours to come, and I was accustomed to her strange speeches, though this struck on my mind more coldly than usual. I made a little jerk forwards; 'I must thank you, please Miss Taroone, for having been so kind to me,' I gulped in an awkward voice. 'And I hope,' I added, as she made no answer, 'I hope I haven't been much of a bother – coming like this, I mean?'

'None, Simon'; was her sole reply. The hand that I had begun to hold out, went back into my pocket, and feeling extremely uncomfortable I half turned away.

'Why, who knows? – ' said the solemn voice, 'Mr Nahum may at this very moment be riding home. Have a candle alight.'

'Thank you, Miss Taroone. Thank you very much indeed.'

With that I turned about and hastened across the darkening garden into the house. My candle stick and matches stood ready on the old oak bench at the foot of the tower. I lit up, and began to climb the cold steps. My heart in my mouth, I hesitated at the hob-nailed door; but managed at last to turn the key in the lock.

With two taller candles kindled, and its curtains drawn over the western window, I at once began to copy out the few last things I wanted for mine in Volume I. But there were two minds in me as midnight drew on, almost two selves, the one busy with pen and ink, the other stealthily listening to every faintest sound in my eyrie, a swift glance now and then up at the darkened glass only setting me more sharply to work. I had never before sat in so enormous a silence; the scratching of my pen its only tongue.

Steadily burned my candles; no sound of hoofs, no owl-cry, no knocking disturbed my peace; the nightingales had long since journeyed South. What I had hoped for, expected, dreaded in this long vigil, I cannot recall; all that I remember of it is that I began to shiver a little at last, partly because my young nerves were on the stretch, and partly because the small hours grew chill. In the very middle of the night there came to my ear what seemed a distant talking or gabbling. It may have been fancy; it may have been Linnet Sara. What certainly was fancy is the notion that, as I started up out of an instant's drowse, a stooping shape had swiftly withdrawn itself from me. But this was merely the shadow of a dream.

I returned at last from the heavy sleep I had fallen into, my forehead resting on the backs of my hands, and they flat on the huge open volume, my whole body stiff with cold, and the first clear grey of daybreak in the East. And suddenly as my awakened eyes stared dully about them in that thin light – the old windows, the strange outlandish objects, the clustering pictures, the countless books, my own ugly writing on my paper – an indescribable despair and anxiety – almost terror even – seized upon me at the rushing thought of my own *ignorance*; of how little I knew, of how unimportant I was. And, again and again, my ignorance. Then I thought of Miss Taroone, of Mr Nahum, of the life before me, and everything yet to do. And a sullen misery swept up in me at these reflections. And once more I wished from the bottom of my heart that I had never come to this house.

But gradually the light broadened. And with it, confidence began to return. The things around me that had seemed strange and hostile became familiar again. I stood up and stretched myself and, I think, muttered a prayer.

To this day I see the marvellous countryside of that morning with its hills and low thick mists and woodlands stretched like a painted scene beneath the windows – and that finger of light from the risen Sun presently piercing across the dark air, and as if by a miracle causing birds and water to awake and sing and shine.

With a kind of grief that was yet rapture in my mind, I stood looking out over the cold lichen-crusted shingled roof of Thrae – towards the East and towards those far horizons. Yet again the apprehension (that was almost a hope) drew over me that at any moment wall and chimney-shaft might thin softly away, and the Transformation Scene begin. I was but just awake: and so too was the world itself, and ever is. And somewhere – Wall or no Wall – was my mother's East Dene . . .

In a while I crept softly downstairs, let myself out, and ran off into the morning. Having climbed the hill from which I had first stared down upon Thrae, I stopped for a moment to recover my breath, and I looked back.

The gilding sun-rays beat low upon the house in the valley. All was still, wondrous, calm. For a moment my heart misgave me at this farewell. The next, in sheer excitement – the cold sweet air, the height, the morning, a few keen beckoning stars – I broke into a kind of Indian war-dance in the thin dewy grass, and then, with a last wave of my hand, like Mr Nahum himself, I set off at a sharp walk on the journey that has not yet come to an end.

MORNING AND MAY

1. *This Is the Key*

This is the Key of the Kingdom
In that Kingdom is a city;
In that city is a town;[1]
In that town there is a street;
In that street there winds a lane;
In that lane there is a yard;
In that yard there is a house;
In that house there waits a room;
In that room an empty bed;
And on that bed a basket –
A Basket of Sweet Flowers:
　Of Flowers, of Flowers;
　A Basket of Sweet Flowers.

Flowers in a Basket;
Basket on the bed;
Bed in the chamber;
Chamber in the house;
House in the weedy yard;
Yard in the winding lane;
Lane in the broad street;
Street in the high town;
Town in the city;
City in the Kingdom –
This is the Key of the Kingdom.
　Of the Kingdom this is the Key.

---

1. That heart of it, within *walls*

2. *A New Year Carol*

Here we bring new water
    from the well so clear,
For to worship God with,
    this happy New Year.

Sing levy dew, sing levy dew,
    the water and the wine;
The seven bright gold wires
    and the bugles that do shine.

Sing reign of Fair Maid,
    with gold upon her toe, –
Open you the West Door,
    and turn the Old Year go.

Sing reign of Fair Maid
    with gold upon her chin, –
Open you the East Door,
    and let the New Year in.
Sing levy dew, sing levy dew,
    the water and the wine;
The seven bright gold wires
    and the bugles they do shine.

3. *Hey! Now the Day Dawns*

'Hay, nou the day dauis;
The jolie Cok crauis;
Nou shroudis the shauis,
   Throu Natur anone.
The thissell-cok cryis
On louers wha lyis,
Nou skaillis the skyis;
   The nicht is neir gone.

Hey! now the day dawns;
The jolly Cock crows;
Thick-leaved the green shaws,
   Through Nature anon.
The thistle-cock cries
On lovers who lies,
All cloudless the skies;
   The night is near gone.

28

'The feildis ouerflouis	*The fields overflow*
With gowans that grouis,	*With daisies a-blow,*
Quhair lilies lyk lou is,	*And lilies like fire shine,*
Als rid as the rone.	*And red is the rowan.*
The turtill that true is,	*The wood-dove that true is*
With nots that reneuis,	*Her crooling reneweth,*
Hir pairtie perseuis;	*And her sweet mate pursueth;*
The nicht is neir gone.	*The night is near gone.*
'Nou Hairtis with Hyndis,	*Now Harts with their Hinds*
Conforme to thair kyndis,	*Conform to their kinds,*
Hie tursis thair tyndis,	*They vaunt their branched*
On grund whair they grone.	*antlers,*
Nou Hurchonis, with Hairis,	*They bell and they groan.*
Ay passis in pairis;	*Now Urchins*[1] *and Hares*
Quhlik deuly declaris	*Keep a-passing in pairs;*
The nicht is neir gone . . .'	*Which duly declares*
	The night is near gone . . .

ALEXANDER MONTGOMERIE

4. *The Sluggard*

'Tis the voice of a sluggard; I heard him complain –
'You have waked me too soon; I must slumber again';
As the door on its hinges, so he on his bed,
Turns his sides, and his shoulders, and his heavy head.
'A little more sleep, and a little more slumber' –
Thus he wastes half his days, and his hours without number;
And when he gets up, he sits folding his hands,
Or walks about saunt'ring, or trifling he stands.

I passed by his garden, and saw the wild brier
The thorn and the thistle grow broader and higher;
The clothes that hang on him are turning to rags;
And his money still wastes till he starves or he begs.

1. Hedgehogs

I made him a visit, still hoping to find
That he took better care for improving his mind;
He told me his dreams, talked of eating and drinking,
But he scarce reads his Bible, and never loves thinking.

Said I then to my heart: 'Here's a lesson for me;
That man's but a picture of what I might be;
But thanks to my friends for their care in my breeding,
Who taught me betimes to love working and reading.'

ISAAC WATTS

5. *Hark, Hark, the Lark*

Hearke, hearke, the Larke at Heaven's gate sings,
　　And Phoebus 'gins arise,
His Steeds to water at those Springs
　　On chaliced Flowres that lyes:
And winking Mary-buds begin
　　To ope their Golden eyes:
With every thing that pretty is,
　　My Lady sweet, arise:
　　　　Arise, arise!

WILLIAM SHAKESPEARE

6. *The Lark Now Leaves His Watery Nest*

The lark now leaves his watery nest,
　　And climbing shakes his dewy wings;
He takes your window for the East,
　　And to implore your light, he sings:
Awake, awake! the morn will never rise
Till she can dress her beauty at your eyes.

The merchant bows unto the seaman's star,
　　The ploughman from the sun his season takes;

But still the lover wonders what they are
    Who look for day before his mistress wakes:
Awake, awake! break through your veils of lawn;
Then draw your curtains, and begin the dawn!

SIR WILLIAM DAVENANT

7. *Early Morn*

When I did wake this morn from sleep,
    It seemed I heard birds in a dream;
Then I arose to take the air –
    The lovely air that made birds scream;
Just as a green hill launched the ship
Of gold, to take its first clear dip.
And it began its journey then,
    As I came forth to take the air;
The timid Stars had vanished quite,
    The Moon was dying with a stare;
Horses, and kine, and sheep were seen
As still as pictures, in fields green.

It seemed as though I had surprised
And trespassed in a golden world
That should have passed while men still slept!
    The joyful birds, the ship of gold,
The horses, kine and sheep did seem
As they would vanish for a dream.

WILLIAM H. DAVIES

8. *Good Morrow*

Pack, clouds, away, and welcome, day!
    With night we banish sorrow.
Sweet air, blow soft, mount, lark, aloft
    To give my Love good morrow.

Wings from the wind to please her mind,
   Notes from the lark I'll borrow:
Bird, prune thy wing, nightingale, sing,
    To give my Love good morrow!
     To give my Love good morrow
    Notes from them all I'll borrow.

Wake from thy nest, robin redbreast!
   Sing, birds, in every furrow,
And from each bill let music shrill
   Give my fair Love good morrow!
Blackbird and thrush in every bush,
   Stare,[1] linnet, and cock-sparrow,
You pretty elves, amongst yourselves
   Sing my fair Love good morrow!
    To give my Love good morrow
    Sing, birds, in every furrow!

         THOMAS HEYWOOD

9. *The Question*

I dreamed that, as I wandered by the way,
  Bare Winter suddenly was changed to Spring,
And gentle odours led my steps astray,
  Mixed with a sound of waters murmuring
Along a shelving bank of turf, which lay
  Under a copse, and hardly dared to fling
Its green arms round the bosom of the stream,
But kissed it and then fled, as thou mightest in dream.

There grew pied wind-flowers and violets,
  Daisies, those pearled Arcturi of the earth,
The constellated flower that never sets;
  Faint oxlips; tender blue-bells, at whose birth
The sod scarce heaved; and that tall flower that wets –
  Like a child, half in tenderness and mirth –

      1. Starling

Its mother's face with Heaven's collected tears,
When the low wind, its playmate's voice, it hears.

And in the warm hedge grew lush eglantine,
   Green cowbind and the moonlight-coloured may
And cherry-blossoms, and white cups, whose wine
   Was the bright dew, yet drained not by the day;
And wild rose, and ivy serpentine
   With its dark buds and leaves, wandering astray;
And flowers azure, black, and streaked with gold,
Fairer than any wakened eyes behold.

And nearer to the river's trembling edge
   There grew broad flag-flowers, purple prankt with white,
And starry river-buds among the sedge,
   And floating water-lilies, broad and bright,
Which lit the oak that overhung the hedge
   With moonlight beams of their own watery light;
And bulrushes, and reeds of such deep green
As soothed the dazzled eye with sober sheen.

Methought that of these visionary flowers
   I made a nosegay, bound in such a way
That the same hues, which in their natural bowers
   Were mingled or opposed, the like array
Kept these imprisoned children of the Hours
   Within my hand – and then, elate and gay,
I hastened to the spot whence I had come,
That I might there present it! – Oh! to whom?

PERCY BYSSHE SHELLEY

10. *The Fresh Air*

The fresh air moves like water round a boat.
   The white clouds wander. Let us wander too.
The whining, wavering plover flap and float.
   That crow is flying after that cuckoo.

Look! Look! ... They're gone. What are the great trees calling?
    Just come a little farther, by that edge
Of green, to where the stormy ploughland, falling
    Wave upon wave, is lapping to the hedge.
Oh, what a lovely bank! Give me your hand.
    Lie down and press your heart against the ground
Let us both listen till we understand,
    Each through the other, every natural sound ...
        I can't hear anything to-day, can you,
        But, far and near: 'Cuckoo! Cuckoo! Cuckoo!'?

HAROLD MONRO

11. *Weathers*

This is the weather the cuckoo likes,
    And so do I;
When the showers betumble the chestnut spikes
    And nestlings fly:
And the little brown nightingale bills his best,
And they sit outside at 'The Travellers' Rest,'
And maids come forth sprig-muslin drest,
And citizens dream of the south and west,
    And so do I.
This is the weather the shepherd shuns,
    And so do I;
When beeches drip in browns and duns,
    And thresh, and ply;
And hill-hid tides throb, throe on throe,
And meadow rivulets overflow,
And drops on gate-bars hang in a row,
And rooks in families homeward go,
    And so do I.

THOMAS HARDY

12. *Green Rain*

Into the scented woods we'll go,
And see the blackthorn swim in snow.
High above, in the budding leaves,
A brooding dove awakes and grieves;
The glades with mingled music stir,
And wildly laughs the woodpecker.
When blackthorn petals pearl the breeze,
There are the twisted hawthorne trees
Thick-set with buds, as clear and pale
As golden water or green hail —
As if a storm of rain had stood
Enchanted in the thorny wood,
And, hearing fairy voices call,
Hung poised, forgetting how to fall.

MARY WEBB

13. *Song on May Morning*

Now the bright morning Star, Dayes harbinger,
Comes dancing from the East, and leads with her
The Flowry *May*, who from her green lap throws
The yellow Cowslip and the pale Primrose.
Hail, bounteous *May*, that dost inspire
Mirth and youth and young desire,
Woods and Groves, are of thy dressing,
Hill and Dale doth boast thy blessing.
Thus we salute thee with our early Song,
And welcome thee, and wish thee long.

JOHN MILTON

14. *Sister, Awake!*

Sister, awake! close not your eyes.
   The day her light discloses,
And the bright morning doth arise
   Out of her bed of roses.

See the clear sun, the world's bright eye,
   In at our window peeping:
Lo, how he blusheth to espy
   Us idle wenches sleeping!

Therefore awake! make haste, I say,
   And let us, without staying,
All in our gowns of green so gay
   Into the park a-maying.

15. *Here We Come A-Piping*

Here we come a-piping,
In Springtime and in May;
Green fruit a-ripening,
And Winter fled away.
The Queen she sits upon the strand,
Fair as lily, white as wand;
Seven billows on the sea,
Horses riding fast and free,
And bells beyond the sand.

16. *As We Dance Round*

As we dance round a-ring-a-ring,
A maiden goes a-maying;

And here a flower, and there a flower,
Through mead and meadow straying:
O gentle one, why dost thou weep? –
Silver to spend with; gold to keep;
Till spin the green round World asleep,
And Heaven its dews be staying.

17. *Old May Song*

All in this pleasant evening, together come are we,
    For the summer springs so fresh, green, and gay;
We tell you of a blossoming and buds on every tree,
    Drawing near unto the merry month of May.

Rise up, the master of this house, put on your charm of gold,
    For the summer springs so fresh, green, and gay;
Be not in pride offended with your name we make so bold,
    Drawing near unto the merry month of May.

Rise up, the mistress of this house, with gold along your breast;
    For the summer springs so fresh, green, and gay;
And if your body be asleep, we hope your soul's at rest,
    Drawing near unto the merry month of May.

Rise up, the children of this house, all in your rich attire,
    For the summer springs so fresh, green, and gay;
And every hair upon your heads shines like the silver wire:
    Drawing near unto the merry month of May.

God bless this house and arbour, your riches and your store,
    For the summer springs so fresh, green, and gay;
We hope the Lord will prosper you, both now and evermore,
    Drawing near unto the merry month of May.

And now comes we must leave you, in peace and plenty here,
  For the summer springs so fresh, green, and gay;
We shall not sing you May again until another year,
  To draw you these cold winters away.

18. *Song of the Mayers*

Remember us poor Mayers all,
  And thus do we begin,
To lead our lives in righteousness,
  Or else we die in sin.

We have been rambling all the night,
  And almost all the day,
And now returning back again,
  We have brought you a bunch of May.

A bunch of May we have brought you,
  And at your door it stands,
It is but a sprout, but it's well budded out
  By the work of our Lord's hands.

The hedges and trees they are so green,
  As green as any leek,
Our Heavenly Father, He watered them
  With his heavenly dew so sweet.

The heavenly gates are open wide,
  Our paths are beaten plain,
And if a man be not too far gone,
  He may return again.

The life of man is but a span,
  It flourishes like a flower;
We are here to-day, and gone to-morrow,
  And are dead in an hour.

The moon shines bright, and the stars give a light,
    A little before it is day,
God bless you all, both great and small,
    And send you a joyful May.

19. *And As for Me*

... And as for me, thogh that I can but lyte,[1]
On bokès for to rede I me delyte,
And to hem yeve[2] I feyth and ful credènce,
And in myn herte have hem in reverence
So hertèly, that there is gamè noon
That fro my bokès maketh me to goon,
But hit be seldom on the holyday,
Save, certeynly, whan that the month of May
Is comen, and that I here the foulès[3] singe
And that the flourès ginnen for to springe, —
Farewel my boke, and my devocioun!
    Now have I than swich[4] a condicioun,
That, of alle the flourès in the mede,
Than love I most these flourès whyte and rede,
Swiche as men callen daysies in our toun.
To hem have I so greet affeccioun,
As I seyde erst, whan comen is the May,
That in my bed ther daweth me no day,
That I nam up, and walking in the mede,
To seen this flour agein the sonne sprede,
When hit uprysith erly by the morwe;[5]
That blisful sightè softneth all my sorwe[6]
    And whan that hit is eve, I rennè blyve,[7]
As soon as evere the sonnè ginneth weste,

1. Know but little
2. Give
3. Birds
4. Such
5. The first thing in the morning
6. Sorrow
7. Run quickly, hasten away

To seen this flour, how it wol go to reste,
For fere of nyght, so hateth she derknesse! . . .

GEOFFREY CHAUCER

20. *The Spring*

What bird so sings, yet so does wail?
O, 'tis the ravished nightingale!
' *Jug, jug, jug, jug, tereu,*' she cries,
And still her woes at midnight rise.
Brave prick-song! who is't now we hear?
None but the lark so shrill and clear;
Now at heaven's gates she claps her wings,
The morn not waking till she sings.
Hark, hark, with what a pretty throat
Poor robin-redbreast tunes his note;
Hark, how the jolly cuckoos sing
Cuckoo – to welcome in the spring!
Cuckoo – to welcome in the spring!

JOHN LYLY

21. *Spring, the Sweet Spring*

Spring, the sweet Spring, is the year's pleasant king;
Then blooms each thing, then maids dance in a ring,
Cold doth not sting, the pretty birds do sing:
    Cuckoo, jug, jug, pu we, to witta woo!

The Palm and May make country houses gay,
Lambs frisk and play, the shepherds pipe all day,
And we hear aye birds tune this merry lay:
    Cuckoo, jug, jug, pu we, to witta woo!

The fields breathe sweet, the daisies kiss our feet,
Young lovers meet, old wives a-sunning sit,
In every street these tunes our ears do greet:
  Cuckoo, jug, jug, pu we, to witta woo!
   Spring, the sweet Spring!

       THOMAS NASH

22. *A May Day*

... And now all nature seemed in love;
The lusty sap began to move;
New juice did stir the embracing vines,
And birds had drawn their valentines.
The jealous trout that now did lie,
Rose at a well-dissembled fly:
There stood my friend with patient skill,
Attending of his trembling quill.[1]
Already were the eaves possessed
With the swift pilgrim's daubèd nest:
The groves already did rejoice
In Philomel's triumphing voice.
The showers were short, the weather mild,
The morning fresh, the evening smiled.
Joan takes her neat-rubbed pail and now
She trips to milk the sand-red cow;
Where, for some sturdy football swain,
Joan strokes[2] a sillabub or twain.
The field and gardens were beset
With tulip, crocus, violet;
And now, though late, the modest rose
Did more than half a blush disclose.
Thus all looked gay, all full of cheer,
To welcome the new-liveried year.

      SIR HENRY WOTTON

  1. Float 2. Milks straight into the bowl

23. *Easter*

I got me flowers to straw thy way,
I got me boughs off many a tree:
But thou wast up by break of day,
And brought'st thy sweets along with thee.

The Sun arising in the East,
Though he give light, and the East perfume,[1]
If they should offer to contest
With thy arising, they presume.

Can there be any day but this,
Though many sunnes to shine endeavour?
We count three hundred, but we misse:
There is but one, and that one ever.

GEORGE HERBERT

24. *Pleasure It Is*

Pleasure it is
    To hear, iwis,[2]
    The birdès sing.
The deer in the dale,
The sheep in the vale,
    The corn springing;
God's purveyance
For sustenance
    It is for man.
Then we always
To Him give praise,
    And thank Him than,
    And thank Him than.

WILLIAM CORNISH

1. Refresh; make sweet   2. Truly, in sooth

MOTHER, HOME, AND SWEETHEART

25. *I Sing of a Maiden*

I sing of a maiden
   That is makeless,[1]
King of all kings
   To her son she ches.[2]

He came all so still
   Where his mother was,
As dew in April
   That falleth on the grass.

He came all so still
   To his mother's bower,
As dew in April
   That falleth on the flower.

He came all so still
   Where his mother lay,
As dew in April
   That falleth on the spray.

Mother and maiden
   Was never none but she;
Well may such a lady
   God's mother be.

1. Mateless and matchless   2. Chose

26. *Lullaby*

Upon my lap my sovereign sits
And sucks upon my breast;
Meantime his love maintains my life
And gives my sense her rest.
 Sing lullaby, my little boy,
 Sing lullaby, mine only joy!

When thou hast taken thy repast,
Repose, my babe, on me;
So may thy mother and thy nurse
Thy cradle also be.
 Sing lullaby, my little boy,
 Sing lullaby, mine only joy!

I grieve that duty doth not work
All that my wishing would,
Because I would not be to thee
But in the best I should.
 Sing lullaby, my little boy,
 Sing lullaby, mine only joy!

Yet as I am, and as I may,
I must and will be thine,
Though all too little for thy self
Vouchsafing to be mine.
 Sing lullaby, my little boy,
 Sing lullaby, mine only joy!

RICHARD ROWLANDS

27. *The Little Black Boy*

My mother bore me in the southern wild,
And I am black, but O! my soul is white;
White as an angel is the English child,
But I am black, as if bereaved of light.

My mother taught me underneath a tree,
And, sitting down before the heat of day,
She took me on her lap and kissèd me,
And, pointing to the east, began to say:

'Look on the rising sun; there God does live,
And gives his light, and gives his heat away;
And flowers and trees and beasts and men receive
Comfort in morning, joy in the noonday.

'And we are put on earth a little space,
That we may learn to bear the beams of love;
And these black bodies and this sunburnt face
Is but a cloud, and like a shady grove.

'For when our souls have learned the heat to bear,
The cloud will vanish; we shall hear his voice,
Saying: "Come out from the grove, my love and care,
And round my golden tent like lambs rejoice." '

Thus did my mother say, and kissèd me;
And thus I say to little English boy.
When I from black and he from white cloud free,
And round the tent of God like lambs we joy,

I'll shade him from the heat, till he can bear
To lean in joy upon our Father's knee;
And then I'll stand and stroke his silver hair,
And be like him, and he will then love me.

WILLIAM BLAKE

28. *The Echoing Green*

The Sun does arise,
And make happy the skies;
The merry bells ring
To welcome the Spring;
The skylark and thrush,
The birds of the bush,
Sing louder around
To the bells' cheerful sound,
While our sports shall be seen
On the Echoing Green.

Old John, with white hair,
Does laugh away care,
Sitting under the oak,
Among the old folk,
They laugh at our play,
And soon they all say:
'Such, such were the joys
When we all, girls and boys,
In our youth time were seen
On the Echoing Green.'

Till the little ones, weary,
No more can be merry;
The sun does descend,
And our sports have an end.
Round the laps of their mothers
Many sisters and brothers,
Like birds in their nest,
Are ready for rest,
And sport no more seen
On the darkening Green.

WILLIAM BLAKE

29. *If I Had But Two Little Wings*

If I had but two little wings
  And were a little feathery bird,
    To you I'd fly, my dear!
But thoughts like these are idle things,
    And I stay here.

But in my sleep to you I fly:
  I'm always with you in my sleep!
    The world is all one's own.
But then one wakes, and where am I?
    All, all alone.

Sleep stays not, though a monarch bids:
  So I love to wake ere break of day:
    For though my sleep be gone,
Yet while 'tis dark, one shuts one's lids,
    And still dreams on.

           SAMUEL TAYLOR COLERIDGE

30. *I Remember*

I remember, I remember,
The house where I was born,
The little window where the sun
Came peeping in at morn;
He never came a wink too soon,
Nor brought too long a day;
But now, I often wish the night
Had borne my breath away.

I remember, I remember,
The roses, red and white,

The violets, and the lily-cups! –
Those flowers made of light!
The lilacs where the robin built,
And where my brother set
The laburnum on his birth-day, –
The tree is living yet!

I remember, I remember,
Where I used to swing,
And thought the air must rush as fresh
To swallows on the wing;
My spirit flew in feathers then,
That is so heavy now,
And summer pools could hardly cool
The fever on my brow!

I remember, I remember,
The fir trees dark and high;
I used to think their slender tops
Were close against the sky:
It was a childish ignorance,
But now 'tis little joy
To know I'm farther off from Heaven
Than when I was a boy.

THOMAS HOOD

31. *Midnight on the Great Western*

In the third-class seat sat the journeying boy,
    And the roof-lamp's oily flame
Played down on his listless form and face,
Bewrapt past knowing to what he was going,
        Or whence he came.

In the band of his hat the journeying boy
    Had a ticket stuck; and a string

Around his neck bore the key of his box,
That twinkled gleams of the lamp's sad beams
   Like a living thing.

What past can be yours, O journeying boy
  Towards a world unknown,
Who calmly, as if incurious quite
On all at stake, can undertake
   This plunge alone?

Knows your soul a sphere, O journeying boy,
  Our rude realms far above,
Whence with spacious vision you mark and mete
This region of sin that you find you in,
   But are not of?

       THOMAS HARDY

32. *The Runaway*

Once when the sun of the year was beginning to fall
We stopped by a mountain pasture to say, 'Whose colt?'
A little Morgan had one forefoot on the wall,
The other curled at his heart. He dipped his head
And snorted to us; and then he had to bolt.
We heard the muffled thunder when he fled
And we saw him or thought we saw him dim and grey
Like a shadow against the curtain of falling flakes.
We said, 'The little fellow's afraid of the snow.
He isn't winter broken.' 'It isn't play
With the little fellow at all. He's running away.
I doubt if even his mother could tell him, "Sakes,
It's only weather." He'd think she didn't know.
Where is his mother? He can't be out alone.'
And now he comes again with a clatter of stone
And mounts the wall again with whited eyes

And all his tail that isn't hair up straight.
He shudders his coat as if to throw off flies.
Whoever it is that leaves him out so late
When everything else has gone to stall and bin
Ought to be told to go and bring him in.

ROBERT FROST

33. *On Eastnor Knoll*

Silent are the woods, and the dim green boughs are
Hushed in the twilight; yonder, in the path through
The apple orchard, is a tired plough-boy
Calling the cows home.

A bright white star blinks, the pale moon rounds, but
Still the red, lurid wreckage of the sunset
Smoulders in smoky fire, and burns on
The misty hill-tops.

Ghostly it grows, and darker, the burning
Fades into smoke, and now the gusty oaks are
A silent army of phantoms thronging
A land of shadows.

JOHN MASEFIELD

34. *Home No More Home to Me*

Home no more home to me, whither must I wander?
    Hunger my driver, I go where I must.
Cold blows the winter wind over hill and heather;
    Thick drives the rain, and my roof is in the dust.

Loved of wise men was the shade of my roof-tree.
　　The true word of welcome was spoken in the door—
Dear days of old, with the faces in the firelight,
　　Kind folks of old, you come again no more.

Home was home then, my dear, full of kindly faces,
　　Home was home then, my dear, happy for the child,
Fire and the windows bright glittered on the moorland;
　　Song, tuneful song, built a palace in wild.
Now, when day dawns on the brow of the moorland,
　　Lone stands the house, and the chimney-stone is cold.
Lone let it stand, now the friends are all departed,
　　The kind hearts, the true hearts, that loved the place of old.

Spring shall come, come again, calling up the moor-fowl,
　　Spring shall bring the sun and rain, bring the bees and flowers;
Red shall the heather bloom over hill and valley,
　　Soft flow the stream through the even-flowing hours;
Fair the day shine as it shone on my childhood —
　　Fair shine the day on the house with open door;
Birds come and cry there and twitter in the chimney —
　　But I go for ever and come again no more.

ROBERT LOUIS STEVENSON

35. *Dalyaunce*

Mundus.　　Welcome, fayre chylde, what is thy name?

Infans.　　I wote not, syr, withouten blame.
　　　　　　　But ofte tyme my moder in her game
　　　　　　　Callèd me dalyaunce.

Mundus.　　Dalyaunce, my swete chylde,
　　　　　　　It is a name that is ryght wylde,
　　　　　　　For whan thou waxest olde.

It is a name of no substaunce
But, my fayre chylde, what woldest thou have?

Infans.   Syr of some comforte I you crave –
Mete and clothe my lyfe to save:
And I your true servaunt shall be.

Mundus.   Fayre chylde, I graunte thee thyne askynge.
I wyll thee fynde[1] whyle thou art yinge[2]
So thou wylte be obedyent to my byddynge.
These garments gaye I gyve to thee.
And also I gyve to thee a name,
And clepe[3] thee Wanton, in every game;
Tyll XIII yere be come and gone,
And than come agayne to me.

[Infans is now called Wanton.]
Wanton.   Gramercy, Worlde, for myne araye,
For now I purpose me to playe.

Mundus.   Fare well, fayre chylde, and have good daye.
All rychelesnesse[4] is kynde[5] for thee.

[Mundus goes out leaving Wanton alone.]
Wanton.   Aha, Wanton is my name!
I can many a quaynte game.
Lo, my toppe I dryve in same,
Se, it torneth rounde!
I can with my scorge-stycke
My felowe upon the heed hytte,
And wyghtly[6] from hym make a skyppe;
And blere[7] on hym my tonge.
If brother or syster do me chyde
I wyll scratche and also byte.

1. Keep   5. Natural
2. Young   6. Nimbly
3. Call   7. Stick out
4. Heedlessness

I can crye, and also kyke,
And mocke them all berewe.
If fader or mother wyll me smyte,
I wyll wrynge[8] with my lyppe;
And lyghtly from hym make a skyppe;
And call my dame shrewe.
Aha, a newe game have I founde:
Se this gynne[9] it renneth rounde;
And here another have I founde,
And yet mo[10] can I fynde.
I can mowe[11] on a man;
And make a lesynge[12] well I can,
And mayntayne it ryght well than.
This connynge[13] came me of kynde.
Ye, syrs,[14] I can well gelde a snayle;
And catche a cowe by the tayle;
This is a fayre connynge!
I can daunce, and also skyppe;
I can playe at the chery pytte;
And I can wystell you a fytte,[15]
Syres, in a whylowe ryne.[16]
Ye, syrs, and every daye
Whan I to scole shall take the waye
Some good mannes gardyn I wyll assaye,
Perys[17] and plommes to plucke.
I can spye a sparowes nest.
I wyll not go to scole but whan me lest,
For there begynneth a sory fest[18]
Whan the mayster sholde lyfte my docke.[19]
But, syrs, whan I was seven yere of age,
I was sent to the Worlde to take wage.
And this seven yere I have ben his page
And kept his commaundement . . .

8. Squiggle	12. Falsehood	16. Willow rind
9. Toy or trap	13. Learning	17. Pears
10. More	14. Yea, sirs	18. Feast
11. Make grimaces	15. Air, tune, stave	19. Gown or coat-tail

36. *Christmas at Sea*

The sheets were frozen hard, and they cut the naked hand;
The decks were like a slide, where a seaman scarce could stand;
The wind was a nor'wester, blowing squally off the sea;
And cliffs and spouting breakers were the only things a-lee.

They heard the surf a-roaring before the break of day;
But 'twas only with the peep of light we saw how ill we lay.
We tumbled every hand on deck instanter, with a shout,
And we gave her the maintops'l, and stood by to go about.

All day we tacked and tacked between the South Head and the
    North;
All day we hauled the frozen sheets, and got no further forth;
All day as cold as charity, in bitter pain and dread,
For very life and nature we tacked from head to head.

We have the South a wider berth, for there the tide-race roared;
But every tack we made we brought the North Head close aboard:
So's we saw the cliffs and houses, and the breakers running high,
And the coastguard in his garden, with his glass against his eye.

The frost was on the village roofs as white as ocean foam;
The good red fires were burning bright in every 'longshore home;
The windows sparkled clear, and the chimneys volleyed out;
And I vow we sniffed the victuals as the vessel went about.

The bells upon the church were rung with a mighty jovial cheer
For it's just that I should tell you how (of all days in the year)
This day of our adversity was blessèd Christmas morn,
And the house above the coastguard's was the house where I was
    born.

O well I saw the pleasant room, the pleasant faces there,
My mother's silver spectacles, my father's silver hair;

And well I saw the firelight, like a flight of homely elves,
Go dancing round the china-plates that stand upon the shelves.

And well I knew the talk they had, the talk that was of me,
Of the shadow on the household and the son that went to sea;
And O the wicked fool I seemed, in every kind of way,
To be here and hauling frozen ropes on blessèd Christmas Day.

They lit the high sea-light, and the dark began to fall.
'All hands to loose topgallant sails,' I heard the captain call,
'By the Lord, she'll never stand it,' our first mate, Jackson, cried.
. . . 'It's the one way or the other, Mr Jackson,' he replied.

She staggered to her bearings, but the sails were new and good.
And the ship smelt up to windward just as though she understood.
As the winter's day was ending, in the entry of the night,
We cleared the weary headland, and passed below the light.

And they heaved a mighty breath, every soul on board but me,
As they saw her nose again pointing handsome out to sea;
But all that I could think of, in the darkness and the cold,
Was just that I was leaving home and my folks were growing old.

ROBERT LOUIS STEVENSON

37. *Twilight*

The twilight is sad and cloudy,
    The wind blows wild and free,
And like the wings of sea-birds
    Flash the white caps of the sea.

But in the fisherman's cottage
    There shines a ruddier light,
And a little face at the window
    Peers out into the night.

Close, close it is pressed to the window,
    As if those childish eyes
Were looking into the darkness,
    To see some form arise.

And a woman's waving shadow
    Is passing to and fro,
Now rising to the ceiling,
    Now bowing and bending low.

What tale do the roaring ocean,
    And the night-wind, bleak and wild,
As they beat at the crazy casement,
    Tell to that little child?

And why do the roaring ocean,
    And the night-wind, wild and bleak,
As they beat at the heart of the mother,
    Drive the colour from her cheek?

HENRY   WADSWORTH   LONGFELLOW

38. *How's My Boy?*

'Ho, sailor of the sea!
How's my boy – my boy?'
'What's your boy's name, good wife,
And in what good ship sailed he?'
'My boy John –
He that went to sea –
What care I for the ship, sailor?
My boy's my boy to me.

'You come back from sea
And not know my John!
I might as well have asked some landsman

58

Yonder down in the town.
There's not an ass in all the parish
But he knows my John.

'How's my boy – my boy?
And unless you let me know,
I'll swear you are no sailor,
Blue jacket or no,
Brass button or no, sailor,
Anchor and crown or no!
Sure his ship was the Jolly Briton.' –
'Speak low, woman, speak low!'

'And why should I speak low, sailor,
About my own boy John?
If I was loud as I am proud
I'd sing him o'er the town!
Why should I speak low, sailor?'
'That good ship went down.'

'How's my boy – my boy?
What care I for the ship, sailor,
I never was aboard her.
Be she afloat, or be she aground,
Sinking or swimming, I'll be bound,
Her owners can afford her!
I say, how's my John?'
'Every man on board went down,
Every man aboard her.'

'How's my boy – my boy?
What care I for the men, sailor?
I'm not their mother –
How's my boy – my boy?
Tell me of him and no other!
How's my boy – my boy?'

SYDNEY DOBELL

39. *Cam' Ye By?*

Cam' ye by the salmon fishers?
Cam' ye by the roperee?
Saw ye a sailor laddie
Waiting on the coast for me?

I ken fahr[1] I'm gyain,[2]
I ken fahs[3] gyain wi' me;
I ha'e a lad o' my ain,
Ye daurna tack 'im fae[4] me.

Stockings of blue silk,
Shoes of patent leather,
Kid to tie them up,
And gold rings on his finger.

Oh for six o'clock!
Oh for seven I weary!
Oh for eight o'clock!
And then I'll see my dearie.

40. *My Boy Tammy*

'Whar hae ye been a' day, my boy Tammy?
Whar hae ye been a' day, my boy Tammy?'
'I've been by burn and flow'ry brae,
Meadow green and mountain grey,
Courtin' o' this young thing just come frae her Mammy.'

1. Where 3. Who's
2. Going 4. From

'And whar gat ye that young thing, my boy Tammy?'
 'I gat her down in yonder howe,[1]
 Smiling on a broomy knowe,[2]
Herding ae wee Lamb and Ewe for her poor Mammy.'

'What said ye to the bonny bairn, my boy Tammy?'
 ' "I hae a house, it cost me dear,
 I've walth o' plenishen and gear,[3]
Ye se get it a', war't ten times mair, gin[4] ye will leave your Mammy." '

'The smile gaed aff her bonny face – "I mauna leave my Mammy!
 She's gi'en me meat, she's gi'en me claes,[5]
 She's been my comfort a' my days,
My father's death brought mony waes – I canna leave my
    Mammy." '

' "We'll tak her hame and mak her fain, mya in kind-hearted
    Lammy,
 We'll gi'e her meat, we'll gi'e her claes,
 We'll be her comfort a' her days":
The wee thing gi'es her hand, and says, "There, gang and ask my
    Mammy." '

'Has she been to kirk wi' thee, my boy Tammy?'
 'She has been to kirk wi' me,
 And the tear was in her ee,
But Oh! she's but a young thing just come frae her Mammy.'

                                HECTOR MACNEILL

1. Dale or hollow   4. If
2. Knoll or hillock   5. Clothes
3. Goods and chattels

41. *Rosy Apple, Lemon or Pear*

Rosy apple, lemon or pear,
Bunch of roses she shall wear;
Gold and silver by her side,
I know who will be the bride.
Take her by her lily-white hand,
  Lead her to the altar;
Give her kisses, – one, two, three, –
  Mother's runaway daughter.

42. *In Praise of Isabel Pennell*

By Saint Mary, my lady,
Your mammy and your daddy
Brought forth a goodly baby!

My maiden Isabell, –
Reflaring[1] rosabell,
The flagrant camamell,

The ruddy rosary,
The sovereign rosemary,
The pretty strawberry,

The columbine, the nepte,[2]
The ieloffer[3] well set,
The proper violet,

Ennewèd, your colour
Is like the daisy flower
After the April shower!

1. Sweet-smelling   3. Gillyflower
2. Cat-mint

Star of the morrow gray,
The blossom on the spray,
The freshest flower of May;

Maidenly demure,
Of womanhood the lure,
Wherefore I make you sure:

It were an heavenly health,
It were an endless wealth,
A life for God himself,

To hear this nightingale,
Among the birdès smale,
Warbling in the vale: –

Dug, dug,
Iug, iug,
Good year and good luck,
With chuk, chuk, chuk, chuk!

JOHN SKELTON

43. *My Sweet Sweeting*

She is so proper and so pure,
Full stedfast, stabill and demure,
There is none such, ye may be sure,
      As my swete swetyng.

In all thys world, as thynketh me,
Is none so plesaunt to my e'e,
That I am glad soo ofte to see,
      As my swete swetyng.

When I behold my swetyng swete,
Her face, her hands, her minion fete,
They seme to me there is none so mete,
   As my swete swetyng.

Above all other prayse must I,
And love my pretty pygsnye,
For none I fynd so womanly
   As my swete swetyng.

44. *Sweet Stay-at-Home*

Sweet Stay-at-Home, sweet Well-content,
Thou knowest of no strange continent:
Thou has not felt thy bosom keep
A gentle motion with the deep;
Thou hast not sailed in Indian seas,
Where scent comes forth in every breeze.
Thou hast not seen the rich grape grow
For miles, as far as eyes can go;
Thou hast not seen a summer's night
When maids could sew by a worm's light;
Nor the North Sea in spring send out
Bright hues that like birds flit about
In solid cages of white ice –
Sweet Stay-at-Home, sweet Love-one-place.
Thou hast not seen black fingers pick
White cotton when the bloom is thick,
Nor heard black throats in harmony;
Nor hast thou sat on stones that lie
Flat on the earth, that once did rise
To hide proud kings from common eyes.
Thou hast not seen plains full of bloom
Where green things had such little room
They pleased the eye like fairer flowers –
Sweet Stay-at-Home, all these long hours.

Sweet Well-content, sweet Love-one-place,
Sweet, simple maid, bless they dear face;
For thou hast made more homely stuff
Nurture thy gentle self enough;
I love thee for a heart that's kind —
Not for the knowledge in thy mind.

WILLIAM H. DAVIES

45. *Waiting*

Rich in the waning light she sat
While the fierce rain on the window spat.
The yellow lamp-glow lit her face,
Shadows cloaked the narrow place
She sat adream in. Then she'd look
Idly upon an idle book;
Anon would rise and musing peer
Out at the misty street and drear;
Or with her loosened dark hair play,
Hiding her fingers' snow away;
And, singing softly, would sing on
When the desire of song had gone.
'O lingering day!' her bosom sighed,
'O laggard Time!' each motion cried.
Last she took the lamp and stood
Rich in its flood,
And looked and looked again at what
Her longing fingers' zeal had wrought;
And turning then did nothing say,
Hiding her thoughts away.

JOHN FREEMAN

46. *The Sick Child*

Child.   O Mother, lay your hand on my brow!
          O mother, mother, where am I now?
          Why is the room so gaunt and great?
          Why am I lying awake so late?

Mother.   Fear not at all: the night is still.
          Nothing is here that means you ill —
          Nothing but lamps the whole town through,
          And never a child awake but you.

Child.   Mother, mother, speak low in my ear,
          Some of the things are so great and near,
          Some are so small and far away,
          I have a fear that I cannot say.
          What have I done, and what do I fear,
          And why are you crying, mother dear?

Mother.   Out in the city, sounds begin.
          Thank the kind God, the carts come in!
          An hour or two more, and God is so kind,
          The day shall be blue in the window blind,
          Then shall my child go sweetly asleep,
          And dream of the birds and the hills of sheep.

                    ROBERT LOUIS STEVENSON

47. *Stillness*

When the words rustle no more,
    And the last work's done,
When the bolt lies deep in the door,
    And Fire, our Sun,
Falls on the dark-laned meadows of the floor;

When from the clock's last chime to the next chime
    Silence beats his drum,
And Space with gaunt grey eyes and her brother Time
    Wheeling and whispering come,
She with the mould of form and he with the loom of rhyme:

Then twittering out in the night my thought-birds flee,
    I am emptied of all my dreams:
I only hear Earth turning, only see
    Ether's long bankless streams,
And only know I should drown if you laid not your hand on me.

JAMES ELROY FLECKER

48. *Lines on Receiving His Mother's Picture*

O that those lips had language! Life has passed
With me but roughly since I heard thee last.
Those lips are thine – thy own sweet smiles I see,
The same that oft in childhood solaced me;
Voice only fails, else how distinct they say,
'Grieve not, my child – chase all thy fears away!' . . .
    My Mother! when I learnt that thou wast dead,
Say, wast thou conscious of the tears I shed?
Hovered thy spirit o'er thy sorrowing son,
Wretch even then, life's journey just begun?
Perhaps thou gav'st me, though unseen, a kiss,
Perhaps a tear, if souls can weep in bliss –
Ah, that maternal smile! it answers – Yes.
I heard the bell tolled on thy burial day,
I saw the hearse that bore thee slow away,
And, turning from my nursery window, drew
A long, long sigh, and wept a last adieu!
But was it such? – It was. Where thou art gone
Adieus and farewells are a sound unknown.

May I but meet thee on that peaceful shore,
The parting word shall pass my lips no more!
Thy maidens, grieved themselves at my concern,
Oft gave me promise of thy quick return.
What ardently I wished, I long believed,
And, disappointed still, was still deceived,
By expectation every day beguiled,
Dupe of *to-morrow* even from a child.
Thus many a sad to-morrow came and went,
Till, all my stock of infant sorrow spent,
I learnt at last submission to my lot.
But, though I less deplored thee, ne'er forgot.

Where once we dwelt our name is heard no more,
Children not thine have trod my nursery floor;
And where the gardener Robin, day by day,
Drew me to school along the public way,
Delighted with my bauble coach, and wrapped
In scarlet mantle warm, and velvet-capped,
'Tis now become a history little known,
That once we called the pastoral house our own.
Short-lived possession! but the record fair
That memory keeps, of all thy kindness there,
Still outlives many a storm, that has effaced
A thousand other themes less deeply traced.
Thy nightly visits to my chamber made,
That thou mightst know me safe and warmly laid;
Thy morning bounties ere I left my home,
The biscuit, or confectionary plum;
The fragrant waters on my cheek bestowed
By thy own hand, till fresh they shone and glowed;
All this, and more endearing still than all,
Thy constant flow of love, that knew no fall . . .

WILLIAM COWPER

49. *The Chimney Sweeper*

When my mother died I was very young,
And my father sold me while yet my tongue
Could scarcely cry ' 'weep! 'weep! 'weep! 'weep!'
So your chimneys I sweep, and in soot I sleep.

There's little Tom Dacre, who cried when his head,
That curled like a lamb's back, was shaved: so I said
'Hush, Tom! never mind it, for when your head's bare
You know that the soot cannot spoil your white hair.'

And so he was quiet, and that very night,
As Tom was a-sleeping, he had such a sight!
That thousands of sweepers, Dick, Joe, Ned, and Jack,
Were all of them locked up in coffins of black.

And by came an Angel who had a bright key,
And he opened the coffins and set them all free;
Then down a green plain leaping, laughing, they run,
And wash in a river, and shine in the Sun.

Then naked and white, all their bags left behind,
They rise upon clouds and sport in the wind;
And the Angel told Tom, if he'd be a good boy,
He'd have God for his father, and never want joy.

And so Tom awoke; and we rose in the dark,
And got with our bags and our brushes to work.
Tho' the morning was cold, Tom was happy and warm;
So if all do their duty they need not fear harm.

WILLIAM BLAKE

50. *Bonnie George Campbell*

Hie upon Hielands,
    and laigh upon Tay,
Bonnie George Campbell
    rode out on a day.

Saddled and briddled
    and booted rade he;
Toom[1] hame cam' the saddle,
    but never cam' he.

Down cam' his auld mither,
    greetin'[2] fu' sair,
And down cam' his bonny wife,
    wingin' her hair: –

'My meadow lies green,
    and my corn is unshorn,
My barn is to build
    and my babe is unborn.'

Saddled and briddled
    and booted rade he;
Toom hame cam' the saddle
    but never cam' he.

51. *The Orphan's Song*

I had a little bird,
I took it from the nest;
I prest it, and blest it,
And nurst it in my breast.

1. Empty   2. Weeping

I set it on the ground,
I danced round and round,
And sang about it so cheerly,
With 'Hey my little bird, and ho my little bird,
And ho but I love thee dearly!'

I make a little feast
Of food soft and sweet,
I hold it in my breast,
And coax it to eat;

I pit, and I pat,
I call it this and that,
And sing about it so cheerly,
With 'Hey my little bird, and ho my little bird,
And ho but I love thee dearly!'

I may kiss, I may sing,
But I can't make it feed,
It taketh no heed
Of any pleasant thing.

I scolded and I socked,
But it minded not a whit,
Its little mouth was locked,
And I could not open it.

Tho' with pit, and with pat,
And with this, and with that,
I sang about it so cheerly,
With 'Hey my little bird, and ho my little bird,
And ho but I love thee dearly!'

But when the day was done,
And the room was at rest,
And I sat all alone
With my birdie in my breast,

And the light had fled,
And not a sound was heard,
Then my little bird
Lifted up its head,

And the little mouth
Loosened its sullen pride,
And it opened, it opened,
With a yearning strong and wide.

.Swifter than I speak
I brought it food once more,
But the poor little beak
Was locked as before.

I sat down again,
And not a creature stirred;
I laid the little bird
Again where it had laid;

And again when nothing stirred,
And not a word I said,
Then my little bird
Lifted up its head,

And the little beak
Loosed its stubborn pride,
And it opened, it opened,
With a yearning strong and wide.

It lay in my breast,
It uttered no cry,
'Twas famished, 'twas famished,
And I couldn't tell why.

I couldn't tell why,
But I saw that it would die,
For all that I kept dancing round and round,
And singing about it so cheerly,
With 'Hey my little bird, and ho my little bird,
And ho but I love thee dearly!'

I never look sad,
I hear what people say,
I laugh when they are gay
And they think I am glad.

My tears never start,
I never say a word,
But I think that my heart
Is like that little bird.

Every day I read,
And I sing, and I play,
But thro' the long day
It taketh no heed.

It taketh no heed
Of any pleasant thing,
I know it doth not read,
I know it doth not sing.

With my mouth I read,
With my hands I play,
My shut heart is shut,
Coax it how you may.

You may coax it how you may
While the day is broad and bright,
But in the dead night
When the guests are gone away,

And no more the music sweet
Up the house doth pass,
Nor the dancing feet
Shake the nursery glass;

And I've heard my aunt
Along the corridor,
And my uncle gaunt
Lock his chamber door;

And upon the stair
All is hushed and still,
And the last wheel
Is silent in the square;

And the nurses snore,
And the dim sheets rise and fall,
And the lamplight's on the wall,
And the mouse is on the floor;

And the curtains of my bed
Are like a heavy cloud,
And the clock ticks loud,
And sounds are in my head;

And little Lizzie sleeps
Softly at my side,
It opens, it opens,
With a yearning strong and wide!

It yearns in my breast,
It utters no cry,
'Tis famished, 'tis famished,
And I feel that I shall die,
I feel that I shall die,
And none will know why.

Tho' the pleasant life is dancing round and round,
And singing about me so cheerly,
With 'Hey my little bird, and ho my little bird,
And ho but I love thee dearly!'

SYDNEY DOBELL

52. *The First Grief*

'Oh! call my brother back to me,
    I cannot play alone;
The summer comes with flower and bee –
    Where is my brother gone?

'The butterfly is glancing bright
    Across the sunbeam's track;
I care not now to chase its flight –
    Oh! call my brother back.

'The flowers run wild – the flowers we sowed
    Around our garden tree;
Our vine is drooping with its load –
    Oh! call him back to me.'

'He would not hear my voice, fair child!
    He may not come to thee;
The face that once like spring-time smiled
    On earth no more thou'lt see.

'A rose's brief, bright life of joy,
    Such unto him was given;
Go – thou must play alone, my boy –
    Thy brother is in heaven!'

'And has he left the birds and flowers,
    And must I call in vain;

And through the long, long summer hours,
    Will he not come again?

'And by the brook, and in the glade,
    Are all our wanderings o'er?
Oh! while my brother with me played,
    Would I had loved him more!'

FELICIA HEMANS

53. *The Poplar Field*

The poplars are felled; farewell to the shade
And the whispering sound of the cool colonnade;
The winds play no more and sing in the leaves,
Nor Ouse on his bosom their image receives.

Twelve years have elapsed since I first took a view
Of my favourite field, and the bank where they grew;
And now in the grass below they are laid,
And the tree is my seat that once lent me a shade.

The blackbird has fled to another retreat
Where the hazels afford him a screen from the heat,
And the scene where his melody charmed me before
Resounds with his sweet-flowing ditty no more.

My fugitive years are all hasting away,
And I must ere long lie as lowly as they
With a turf on my breast, and a stone at my head,
Ere another such grove shall arise in its stead.

'Tis a sight to engage me, if anything can,
To muse on the perishing pleasures of man;
Though his life be a dream, his enjoyments, I see,
Have a being less durable even than he.

WILLIAM COWPER

54. *Farewell*

Not soon shall I forget — a sheet
Of golden water, cold and sweet,
The young moon with her head in veils
Of silver, and the nightingales.

A wain of hay came up the lane —
O fields I shall not walk again,
And trees I shall not see, so still
Against a sky of daffodil!

Fields where my happy heart had rest,
And where my heart was heaviest,
I shall remember them at peace
Drenched in moon-silver like a fleece.

The golden water sweet and cold,
The moon of silver and of gold,
The dew upon the gray grass-spears,
I shall remember them with tears.

KATHARINE TYNAN

55. *Ye Banks and Braes o' Bonnie Doon*

Ye banks and braes o' bonnie Doon,
How can ye bloom sae fair?
How can ye chant, ye little birds,
And I sae fu' o' care?

Thou'll break my heart, thou bonnie bird
That sings upon the bough;
Thou minds me o' the happy days
When my fause Luve was true.

Thou'll break my heart, thou bonnie bird
 That sings beside thy mate;
For sae I sat, and sae I sang,
 And wist na o' my fate.

Aft hae I roved by bonnie Doon
 To see the woodbine twine,
And ilka[1] bird sang o' its love;
 And sae did I o' mine.

Wi' lightsome heart I pu'd a rose,
 Frae aff its thorny tree;
And my fause luver staw[2] the rose,
 But left the thorn wi' me.

ROBERT BURNS

56. *To a River in the South*

Call me no more, O gentle stream,
To wander through thy sunny dream,
No more to lean at twilight cool
Above thy weir and glimmering pool.

Surely I know thy hoary dawns,
The silver crisp on all thy lawns,
The softly swirling undersong
That rocks thy reeds the winter long.

Surely I know the joys that ring
Through the green deeps of leafy spring;
I know the elfin cups and domes
That are their small and secret homes.

1. Every   2. Stole

Yet is the light for ever lost
That daily once thy meadows crossed,
The voice no more by thee is heard
That matched the song of stream and bird.

Call me no more! – thy waters roll
Here, in the world that is my soul,
And here, though Earth be drowned in night,
Old love shall dwell with old delight.

HENRY NEWBOLT

57. *The Deserted House*

There's no smoke in the chimney,
    And the rain beats on the floor;
There's no glass in the window,
    There's no wood in the door;
The heather grows behind the house,
    And the sand lies before.

No hand hath trained the ivy,
    The walls are gray and bare;
The boats upon the sea sail by,
    Nor ever tarry there.
No beast of the field comes nigh,
    Nor any bird of the air.

MARY COLERIDGE

58. *An Old Woman of the Roads*

O, to have a little house!
    To own the hearth and stool and all!
The heaped-up sods upon the fire,
    The pile of turf against the wall!

To have a clock with weights and chains
    And pendulum swinging up and down!
A dresser filled with shining delph,
    Speckled and white and blue and brown!

I could be busy all the day
    Clearing and sweeping hearth and floor,
And fixing on their shelf again
    My white and blue and speckled store!

I could be quiet there at night
    Beside the fire and by myself,
Sure of a bed, and loth to leave
    The ticking clock and the shining delph!

Och! but I'm weary of mist and dark,
    And roads where there's never a house or bush,
And tired I am of bog and road
    And the crying wind and the lonesome hush!

And I am praying to God on high,
    And I am praying Him night and day,
For a little house — a house of my own —
    Out of the wind's and the rain's way.

PADRAIC COLUM

59. *A Deserted Home*

Here where the fields lie lonely and untended,
    Once stood the old house grey among the trees,
Once to the hills rolled the waves of the cornland —
    Long waves and golden, softer than the sea's.

Long, long ago has the ploughshare rusted,
    Long has the barn stood roofless and forlorn;

But oh! far away are some who still remember
   The songs of the young girls binding up the corn.

Here where the windows shone across the darkness,
   Here where the stars once watched above the fold,
Still watch the stars, but the sheepfold is empty;
   Falls now the rain where the hearth glowed of old.

Here where the leagues of melancholy lough-sedge
   Moan in the wind round the grey forsaken shore,
Once waved the corn in the mid-month of autumn,
   Once sped the dance when the corn was on the floor.

                  SIDNEY ROYSE LYSAGHT

60. *Under the Woods*

When these old woods were young
The thrushes' ancestors
As sweetly sung
In the old years.

There was no garden here,
Apples nor mistletoe;
No children dear
Ran to and fro.

New then was this thatched cot,
But the keeper was old,
And he had not
Much lead or gold.

Most silent beech and yew:
As he went round about
The woods to view
Seldom he shot.

But now that he is gone
Out of most memories,
Still lingers on,
A stoat of his,

But one, shrivelled and green,
And with no scent at all,
And barely seen
On this shed wall.

EDWARD THOMAS

61. *Blows the Wind To-day*

Blows the wind to-day, and the sun and the rain are flying,
    Blows the wind on the moors to-day and now,
Where about the graves of the martyrs the whaups are crying,
    My heart remembers how!

Grey recumbent tombs of the dead in desert places,
    Standing stones on the vacant wine-red moor,
Hills of sheep, and the howes of the silent vanished races,
    And winds, austere and pure:

Be it granted me to behold you again in dying,
    Hills of home! and to hear again the call;
Hear about the graves of the martyrs the peewees crying,
    And hear no more at all.

ROBERT LOUIS STEVENSON

62. *The Twa Brothers*

There were twa brethren in the north,
    They went[1] to the school thegither;
The one unto the other said,
    'Will you try a warsle[2] afore?'

They warsled up, they warsled down,
    Till Sir John fell to the ground,
And there was a knife in Sir Willie's pouch,
    Gied him a deadlie wound.

'O brither dear, take me on your back,
    Carry me to yon burn clear,
And wash the blood from off my wound,
    And it will bleed nae mair.'

He took him up upon his back,
    Carried him to yon burn clear,
And washed the blood from off his wound,
    And aye it bled the mair.

'O brither dear, take me on your back,
    Carry me to yon kirk-yard,
And dig a grave baith wide and deep,
    And lay my body there.'

He's taen him up upon his back,
    Carried him to yon kirk-yard,
And dug a grave baith deep and wide,
    And laid his body there.

'But what will I say to my father dear,
    Gin[3] he chance to say, Willie, whar's John?'

1. Had been   3. If
2. Wrestle

'Oh say that he's to England gone,
  To buy him a cask of wine.'

'And what will I say to my mother dear,
  Gin she chance to say, Willie, whar's John?'
'Oh say that he's to England gone,
  To buy her a new silk gown.'

'And what will I say to my sister dear,
  Gin she chance to say, 'Willie, whar's John?'
'Oh say that he's to England gone,
  To buy her a wedding ring.'

'But what will I say to her you lo'e dear,
  Gin she cry, Why tarries my John?'
'Oh tell her I lie in Kirk-land fair,
  And home shall never come.'

63. *The Dead Knight*

The cleanly rush of the mountain air,
And the mumbling, grumbling humble-bees,
Are the only things that wander there,
The pitiful bones are laid at ease,
The grass has grown in his tangled hair,
And a rambling bramble binds his knees.

To shrieve his soul from the pangs of hell,
The only requiem-bells that rang
Were the hare-bell and the heather-bell.
Hushed he is with the holy spell
In the gentle hymn the wind sang,
And he lies quiet, and sleeps well.

He is bleached and blanched with the summer sun;
The misty rain and the cold dew
Have altered him from the kingly one
(That his lady loved, and his men knew)
And dwindled him to a skeleton.

The vetches have twined about his bones,
The straggling ivy twists and creeps
In his eye-sockets; the nettle keeps
Vigil about him while he sleeps.
Over his body the wind moans
With a dreary tune throughout the day,
In a chorus wistful, eerie, thin
As the gull's cry — as the cry in the bay,
The mournful word the seas say
When tides are wandering out or in.

JOHN MASEFIELD

64. *Sheath and Knife*

One king's daughter said to anither,
  Brume blumes bonnie and grows sae fair,
'We'll gae ride like sister and brither,'
  And we'll neer gae down to the brume nae mair.

'We'll ride doun into yonder valley,
  Brume blumes bonnie and grows sae fair,
Whare the greene greene trees are budding sae gaily.
  And we'll neer gae down to the brume nae mair.

'Wi' hawke and hounde we will hunt sae rarely,
  Brume blumes bonnie and grows sae fair,
And we'll come back in the morning early.'
  And we'll neer gae down to the brume nae mair.

They rade on like sister and brither,
  Brume blumes bonnie and grows sae fair,
And they hunted and hawket in the valley thegither.
  And we'll neer gae down to the brume nae mair.

'Now, lady, hauld my horse and my hawk,
  Brume blumes bonnie and grows sae fair,
For I maun na[1] ride, and I daur na[2] walk,
  And we'll neer gae down to the brume nae mair.

'But set me doun be the rute o' this tree,
  Brume blumes bonnie and grows sae fair,
For there ha'e I dreamt that my bed sall be.'
  And we'll neer gae down to the brume nae mair.

The ae king's daughter did lift doun the ither,
  Brume blumes bonnie and grows sae fair,
She was licht in her armis like ony fether.
  And we'll neer gae down to the brume nae mair.

Bonnie Lady Ann sat doun be the tree,
  Brume blumes bonnie and grows sae fair,
And a wide grave was houkit[3] whare nane suld be.
  And we'll neer gae down to the brume nae mair.

The hawk had nae lure, and horse had nae master,
  Brume blumes bonnie and grows sae fair,
And the faithless hounds thro' the woods ran faster.
  And we'll neer gae down to the brume nae mair.

The one king's daughter had ridden awa',
  Brume blumes bonnie and grows sae fair,
But bonnie Lady Ann lay in the deed-thraw.[4]
  And we'll neer gae down to the brume nae mair.

1. Must not	3. Dug, delved
2. Dare not	4. Her death-throes

65. *I Have a Young Sister*

I have a yong suster
   fer beyondyn the se;
Many be the drowryis
   that che sente me.

Che sente me the cherye,
   withoutyn ony ston,
And so che dede (the) dowe,
   withoutyn ony bon.

Sche sente me the brere,
   withoutyn ony rynde.
Sche bad me love my lem-
     man
   withoute longyng.

How shuld ony cherye
   be withoute ston?
And how shuld ony dowe
   ben withoute bon?

How shuld any brere
   ben withoute rynde?
How shuld I love my lemman
   withoute longyng?

Quan the cherye was a flour,
   than hadde it non ston;
Quan the dowe was an ey,
   than hadde it non bon.

I have a young sister
   Far beyond the sea;
Many are the keepsakes
   That she's sent me.

She sent me a cherry —
   It hadn't any stone;
And so she did a wood dove
   Withouten any bone.

She sent me a briar
   Withouten any rind;
She bad me love my sweet-
     heart
   Withouten longing in my
     mind.

How should any cherry
   Be withouten stone?
And how should any wood
     dove
   Be withouten bone?

How should any briar,
   Be withouten rind?
And how love a sweetheart
   Withouten longing in my
     mind?

When the cherry was a flower
   Then it had no stone;
When the wood-dove was an
     egg
   Then it had no bone.

Quan the brere was onbred,
  than hadde it non rynde;
Quan the mayden hayt that
    che lovit,
    che is withoute longyng.

When the briar was unbred
  Then it had no rind;
And when a maid hath that
    she loves,
    She longs not in her mind.

66. *Annabel Lee*

It was many and many a year ago,
  In a kingdom by the sea,
That a maiden there lived whom you may know
  By the name of Annabel Lee;
And this maiden she lived with no other thought
  Than to love and be loved by me.

I was a child and she was a child,
  In this kingdom by the sea;
But we loved with a love that was more than love –
  I and my Annabel Lee;
With a love that the winged seraphs of heaven
  Coveted her and me.

And this was the reason that, long ago
  In this kingdom by the sea,
A wind blew out of a cloud, chilling
  My beautiful Annabel Lee;
So that her highborn kinsman came
  And bore her away from me,
To shut her up in a sepulchre
  In this kingdom by the sea.

The angels, not half so happy in heaven,
  Went envying her and me –
Yes! – that was the reason (as all men know,
  In this kingdom by the sea)

That the wind came out of the cloud by night,
   Chilling and killing my Annabel Lee.

But our love it was stronger by far than the love
   Of those who were older than we,
   Of many far wiser than we;
And neither the angels in heaven above
   Nor the demons down under the sea
Can ever dissever my soul from the soul
   Of the beautiful Annabel Lee.

For the moon never beams without bringing me dreams
   Of the beautiful Annabel Lee;
And the stars never rise but I feel the bright eyes
   Of the beautiful Annabel Lee;
And so, all the night-tide, I lie down by the side
Of my darling – my darling – my life and my bride,
   In the sepulchre by the sea,
In her tomb by the sounding sea.

EDGAR ALLAN POE

67. *The Shell*

And then I pressed the shell
   Close to my ear
And listened well,
And straightway like a bell
   Came low and clear
The slow, sad murmur of far distant seas,
Whipped by an icy breeze
   Upon a shore
Windswept and desolate.
   It was a sunless strand that never bore
The footprint of a man,
   Nor felt the weight

Since time began
Of any human quality or stir
Save what the dreary winds and waves incur.
And in the hush of waters was the sound
Of pebbles rolling round,
For ever rolling with a hollow sound.
And bubbling sea-weeds as the waters go
Swish to and fro
Their long, cold tentacles of slimy grey.
There was no day,
Nor ever came a night
Setting the stars alight
To wonder at the moon:
Was twilight only and the frightened croon,
Smitten to whimpers, of the dreary wind
And waves that journeyed blind –
And then I loosed my ear – oh, it was sweet
To hear a cart go jolting down the street!

JAMES STEPHENS

FEASTS: FAIRS:
BEGGARS: GIPSIES

68. *London Bridge*

London Bridge is broken down,
   Dance o'er my Lady Lee,
London Bridge is broken down,
   With a gay lady.

How shall we built it up again?
   Dance o'er my Lady Lee,
How shall we build it up again?
   With a gay lady.

Silver and gold will be stole away,
   Dance o'er my Lady Lee,
Silver and gold will be stole away,
   With a gay lady.

Build it up with iron and steel,
   Dance o'er my Lady Lee,
Build it up with iron and steel,
   With a gay lady.

Iron and steel will bend and bow,
   Dance o'er my Lady Lee,
Iron and steel will bend and bow,
   With a gay lady.

Build it up with wood and clay,
   Dance o'er my Lady Lee,
Build it up with wood and clay,
   With a gay lady.

Wood and clay will wash away,
   Dance o'er my Lady Lee,
Wood and clay will wash away,
   With a gay lady.

Build it up with stone so strong,
   Dance o'er my Lady Lee,
Huzza! 'twill last for ages long,
   With a gay lady.

69. *Holy Thursday*

'Twas on a Holy Thursday, their innocent faces clean,
Came children walking two and two, in red and blue and green,
Grey-headed beadles walked before, with wands as white as snow,
Till into the high dome of Paul's they like Thames' waters flow.

O what a multitude they seemed, these flowers of London town!
Seated in companies they sit with radiance all their own.
The hum of multitudes was there, but multitudes of lambs,
Thousands of little boys and girls raising their innocent hands.

Now, like a mighty wind they raise to Heaven the voice of song,
Or like harmonious thunderings the seats of Heaven among.
Beneath them sit the agèd men, wise guardians of the poor;
Then cherish pity, lest you drive an angel from your door.

WILLIAM BLAKE

70. *The Mayors*

This city and this country has brought forth many mayors,
To sit in state and give forth laws out of their old oak chairs,
With face as brown as any nut with drinking of strong ale;
Good English hospitality, O then it did not fail!
With scarlet gowns and broad gold lace would make a yeoman
   sweat,
With stockings rolled above their knees and shoes as black as jet,

With eating beef and drinking beer, O they were stout and hale!
Good English hospitality, O then it did not fail!
Thus sitting at the table wide, the Mayor and Aldermen
Were fit to give law to the city; each ate as much as ten:
The hungry poor entered the hall to eat good beef and ale –
Good English hospitality, O then it did not fail!

WILLIAM BLAKE

71. *The Fine Old English Gentleman*

I'll sing you a good old song,
　　Made by a good old pate,
Of a fine old English gentleman
　　Who had an old estate,
And who kept up his old mansion
　　At a bountiful old rate;
With a good old porter to relieve
　　The old poor at his gate,
Like a fine old English gentleman
　　All of the olden time.

His hall so old was hung around
　　With pikes and guns and bows,
And swords, and good old bucklers,
　　That had stood some tough old blows;
'Twas there *his worship* held his state
　　In doublet and trunk hose,
And quaffed his cup of good old sack,
　　To warm his good old nose,
Like a fine old English gentleman
　　All of the olden time.

When winter's cold brought frost and snow,
    He opened house to all;
And though threescore and ten his years,
    He featly led the ball;
Nor was the houseless wanderer
    E'er driven from his hall;
For while he feasted all the great,
    He ne'er forgot the small;
Like a fine old English gentleman
    All of the olden time.

But time, though old, is strong in flight,
    And years rolled swiftly by;
And Autumn's falling leaves proclaimed
    This good old man must die!
He laid him down right tranquilly,
    Gave up life's latest sigh;
And mournful stillness reigned around,
    And tears bedewed each eye,
For this fine old English gentleman
    All of the olden time.

Now surely this is better far
    Than all the new parade
Of theatres and fancy balls,
    'At home' and masquerade:
And much more economical,
    For all his bills were paid.
Then leave your new vagaries quite,
    An take up the old trade
Of a fine old English gentleman,
    All of the olden time.

72. *Bring Us In Good Ale*

Bring us in good ale, and bring us in good ale;
For our blessed Lady sake bring us in good ale!

Bring us in no browne bred, for that is made of brane,[1]
Nor bring us in no white bred, for therein is no gane,
But bring us in good ale!

Bring us in no befe, or there is many bones,
But bring us in good ale, for that goth downe at ones,
And bring us in good ale!

Bring us in no bacon, for that is passing fat,
But bring us in good ale, and gife us enought of that;
And bring us in good ale!

Bring us in no mutton, for that is often lene,
Nor bring us in no tripes, for they be seldom clene,
But bring us in good ale!

Bring us in no egges, for there are many schelles,
But bring us in good ale, and gife us nothing elles;
And bring us in good ale!

Bring us in no butter, for therein are many hores,[2]
Nor bring us in no pigges flesch, for that will make us bores,
But bring us in good ale!

Bring us in no podinges, for therein is all Godes good,[3]
Nor bring us in no venesen, for that is not for our blod;
But bring us in good ale!

Bring us in no capons flesch, for that is ofté dere,
Nor bring us in no dokes[4] flesch, for they slober in the mere,
But bring us in good ale!

1. Bran   3. Yeast
2. Hairs   4. Duck's

73. *The Vision of Mac Conglinne*

A vision that appeared to me,
An apparition wonderful
      I tell to all:
There was a coracle all of lard
Within a Port of New-Milk Lake
      Upon the world's smooth sea.

We went into that man-of-war,
'Twas warrior-like to take the road
      O'er ocean's heaving waves.
Our oar-strokes then we pulled
Across the level of the main,
Throwing the sea's harvest up
      Like honey, the sea-soil.

The fort we reached was beautiful,
With works of custards thick,
      Beyond the lake.
Fresh butter was the bridge in front,
The rubble dyke was fair white wheat,
      Bacon the palisade.

Stately, pleasantly it sat,
A compact house and strong.
      Then I went in:
The door of it was hung beef,
The threshold was dry bread,
      Cheese-curds the walls . . .

Behind it was a well of wine,
Beer and bragget in streams,
      Each full pool to the taste.
Malt in smooth wavy sea
Over a lard-spring's brink
      Flowed through the floor . . .

A row of fragrant apple-trees,
An orchard in its pink-tipped bloom,
      Between it and the hill.
A forest tall of real leeks,
Of onions and of carrots, stood
      Behind the house.

Within, a household generous,
A welcome of red, firm-fed men,
      Around the fire:
Seven bead-strings and necklets seven
Of cheeses and of bits of tripe
      Round each man's neck.

The Chief in cloak of beefy fat
Beside his noble wife and fair
      I then beheld.
Below the lofty cauldron's spit
Then the Dispenser I beheld,
      His fleshfork on his back.

74. *Stool Ball*

... Now the milkmaids' pails are deckt with flowers,
And men begin to drink in bowers,
The mackarels come up in shoals,
To fill the mouths of hungry souls;
Sweet sillabubs, and lip-loved tansey,
For William is prepared by Nancy.
Much time is wasted now away,
At pigeon-holes, and nine-pin play,
Whilst hob-nail Dick, and simp'ring Frances,
Trip it away in country dances;
At stool-ball and at barley-break,
Wherewith they harmless pastime make ...

75. *Milking Pails*

Mary's gone a-milking,
   A rea, a ria, a roses,
Mary's gone a-milking,
   Gentle sweet mother o' mine.

Take your pails and go after her,
   A rea, a ria, a roses,
Take your pails and go after her,
   Gentle sweet daughter o' mine.

Buy me a pair of new milking pails,
   A rea, a ria, a roses,
Buy me a pair of new milking pails,
   Gentle sweet mother o' mine.

Where's the money to come from,
   A rea, a ria, a roses,
Where's the money to come from,
   Gentle sweet daughter o' mine?

Sell my father's feather bed,
   A rea, a ria, a roses,
Sell my father's feather bed,
   Gentle sweet mother o' mine.

What's your father to sleep on,
   A rea, a ria, a roses,
What's your father to sleep on,
   Gentle sweet daughter o' mine?

Put him in the truckle bed,
   A rea, a ria, a roses,
Put him in the truckle bed,
   Gentle sweet mother o' mine.

What are the children to sleep on,
  A rea, a ria, a roses,
What are the children to sleep on,
  Gentle sweet daughter o' mine?

Put them in the pig-sty,
  A rea, a ria, a roses,
Put them in the pig-sty,
  Gentle sweet mother o' mine.

What are the pigs to lie in,
  A rea, a ria, a roses,
What are the pigs to lie in,
  Gentle sweet daughter o' mine?

Put them in the washing-tubs,
  A rea, a ria, a roses,
Put them in the washing-tubs,
  Gentle sweet mother o' mine.

What am I to wash in,
  A rea, a ria, a roses,
What am I to wash in,
  Gentle sweet daughter o' mine?

Wash in the thimble,
  A rea, a ria, a roses,
Wash in the thimble,
  Gentle sweet mother o' mine.

Thimble won't hold your father's shirt,
  A rea, a ria, a roses,
Thimble won't hold your father's shirt,
  Gentle sweet daughter o' mine.

Wash in the river,
  A rea, a ria, a roses,

Wash in the river,
Gentle sweet mother o' mine.

Suppose the clothes should blow away,
A rea, a ria, a roses,
Suppose the clothes should blow away,
Gentle sweet daughter o' mine?

Set a man to watch them,
A rea, a ria, a roses,
Set a man to watch them,
Gentle sweet mother o' mine.

Suppose the man should go to sleep,
A rea, a ria, a roses,
Suppose the man should go to sleep,
Gentle sweet daughter o' mine?

Take a boat and go after them,
A rea, a ria, a roses,
Take a boat and go after them,
Gentle sweet mother o' mine.

Suppose the boat should be upset,
A rea, a ria, a roses,
Suppose the boat should be upset,
Gentle sweet daughter o' mine?

Then that would be an end of you,
A rea, a ria, a roses,
Then that would be an end of you,
Gentle sweet mother o' mine.

76. *The Pedlar's Song*

Lawne as white as driven Snow,
Cypresse blacke as ere was Crow,

Cloves as sweete as Damaske Roses,
Maskes for faces, and for noses,
Bugle-bracelet, Necke-lace Amber,
Perfume for a Ladies Chamber:
Golden Quoifes, and Stomachers
For my Lads, to give their deers:
Pins, and peaking-stickes of steele:
What Maids lacke from head to heele:
   Come buy of me, come: come buy, come buy,
   Buy Lads, or else your Lasses cry: Come buy.

WILLIAM SHAKESPEARE

77. *Fine Knacks for Ladies*

Fine knacks for ladies! cheap, choice, brave, and new,
   Good pennyworths — but money cannot move:
I keep a fair but for the Fair to view —
   A beggar may be liberal of love.
Though all my wares be trash, the heart is true,
           The heart is true.

Great gifts are guiles and look for gifts again;
   My trifles come as treasures from my mind:
It is a priceless jewel to be plain;
   Sometimes in shell the orient'st pearls we find: —
Of others take a sheaf, of me a grain!
           Of me a grain! . . .

78. *Oh! Dear!*

Oh! dear! what can the matter be?
Dear! dear! what can the matter be?
Oh! dear! what can the matter be?
Johnny's so long at the fair.

He promised he'd buy me a fairing should please me,
And then for a kiss, oh! he vowed he would tease me,
He promised he'd bring me a bunch of blue ribbons
To tie up my bonny brown hair.

And it's oh! dear! what can the matter be?
Dear! dear! what can the matter be?
Oh! dear! what can the matter be?
Johnny's so long at the fair.

He promised he'd bring me a basket of posies,
A garland of lilies, a garland of roses,
A little straw hat, to set off the blue ribbons
That tie up my bonny brown hair.

And it's oh! dear! what can the matter be?
Dear! dear! what can the matter be?
Oh! dear! what can the matter be?
Johnny's so long at the fair.

79. *Sledburn Fair*

I'd oft heard tell of this Sledburn fair,
    And fain I would gan thither,
'Twere in the prime of summer-time,
    In fine and pleasant weather;
My Dad and Mam they did agree
    That Nell and I should gae
See for to view this Sledburn fair,
    And ride on Dobbin, oh . . .

So Nell gat on and I gat on,
    And we both rode off together,
And everybody we did meet
    Enquired how far 'twas thither?

Until we came to t'other field end,
   'Twas about steeple high,
'See yonder, Nell, see yonder, Nell,
   There's Sledburn town,' cried I.

And when we reached this famous town
   We enquirèd for an alehouse,
We lookèd up and saw a sign
   As high as any gallows;
We called for Harry, the ostler,
   To give our horse some hay,
For we had come to Sledburn Fair
   And meant to stop all day.

The landlord then himself came out
   And led us up an entry;
He took us in the finest room
   As if we'd been quite gentry.
And puddings and sauce they did so smell,
   Pies and roast beef so rare,
'Oh, Zooks!' says Nell, 'we've acted well
   In coming to Sledburn Fair.'

80. *Widdecombe Fair*

'Tom Pearse, Tom Pearse, lend me your gray mare,'
   All along, down along, out along, lee.
'For I want for to go to Widdecombe Fair,
   Wi' Bill Brewer, Jan Stewer, Peter Gurney, Peter Davy, Dan'l
     Whiddon, Harry Hawk,
   Old Uncle Tom Cobley and all.'
     Old Uncle Tom Cobley and all.

'And when shall I see again my gray mare?'
   All along, down along, out along, lee.

'By Friday soon, or Saturday noon,
    Wi' Bill Brewer, Jan Stewer, Peter Gurney, Peter Davy, Dan'l
      Whiddon, Harry Hawk,
    Old Uncle Tom Cobley and all.'
        Old Uncle Tom Cobley and all.

Then Friday came and Saturday noon,
    All along, down along, out along, lee.
But Tom Pearse's old mare hath not trotted home,
    Wi' Bill Brewer, Jan Stewer, Peter Gurney, Peter Davy, Dan'l
      Whiddon, Harry Hawk,
    Old Uncle Tom Cobley and all.
        Old Uncle Tom Cobley and all.

So Tom Pearse he got up to the top o' the hill,
    All along, down along, out along, lee.
And he seed his old mare down a-making her will,
    Wi' Bill Brewer, Jan Stewer, Peter Gurney, Peter Davy, Dan'l
      Whiddon, Harry Hawk,
    Old Uncle Tom Cobley and all.
        Old Uncle Tom Cobley and all.

So Tom Pearse's old mare her took sick and her died,
    All along, down along, out along, lee.
And Tom he sat down on a stone, and he cried
    Wi' Bill Brewer, Jan Stewer, Peter Gurney, Peter Davy, Dan'l
      Whiddon, Harry Hawk,
    Old Uncle Tom Cobley and all.
        Old Uncle Tom Cobley and all.

But this isn't the end o' this shocking affair,
    All along, down along, out along, lee.
Nor, though they be dead, of the horrid career
    Of Bill Brewer, Jan Stewer, Peter Gurney, Peter Davy, Dan'l
      Whiddon, Harry Hawk,
    Old Uncle Tom Cobley and all.
        Old Uncle Tom Cobley and all.

When the wind whistles cold on the moor of a night,
    All along, down along, out along, lee.
Tom Pearse's old mare doth appear, gashly white,
    Wi' Bill Brewer, Jan Stewer, Peter Gurney, Peter Davy, Dan'l
        Whiddon, Harry Hawk,
    Old Uncle Tom Cobley and all.
            Old Uncle Tom Cobley and all.

And all the long night he heard skirling and groans,
    All along, down along, out along, lee.
From Tom Pearse's old mare in her rattling bones,
    And from Bill Brewer, Jan Stewer, Peter Gurney, Peter Davy,
        Dan'l Whiddon, Harry Hawk,
    Old Uncle Tom Cobley and all.
            Old Uncle Tom Cobley and all.

81. *Gipsies*

The snow falls deep; the forest lies alone;
The boy goes hasty for his load of brakes,[1]
Then thinks upon the fire and hurries back;
The gipsy knocks his hands and tucks them up,
And seeks his squalid camp, half hid in snow,
Beneath the oak which breaks away the wind,
And bushes close in snow-like hovel warm;
There tainted mutton wastes upon the coals,
And the half-wasted dog squats close and rubs,
Then feels the heat too strong, and goes aloof;
He watches well, but none a bit can spare,
And vainly waits the morsel thrown away.
'Tis thus they live – a picture to the place,
A quiet, pilfering, unprotected race.

JOHN CLARE

1. Bracken

82. *The Idlers*

The gipsies lit their fires by the chalk-pit gate anew,
And the hobbled horses supped in the further dusk and dew;
The gnats flocked round the smoke like idlers as they were
And through the goss and bushes the owls began to churr.

An ell above the woods the last of sunset glowed
With a dusky gold that filled the pond beside the road;
The cricketers had done, the leas all silent lay,
And the carrier's clattering wheels went past and died away.

The gipsies lolled and gossiped, and ate their stolen swedes,
Made merry with mouth-organs, worked toys with piths of reeds:
The old wives puffed their pipes, nigh as black as their hair,
And not one of them all seemed to know the name of care.

EDMUND BLUNDEN

83. *The Wraggle Taggle Gipsies*

There were three gipsies a-come to my door,
And down-stairs ran this a-lady, O!
One sang high, and another sang low,
And the other sang, Bonny, bonny Biscay, O!

Then she pulled off her silk-finished gown
And put on hose of leather, O!
The ragged, ragged rags about our door –
She's gone with the wraggle taggle gipsies, O!

It was late last night, when my lord came home,
Enquiring for his a-lady, O!
The servants said, on every hand:
'She's gone with the wraggle taggle gipsies, O!'

'O saddle to me my milk-white steed,
Go and fetch me my pony, O!
That I may ride and seek my bride,
Who is gone with the wraggle taggle gipsies, O!'

O he rode high and he rode low,
He rode through woods and copses too,
Until he came to an open field,
And there he espied his a-lady, O!

'What makes you leave your house and land?
What makes you leave your money, O?
What makes you leave your new-wedded lord;
To go with the wraggle taggle gipsies, O!'

'What care I for my house and my land?
What care I for my money, O?
What care I for my new-wedded lord?
I'm off with the wraggle taggle gipsies, O!'

'Last night you slept on a goose-feather bed,
With the sheet turned down so bravely, O!
And to-night you'll sleep in a cold open field,
Along with the wraggle taggle gipsies, O!'

'What care I for a goose-feather bed,
With the sheet turned down so bravely, O?
For to-night I shall sleep in a cold open field,
Along with the wraggle taggle gipsies, O!'

84. *Where Do the Gipsies Come From?*

Where do the gipsies come from?
The gipsies come from Egypt.
The fiery sun begot them,
    Their dam was the desert dry.

She lay there stripped and basking,
And gave them suck for the asking,
And an Emperor's bone to play with,
    Whenever she heard them cry.

What did the gipsies do there?
They built a tomb for Pharaoh,
They built a tomb for Pharaoh,
    So tall it touched the sky.
They buried him deep inside it,
Then let what would betide it,
They saddled their lean-ribbed ponies
    And left him there to die.

What do the gipsies do now?
They follow the Sun, their father,
They follow the Sun, their father,
    They know not whither nor why.
Whatever they find they take it,
And if it's a law they break it.
So never you talk to a gipsy,
    Or look in a gipsy's eye.

H. H. BASHFORD

85. *Beggars*

What noise of viols is so sweet
    As when our merry clappers ring?
What mirth doth want when beggars meet?
    A beggar's life is for a king.
Eat, drink, and play, sleep when we list,
Go where we will – so stocks be missed.
    Bright shines the sun; play, beggars, play!
    Here's scraps enough to serve to-day.

The world is ours, and ours alone;
   For we alone have world at will.
We purchase not — all is our own;
   Both fields and street we beggars fill.
   Bright shines the sun; play, beggars, play!
   Here's scraps enough to serve to-day.

FRANCIS DAVIDSON

86. *Weep, Weep, Ye Woodmen!*

Weep, weep, ye woodmen! wail;
   Your hands with sorrow wring!
Your master Robin Hood lies dead,
   Therefore sigh as you sing.

Here lie his primer and his beads,
   His bent bow and his arrows keen,
His good sword and his holy cross:
   Now cast on flowers fresh and green.

And, as they fall, shed tears and say
   Well, well-a-day! well, well-a-day!
Thus cast ye flowers fresh, and sing,
   And on to Wakefield take your way.

ANTHONY MUNDAY

87. *My Handsome Gilderoy*

Gilderoy was a bonnie boy,
   Had roses tull[1] his shoone,
His stockings were of silken soy,
   Wi' garters hanging doune:

1. To

It was, I weene, a comelie sight,
    To see sae trim a boy;
He was my joy and heart's delight,
    My handsome Gilderoy.

Oh! sike twe[2] charming een he had,
    A breath as sweet as rose;
He never ware a Highland plaid,
    But costly silken clothes.
He gained the luve of ladies gay,
    Nane eir tull him was coy,
Ah! wae is mee! I mourn the day,
    For my dear Gilderoy.

My Gilderoy and I were born
    Baith in one toun together;
We scant[3] were seven years beforn
    We gan to luve each other;
Our daddies and our mammies thay
    Were fill'd wi' mickle joy,
To think upon the bridal day
    'Twixt me and Gilderoy.

For Gilderoy, that luve of mine,
    Gude waith! I freely bought
A wedding sark of Holland fine
    Wi' silken flowers wrought:
And he gied me a wedding ring,
    Which I received with joy,
Nae lad nor lassies eir could sing
    Like me and Gilderoy.

Wi' mickle joy we spent our prime,
    Till we were baith sixteen,

2. Such two   3. Scarce

And aft we past the langsome time
   Among the leaves sae green:
Aft on the banks we'd sit us thair,
   And sweetly kiss and toy;
Wi' garlands gay wad deck my hair
   My handsome Gilderoy.

Oh! that he still had been content
   Wi' me to lead his life;
But, ah! his manfu' heart was bent
   To stir in feats of strife.
And he in many a venturous deed
   His courage bauld wad try;
And now this gars[4] mine heart to bleed
   For my dear Gilderoy.

And when of me his leave he tuik,
   The tears they wet mine ee;
I gave tull him a parting luik,
   'My benison gang wi' thee!
God speed thee weil, mine ain dear heart,
   For gane is all my joy;
My heart is rent, sith we maun part,
   My handsome Gilderoy!'

My Gilderoy, baith far and near,
   Was feared in ev'ry toun,
And bauldly bare away the gear
   Of many a lawland loun:
Nane eir durst meet him man to man,
   He was sae brave a boy;
At length wi' numbers he was tane,
   My winsome Gilderoy.

Wae worth the loun that made the laws,
   To hang a man for gear,

    4. Makes

To 'reave of life for ox or ass,
  For sheep, or horse, or mare:
Had not their laws been made sae strick,
  I neir had lost my joy;
Wi' sorrow neir had wat my cheek
  For my dear Gilderoy.

Giff [5] Gilderoy had done amisse,
  He mought hae banisht been,
Ah, what fair cruelty is this,
  To hang sike handsome men!
To hang the flower o' Scottish land,
  Sae sweet and fair a boy;
Nae lady had so white a hand
  As thee, my Gilderoy.

Of Gilderoy sae fraid they were,
  They bound him mickle strong,
Tull Edenburrow they led him thair,
  And on a gallows hung:
They hung him high aboon the rest,
  He was so trim a boy:
Thair dyed the youth whom I lued best,
  My handsome Gilderoy.

Thus having yielded up his breath,
  I bare his corpse away;
Wi' tears, that trickled for his death,
  I washt his comely clay;
And siker [6] in a grave sae deep
  I laid the dear-lued boy,
And now for evir maun I weep
  My winsome Gilderoy.

5. If   6. Safely

BEASTS OF THE FIELD:
FOWLS OF THE AIR

88. *Bingo*

The miller's mill-dog lay at the mill-door,
And his name was Little Bingo.
B with an I, I with an N, N with a G, G with an O,
And his name was Little Bingo.

The miller he bought a cask of ale,
And he called it right good Stingo.
S with a T, T with an I, I with an N, N with a G, G with an O,
And he called it right good Stingo.

The miller he went to town one day,
And he bought a wedding Ring-o!
R with an I, I with an N, N with a G, G with an O,
And he bought a wedding Ring-o!

89. *The Irish Harper and His Dog*

On the green banks of Shannon, when Sheelah was nigh,
No blithe Irish lad was so happy as I;
No harp like my own could so cheerily play,
And wherever I went was my poor dog Tray.

When at last I was forced from my Sheelah to part,
She said — while the sorrow was big at her heart —
'Oh! remember your Sheelah, when far, far away,
And be kind, my dear Pat, to our poor dog Tray.'

Poor dog! he was faithful and kind, to be sure,
And he constantly loved me, although I was poor;
When the sour-looking folks sent me heartless away,
I had always a friend in my poor dog Tray.

When the road was so dark, and the night was so cold,
And Pat and his dog were grown weary and old,
How snugly we slept in my old coat of grey,
And he licked me for kindness – my poor dog Tray.

Though my wallet was scant, I remembered his case,
Nor refused my last crust to his pitiful face;
But he died at my feet on a cold winter day,
And I played a lament for my poor dog Tray.

Where now shall I go, poor, forsaken, and blind?
Can I find one to guide me, so faithful and kind?
To my sweet native village, so far, far away,
I can never return with my poor dog Tray.

THOMAS CAMPBELL

90. *Poor Old Horse*

My clothing was once of the linsey woolsey fine,
My tail it grew at length, my coat did likewise shine;
But now I'm growing old; my beauty does decay,
My master frowns upon me; one day I heard him say,
Poor old horse: poor old horse.

Once I was kept in the stable snug and warm,
To keep my tender limbs from any cold or harm;
But now, in open fields, I am forced for to go,
In all sorts of weather, let it be hail, rain, freeze, or snow.
Poor old horse: poor old horse.

Once I was fed on the very best corn and hay
That ever grew in yon fields, or in yon meadows gay;
But now there's no such doing can I find at all,
I'm glad to pick the green sprouts that grow behind yon wall.
Poor old horse: poor old horse.

'You are old, you are cold, you are deaf, dull, dumb and slow,
You are not fit for anything, or in my team to draw.
You have eaten all my hay, you have spoiled all my straw,
So hang him, whip, stick him, to the huntsman let him go.'
Poor old horse: poor old horse.

My hide unto the tanners then I would freely give,
My body to the hound dogs, I would rather die than live,
Likewise my poor old bones that have carried you many a mile,
Over hedges, ditches, brooks, bridges, likewise gates and stiles.
Poor old horse: poor old horse.

91. *Ay Me, Alas, Heigh Ho!*

Ay me, alas, heigh ho, heigh ho!
Thus doth Messalina go
Up and down the house a-crying,
For her monkey lies a-dying.
Death, thou art too cruel
To bereave her of her jewel,
Or to make a seizure
Of her only treasure.
If her monkey die,
She will sit and cry,
Fie fie fie fie fie!

92. *The Fly*

Once musing as I sat,
And candle burning by,
When all were hushed, I might discern
A simple, sely fly;
That flew before mine eyes,

With free rejoicing heart,
And here and there with wings did play,
As void of pain and smart.
Sometime by me she sat
When she had played her fill;
And ever when she rested had
About she fluttered still.
When I perceived her well
Rejoicing in her place,
'O happy fly!' (quoth I), and eke
O worm in happy case!
Which of us two is best?
I that have reason? No:
But thou that reason art without,
And therefore void of woe.
I live, and so dost thou:
But I live all in pain,
And subject am to one, alas!
That makes my grief her gain.
Thou livest, but feel'st no grief;
No love doth thee torment.
A happy thing for me it were
(If God were so content)
That thou with pen were placèd here,
And I sat in thy place:
Then I should joy as thou dost now,
And thou should'st wail thy case.

BARNABE GOOGE

93. *Bête Humaine*

Riding through Ruwu swamp, about sunrise,
I saw the world awake; and as the ray
Touched the tall grasses where they sleeping lay,
Lo, the bright air alive with dragonflies:

With brittle wings aquiver, and great eyes
Piloting crimson bodies, slender and gay.
I aimed at one, and struck it, and it lay
Broken and lifeless, with fast-fading dyes . . .

Then my soul sickened with a sudden pain
And horror, at my own careless cruelty,
That in an idle moment I had slain
A creature whose sweet life it is to fly:
Like beasts that prey with tooth and claw . . .
      Nay, they
Must slay to live, but what excuse had I?

FRANCIS BRETT YOUNG

94. *The Lamb*

Little Lamb, who made thee?
Dost thou know who made thee?
Gave thee life, and bid thee feed,
By the stream, and o'er the mead;
Gave thee clothing of delight,
Softest clothing, woolly, bright;
Gave thee such a tender voice,
Making all the vales rejoice?
    Little Lamb, who made thee?
    Dost thou know who made thee?

    Little Lamb, I'll tell thee,
    Little Lamb, I'll tell thee:
He is called by thy name,
For he calls Himself a Lamb.
He is meek, and He is mild;
He became a little child.

I a child, and thou a lamb,
We are callèd by His name.
Little Lamb, God bless thee!
Little Lamb, God bless thee!

WILLIAM BLAKE

95. *The Sale of the Pet Lamb*

Oh! poverty is a weary thing, 'tis full of grief and pain;
It boweth down the heart of man, and dulls his cunning brain;
It maketh even the little child with heavy sighs complain . . .

A thousand flocks were on the hills, a thousand flocks and more,
Feeding in sunshine pleasantly; they were the rich man's store:
There was the while one little lamb beside a cottage door;

A little lamb that rested with the children 'neath the tree,
That ate, meek creature, from their hands, and nestled to the knee;
That had a place within their hearts, one of the family.

But want, even as an armèd man, came down upon their shed,
The father laboured all day long that his children might be fed,
And, one by one, their household things were sold to buy them bread.

That father, with a downcast eye, upon his threshold stood,
Gaunt poverty each pleasant thought had in his heart subdued.
'What is the creature's life to us?' said he: ' 'twill buy us food.

'Ay, though the children weep all day, and with down-drooping head
Each does his small task mournfully, the hungry must be fed;
And that which has a price to bring must go to buy us bread.'

It went. Oh! parting has a pang the hardest heart to wring,
But the tender soul of a little child with fervent love doth cling,
With love that hath no feignings false, unto each gentle thing.

Therefore most sorrowful it was those children small to see,
Most sorrowful to hear them plead for the lamb so piteously:
'Oh! mother dear, it loveth us; and what beside have we?'

'Let's take him to the broad green hill!' in his impotent despair
Said one strong boy: 'let's take him off, the hills are wide and
    fair;
I know a little hiding-place, and we will keep him there.'

Oh vain! They took the little lamb, and straightway tied him down,
With a strong cord they tied him fast; and o'er the common
    brown,
And o'er the hot and flinty roads, they took him to the town.

The little children through that day, and throughout all the
    morrow,
From every thing about the house a mournful thought did borrow;
The very bread they had to eat was food unto their sorrow.

Oh! poverty is a weary thing, 'tis full of grief and pain;
It keepeth down the soul of man, as with an iron chain;
It maketh even the little child with heavy sighs complain.

MARY HOWITT

96. *A Child's Pet*

When I sailed out of Baltimore
    With twice a thousand head of sheep,
They would not eat, they would not drink,
    But bleated o'er the deep.

Inside the pens we crawled each day,
    To sort the living from the dead;
And when we reached the Mersey's mouth,
    Had lost five hundred head.

Yet every night and day one sheep,
    That had no fear of man or sea,
Stuck through the bars its pleading face,
    And it was stroked by me.

And to the sheep-men standing near,
    'You see,' I said, 'this one tame sheep:
It seems a child has lost her pet,
    And cried herself to sleep.'

So every time we passed it by,
    Sailing to England's slaughter-house,
Eight ragged sheep-men – tramps and thieves –
    Would stroke that sheep's black nose.

WILLIAM H. DAVIES

97. *The Snare*

I hear a sudden cry of pain!
    There is a rabbit in a snare:
Now I hear the cry again,
    But I cannot tell from where.

But I cannot tell from where
    He is calling out for aid;
Crying on the frightened air,
    Making everything afraid.

Making everything afraid,
    Wrinkling up his little face,

As he cries again for aid;
　　And I cannot find the place!

And I cannot find the place
　　Where his paw is in the snare:
Little one! Oh, little one!
　　I am searching everywhere.

JAMES STEPHENS

98. *The Monk and His Pet Cat*

I and my white Pangur
Have each his special art:
His mind is set on hunting mice,
Mine is upon my special craft.

I love to rest – better than any fame! –
With close study at my little book;
White Pangur does not envy me:
He loves his childish play.

When in our house we two are all alone –
A tale without tedium!
We have – sport never-ending!
Something to exercise our wit.

At times by feats of derring-do
A mouse sticks in his net,
While into my net there drops
A difficult problem of hard meaning.

He points his full shining eye
Against the fence of the wall:
I point my clear though feeble eye
Against the keenness of science.

He rejoices with quick leaps
When in his sharp claw sticks a mouse:
I too rejoice when I have grasped
A problem difficult and dearly loved.

Though we are thus at all times,
Neither hinders the other,
Each of us pleased with his own art
Amuses himself alone.

He is a master of the work
Which every day he does:
While I am at my own work
To bring difficulty to clearness.

99. *The Tyger*

Tyger! Tyger! burning bright
In the forests of the night,
What immortal hand or eye
Could frame thy fearful symmetry?

In what distant deeps or skies
Burnt the fire of thine eyes?
On what wings dare he aspire?
What the hand dare seize the fire?

And what shoulder, and what art,
Could twist the sinews of thy heart?
And when thy heart began to beat,
What dread hand? and what dread feet?

What the hammer? what the chain?
In what furnace was thy brain?
What the anvil? what dread grasp
Dare its deadly terrors clasp?

When the stars threw down their spears,
And watered heaven with their tears,
Did he smile his work to see?
Did he who made the Lamb make thee?

Tyger! Tyger! burning bright
In the forests of the night,
What immortal hand or eye,
Dare frame thy fearful symmetry?

WILLIAM BLAKE

100. *The Nymph Complaining for the Death of Her Fawn*

The wanton Troopers riding by
Have shot my Fawn, and it will dye.
Ungentle men! they cannot thrive
Who killed thee. Thou ne'er didst alive
Them any Harm: alas! nor cou'd
Thy Death yet do them any Good . . .
For it was full of sport, and light
Of foot and heart, and did invite
Me to its game; it seemed to bless
Itself in me; how could I less
Than love it? O, I cannot be
Unkind to a beast that loveth me . . .
    With sweetest Milk, and Sugar, first
I it at mine own Fingers nurst;
And as it grew, so every Day
It waxed more white and sweet than they.
It had so sweet a Breath! And oft
I blushed to see its Foot more soft,
And white (shall I say than my Hand?)
Nay, any Ladie's of the Land.

It is a wond'rous Thing how fleet
'Twas on those little Silver Feet;
With what a pretty skipping Grace,
It oft would challenge me the Race;
And when't had left me far away,
'Twould stay, and run again, and stay;
For it was nimbler much than Hindes,
And trot as if on the Four Winds.
    I have a Garden of my own,
But so with Roses over-grown,
And Lillies, that you would it guess
To be a little Wilderness;
And all the Spring Time of the Year
It only lovèd to be there.
Among the Beds of Lillies I
Have sought it oft, where it should lye;
Yet could not, till it self would rise,
Find it, although before mine Eyes:
For, in the flaxen Lillies' Shade,
It like a Bank of Lillies laid.
Upon the Roses it would feed,
Until its Lips ev'n seemed to bleed;
And then to me 'twould boldly trip,
And print those Roses on my Lip.
But all its chief Delight was still
On Roses thus itself to fill,
And its pure Virgin Limbs to fold
It whitest sheets of Lillies cold:
Had it lived long, it would have been
Lillies without, Roses within . . .

ANDREW MARVELL

101. *Of All the Birds*

Of all the birds that I do know,
    Philip my sparrow hath no peer;
For sit she high, or sit she low,
    Be she far off, or be she near,
There is no bird so fair, so fine,
Nor yet so fresh as this of mine;
For when she once hath felt a fit,
Philip will cry still: *Yet, yet, yet.*

Come in a morning merrily
    When Philip hath been lately fed;
Or in an evening soberly
    When Philip list to go to bed;
It is a heaven to hear my Phipp,
How she can chirp with merry lip,
For when she once hath felt a fit,
Philip will cry still: *Yet, yet, yet.*

She never wanders far abroad,
    But is at home when I do call.
If I command she lays on load [1]
    With lips, with teeth, with tongue and all.
She chants, she chirps, she makes such cheer,
That I believe she hath no peer.
For when she once hath felt the fit,
Philip will cry still: *Yet, yet, yet.*

And yet besides all this good sport
    My Philip can both sing and dance,
With new found toys of sundry sort
    My Philip can both prick and prance.
And if you say but: Fend cut, [2] Phipp!
Lord, how the peat [3] will turn and skip!

    1. Lustily   2. *Cave!*   3. Pretty dear

For when she once hath felt the fit,
Philip will cry still: *Yet, yet, yet*.

And to tell truth he were to blame –
    Having so fine a bird as she,
To make him all this goodly game
    Without suspect or jealousy –
He were a churl and knew no good,
Would see her faint for lack of food,
For when she once hath felt the fit,
Philip will cry still: *Yet, yet, yet*.

102. *The Dead Sparrow*

Tell me not of joy; there's none,
Now my little Sparrow's gone:
        He, just as you,
        Would try and woo,
He would chirp and flatter me;
He would hang the wing awhile –
Till at length he saw me smile
Lord, how sullen he would be!

He would catch a crumb, and then
Sporting, let it go agen;
        He from my lip
        Would moisture sip;
He would from my trencher feed;
Then would hop, and then would run,
And cry *Philip* when he'd done.
O! whose heart can choose but bleed?

O how eager would he fight,
And ne'er hurt, though he did bite.
        No morn did pass,
        But on my glass

He would sit, and mark and do
What I did – now ruffle all
His feathers o'er, now let 'em fall;
And then straightway sleek them too.

Whence will Cupid get his darts
Feathered now to pierce our hearts?
    A wound he may
    Not, Love, convey,
Now this faithful bird is gone;
  O let mournful turtles join
  With loving red-breasts, and combine
To sing dirges o'er his stone!

              WILLIAM CARTWRIGHT

103. *On a Little Bird*

Here lies a little bird.
  Once all day long
In Martha's house was heard
  His rippling song.

Tread lightly where he lies
  Beneath this stone
With nerveless wings, closed eyes,
  And sweet voice gone.

            MARTIN ARMSTRONG

104. *Adlestrop*

Yes. I remember Adlestrop –
The name, because one afternoon
Of heat the express-train drew up there
Unwontedly. It was late June.

The steam hissed. Someone cleared his throat.
No one left and no one came
On the bare platform. What I saw
Was Adlestrop – only the name

And willows, willow-herb, and grass,
And meadowsweet, and haycocks dry,
No whit less still and lonely fair
Than the high cloudlets in the sky.

And for that minute a blackbird sang
Close by, and round him, mistier,
Farther and farther, all the birds
Of Oxfordshire and Gloucestershire.

EDWARD THOMAS

105. *The Reverie of Poor Susan*

At the corner of Wood Street, when daylight appears,
Hangs a Thrush that sings loud, it has sung for three years.
Poor Susan has passed by the spot, and has heard
In the silence of morning the song of the bird.

'Tis a note of enchantment; what ails her? She sees
A mountain ascending, a vision of trees;
Bright volumes of vapour through Lothbury glide,
And a river flows on through the vale of Cheapside.

Green pastures she views in the midst of the dale
Down which she so often has tripped with her pail;
And a single small cottage, a nest like a dove's,
The one only dwelling on earth that she loves.

She looks, and her heart is in heaven: but they fade,
The mist and the river, the hill and the shade;
The stream will not flow, and the hill will not rise,
And the colours have all passed away from her eyes!

WILLIAM WORDSWORTH

106. *The Thrush's Song*

Dear, dear, dear,
   Is the rocky glen.
Far away, far away, far away
   The haunts of men.

Here shall we dwell in love
With the lark and the dove,
Cuckoo and cornrail;
Feast on the banded snail,
   Worm and gilded fly;
Drink of the crystal rill
Winding adown the hill,
   Never to dry.

With glee, with glee, with glee,
   Cheer up, cheer up, cheer up, here
Nothing to harm us, then sing merrily,
   Sing to the loved ones whose nest is near –
   Qui, qui, qui, kweeu quip,
   Tiurru, tiurru, chipiwi,
   Too-tee, too-tee, chiu choo,
   Chirri, chirri, chooee,
   Quiu, qui, qui.

W. MACGILLIVRAY

107. *Sweet Suffolk Owl*

Sweet Suffolk Owl, so trimly dight
With feathers, like a lady bright,
Thou sing'st alone, sitting by night,
    Te whit! Te whoo! Te whit! To whit!

Thy note that forth so freely rolls
With shrill command the mouse controls;
And sings a dirge for dying souls –
    Te whit! Te whoo! Te whit! To whit!

THOMAS VAUTOR

108. *Who? Who?*

'Who – Who – the bride will be?'
'The owl she the bride shall be.'
    The owl quoth,
    Again to them both,
'I am sure a grim ladye;
    Not I the bride can be,
    I not the bride can be!'

109. *When Cats Run Home*

When cats run home and light is come,
  And dew is cold upon the ground,
And the far-off stream is dumb,
  And the whirring sail goes round,
  And the whirring sail goes round;
    Alone and warming his five wits,
    The white owl in the belfry sits.

When merry milkmaids click the latch,
   And rarely smells the new-mown hay,
And the cock hath sung beneath the thatch
   Twice or thrice his roundelay,
   Twice or thrice his roundelay;
      Alone and warming his five wits,
      The white owl in the belfry sits.

ALFRED, LORD TENNYSON

110. *Once*

Once I was a monarch's daughter,
   And sat on a lady's knee;
But am now a nightly rover,
   Banished to the ivy tree.

Crying hoo, hoo, hoo, hoo, hoo, hoo,
   Hoo, hoo, hoo, my feet are cold.
Pity me, for here you see me
   Persecuted, poor, and old.

111. *The Water-Ousel*

Where on the wrinkled stream the willows lean,
And fling a very ecstacy of green
Down the dim crystal; and the chestnut tree
Admires her large-leaved shadow, swift and free,
A water-ousel came, with such a flight
As archangels might envy. Soft and bright
Upon a water-kissing bough she lit,
And washed and preened her silver breast, though it
Was dazzling fair before. Then twittering
She sang, and made obeisance to the Spring.

And in the wavering amber at her feet
Her silent shadow, with obedience meet,
Made her quick, imitative curtsies, too.
Maybe she dreamed a nest, so safe and dear,
Where the keen spray leaps whitely to the weir;
And smooth, warms eggs that hold a mystery;
And stirrings of life and twitterings, that she
Is passionately glad of; and a breast
As silver-white as hers, which without rest
Or languor, borne by spread wings swift and strong,
Shall fly upon her service all day long.
She hears a presage in the ancient thunder
Of the silken fall, and her small soul in wonder
Makes preparation as she deems most right,
Repurifying what before was white
Against the day when, like a beautiful dream,
Two little ousels shall fly with her down stream,
And even the poor, dumb shadow-bird shall flit
With two small shadows following after it.

MARY WEBB

112. *L'Oiseau Bleu*

The lake lay blue below the hill.
    O'er it, as I looked, there flew
Across the waters, cold and still,
    A bird whose wings were palest blue.

The sky above was blue at last,
    The sky beneath me blue in blue.
A moment, ere the bird had passed,
    It caught his image as he flew.

MARY COLERIDGE

113. *I Had a Dove*

I had a dove and the sweet dove died;
    And I have thought it died of grieving:
O what could it grieve for? Its feet were tied,
    With a silken thread of my own hand's weaving;
    Sweet little red feet! why should you die –
Why should you leave me, sweet bird! Why?
You lived alone in the forest-tree,
Why, pretty thing! would you not live with me?
I kissed you oft and gave you white peas;
Why not live sweetly, as in the green trees?

JOHN KEATS

114. *Philomel*

As it fell upon a day
In the merry month of May,
Sitting in a pleasant shade
Which a grove of myrtles made,
Beasts did leap and birds did sing,
Trees did grow and plants did spring;
Everything did banish moan
Save the Nightingale alone:
She, poor bird, as all forlorn
Leaned her breast up-till a thorn,
And there sung the doleful'st ditty.
That to hear it was great pity.
Fie, fie, fie! now would she cry;
Tereu, tereu! by and by;
That to hear her so complain
Scarce I could from tears refrain;
For her griefs so lively shown
Made me think upon mine own.

Ah! thought I, thou mourn'st in vain,
None takes pity on thy pain:
Senseless trees they cannot hear thee,
Ruthless beasts they will not cheer thee:
King Pandion he is dead,
All thy friends are lapped in lead;
All thy fellow birds do sing
Careless of thy sorrowing:
Even so, poor bird, like thee,
None alive will pity me.

RICHARD BARNFIELD

115. *A Sparrow-Hawk*

A sparhawk proud did hold in wicked jail
Music's sweet chorister, the Nightingale:
To whom with sighs she said: 'O set me free,
And in my song I'll praise no bird but thee.'
The Hawk replied: 'I will not lose my diet
To let a thousand such enjoy their quiet.'

116. *The Eagle*

He clasps the crag with crooked hands;
Close to the sun in lonely lands,
Ringed with the azure world, he stands.

The wrinkled sea beneath him crawls;
He watches from his mountain walls,
And like a thunderbolt he falls.

ALFRED, LORD TENNYSON

117. *The Twa Corbies*

As I was walking all alane,
I heard twa corbies making a mane,
And tane unto the tither say: —
'Where sall we gang and dine to-day?'

' — In behint yon auld fail dyke,[1]
I wat there lies a new-slain Knight;
And naebody kens that he lies there
But his hawk, his hound, and lady fair.

'His hound is to the hunting gane,
His hawk to fetch the wild-fowl hame,
His lady's ta'en another mate,
So we may mak our dinner sweet.

'Ye'll sit on his white hause-bane,
And I'll pick out his bonnie blue een.
Wi' ae lock o' his gowden hair
We'll theek[2] our nest when it grows bare.

'Mony a one for his maks mane,
But nane sall ken where he is gane.
O'er his white banes, where they are bare,
The wind sall blaw for evermair.'

118. *In the Wilderness*

Christ of His gentleness
Thirsting and hungering
Walked in the wilderness;

1. Green-walled ditch   2. Thatch, mend

Soft words of grace He spoke
Unto lost desert-folk
That listened wondering.
He heard the bitterns call
From ruined palace-wall,
Answered them brotherly.
He held communion
With the she-pelican
Of the lonely piety.
Basilisk, cockatrice,
Flocked to His homilies,
With mail of dread device,
With monstrous barbèd stings,
With eager dragon-eyes;
Great rats on leather wings
And poor blind broken things,
Foul in their miseries.
And ever with Him went,
Of all His wanderings
Comrade, with ragged coat,
Gaunt ribs – poor innocent –
Bleeding foot, burning throat,
The guileless old scape-goat;
For forty nights and days
Followed in Jesus' ways,
Sure guard behind Him kept,
Tears like a lover wept.

ROBERT GRAVES

119. *Stupidity Street*

I saw with open eyes
Singing birds sweet
Sold in the shops
For the people to eat,

Sold in the shops of
Stupidity Street.

I saw in vision
The worm in the wheat,
And in the shops nothing
For people to eat;
Nothing for sale in
Stupidity Street.

RALPH HODGSON

120. *Come Wary One*

'Come wary one, come slender feet,
Come pretty bird and sing to me,
I have a cage of wizard wood
With perch of ebony;
Come pretty bird, there's dainty food,
There's cherry, plum, and strawberry,
In my red cage, my wizard cage,
The cage I made for thee.'

The bird flew down, the bird flew in,
The cherries they were dried and dead,
She tied him with a silken skein
To a perch of molten lead;
And first most dire he did complain,
And next he sulky sad did fall,
Chained to his perch, his burning perch,
He would not sing at all.

There came an elf, a silent elf,
A silver wand hung by his side,
And when that wand lay on the door,
The door did open wide.

The pretty bird with beak he tore
That silken skein, then out flew he,
From that red cage, that greedy cage,
That cage of wizardry.

RUTH MANNING-SANDERS

121. *Upon the Lark and the Fowler*

Thou simple Bird what mak'st thou here to play?
Look, there's the Fowler, prethee come away.
Dost not behold the Net? Look there 'tis spread,
Venture a little further thou art dead.
Is there not room enough in all the Field
For thee to play in, but thou needs must yield
To the deceitful glitt'ring of a Glass,
Placed betwixt Nets to bring thy death to pass?
Bird, if thou art so much for dazling light,
Look, there's the Sun above thee, dart upright.
Thy nature is to soar up to the Sky,
Why wilt thou come down to the nets, and dye?
Take no heed to the Fowler's tempting Call;
This whistle he enchanteth Birds withal.
Or if thou seest a live Bird in his net,
Believe she's there 'cause thence she cannot get.
Look how he tempteth thee with his Decoy,
That he may rob thee of thy Life, thy Joy:
Come, prethee Bird, I prethee come away,
Why should this net thee take, when 'scape thou may?
Hadst thou not Wings, or were thy feathers pulled,
Or wast thou blind or fast asleep wer't lulled:
The case would somewhat alter, but for thee,
Thy eyes are ope, and thou has Wings to flee.

Remember that thy Song is in thy Rise,
Not in thy Fall, Earth's not thy Paradise.
Keep up aloft then, let thy circuits be
Above, where Birds from Fowlers nets are free . . .

JOHN BUNYAN

122. *The Birds*

He.   Where thou dwellest, in what Grove,
       Tell me Fair One, tell me Love;
       Where thou thy charming nest dost build,
       O thou pride of every field!

She.   Yonder stands a lonely tree,
       There I live and mourn for thee;
       Morning drinks my silent tear,
       And evening winds my sorrow bear.

He.   O thou summer's harmony,
       I have lived and mourned for thee;
       Each day I mourn along the wood,
       And night hath heard my sorrows loud.

She.   Dost thou truly long for me?
       And am I thus sweet to thee?
       Sorrow now is at an end,
       O my lover and my Friend!

He.   Come, on wings of joy we'll fly
       To where my bower hangs on high;
       Come, and make thy calm retreat
       Among green leaves and blossoms sweet.

WILLIAM BLAKE

123. *Two Pewits*

Under the after-sunset sky
Two pewits sport and cry,
More white than is the moon on high
Riding the dark surge silently;
More black than earth. Their cry
Is the one sound under the sky.
They alone move, now low, now high,
And merrily they cry
To the mischievous Spring sky,
Plunging earthward, tossing high,
Over the ghost who wonders why
So merrily they cry and fly,
Nor choose 'twixt earth and sky,
While the moon's quarter silently
Rides, and earth rests as silently.

EDWARD THOMAS

124. *To a Waterfowl*

Whither, midst falling dew,
While glow the heavens with the last steps of day,
Far, through their rosy depths, dost thou pursue
    Thy solitary way?

Vainly the fowler's eye
Might mark thy distant flight to do thee wrong,
As, darkly painted on the crimson sky,
    Thy figure floats along.

Seek'st thou the plashy brink
Of weedy lake, or marge of river wide,
Or where the rocking billows rise and sink
    On the chafed ocean-side?

There is a Power whose care
Teaches thy way along that pathless coast, –
The desert and illimitable air, –
    Lone wandering, but not lost.

All day thy wings have fanned
At that far height, the cold thin atmosphere,
Yet stoop not, weary, to the welcome land,
    Though the dark night is near.

And soon that toil shall end;
Soon shall thou find a summer home, and rest,
And scream among thy fellows; reeds shall bend,
    Soon, o'er thy sheltered nest.

Thou'rt gone: the abyss of heaven
Hath swallowed up thy form; yet, on my heart
Deeply hath sunk the lesson thou hast given,
    And shall not soon depart.

He who, from zone to zone,
Guides through the boundless sky thy certain flight,
In the long way that I must tread alone,
    Will lead my steps aright.

WILLIAM CULLEN BRYANT

125. *Midnight*

. . . Midnight was come, when every vital thing
With sweet sound sleep their weary limbs did rest,
The beasts were still, the little birds that sing
Now sweetly slept, beside their mother's breast,
The old and all were shrouded in their nest:
   The waters calm, the cruel seas did cease,
   The woods, and fields, and all things held their peace.

The golden stars were whirled amid their race,
And on the earth did laugh with twinkling light,
When each thing, nestled in his resting place,
Forgat day's pain with pleasure of the night:
The hare had not the greedy hounds in sight,
   The fearful deer of death stood not in doubt,
   The partridge dreamed not of the falcon's foot.

The ugly bear now minded not the stake,
Nor how the cruel mastives do him tear;
The stag lay still unrousèd from the brake;
The foamy boar feared not the hunter's spear:
All things were still, in desert, bush, and brere:[1]
   With quiet heart, now from their travails ceased,
   Soundly they slept in midst of all their rest.

THOMAS SACKVILLE, LORD BUCKHURST

1. Briar: wildwood

ELPHIN, OUPH, AND FAY

126. *Come unto These Yellow Sands*

(*Ariel singing*)   Come unto these yellow sands,
            And then take hands:
      Curtsied when you have, and kist,
          The wilde waves whist:
   Foote it featly heere, and there,
 And sweete Sprights the burthen beare.
  Harke, harke, *bowgh wawgh*:
  The watch-dogges barke, *bowgh wawgh*.
     Hark, hark, I heare,
   The straine of strutting Chanticlere
       Cry *Cockadidle-dowe*.

                WILLIAM SHAKESPEARE

127. *The Elves' Dance*

Round about, round about
  In a fair ring-a,
Thus we dance, thus we dance
  And thus we sing-a,
Trip and go, to and fro
  Over this green-a,
All about, in and out,
  For our brave Queen-a.

128. *By the Moon*

By the moone we sport and play,
With the night begins our day:
As we daunce the deaw doth fall,
Trip it little urchins all:

149

Lightly as the little Bee,
Two by two, and three by three:
And about go we, and about go wee.

I do come about the coppes,
Leaping upon flowers toppes:
Then I get upon a flie,
Shee carries me above the skie:
And trip and goe.

When a deawe drop falleth downe,
And doth light upon my crowne,
Then I shake my head and skip,
And about I trip.
Two by two, and three by three:
And about go we, and about go wee.

THOMAS RAVENSCROFT

129. *For a Mocking Voice*

Who calls? Who calls? Who?
Did you call? Did you? –
I call! I call! I!
Follow where I fly. –
Where? O where? O where?
On Earth or in the Air? –
Where you come, I'm gone!
Where you fly, I've flown! –
Stay! ah, stay! ah, stay,
Pretty Elf, and play!
Tell me where you are –
Ha, ha, ha, ha, ha!

ELEANOR FARJEON

130. *Where the Bee Sucks*

Where the Bee sucks, there suck I,
In a Cowslip's bell I lie,
There I cowch when Owles do crie;
On the Batt's back I doe flie
    After Sommer merrily.
Merrily, merrily, shall I live now
Under the blossom that hangs on the Bow.

            WILLIAM SHAKESPEARE

131. *Echo*

How see you Echo? When she calls I see
Her pale face looking down through some great tree,
Whose world of green is like a moving sea,
That shells re-echo.
I see her with a white face like a mask,
That vanishes to come again; damask
Her cheek, but deeply pale,
Her eyes are green,
With a silver sheen,
And she mocks the thing you ask.
'O Echo!' (hear the children calling) 'are you there?' . . .
'Where?' . . .

When the wind blows over the hill,
She hides with a vagrant will,
And call you may loud, and call you may long,
She lays finger on lip when the winds are strong,
And for all your pains she is still.
But when young plants spring, and the chiff-chaffs sing,
And the scarlet capped woodpecker flies through the vale,
She is out all day,

Through the fragrant May,
To babble and tattle her Yea and Nay.
'O Echo!' (still the children call) 'Where are you?
      where?' . . .
'Air . . .'

VISCOUNTESS GREY

132. *The Splendour Falls*

The splendour falls on castle walls
    And snowy summits old in story:
The long light shakes across the lakes,
    And the wild cataract leaps in glory.
Blow, bugle, blow, set the wild echoes flying,
Blow, bugle; answer, echoes, dying, dying, dying.

O hark, O hear! how thin and clear,
    And thinner, clearer, farther going!
O sweet and far from cliff and scar
    The horns of Elfland faintly blowing!
Blow, let us hear the purple glens replying:
Blow, bugle; answer, echoes, dying, dying, dying.

O love, they die in yon rich sky,
    They faint on hill or field or river:
Our echoes roll from soul to soul,
    And grow for ever and for ever
Blow, bugle, blow, set the wild echoes flying,
And answer, echoes, answer, dying, dying, dying.

ALFRED, LORD TENNYSON

133. *The Fairies*

Up the airy mountain,
   Down the rushy glen,
We daren't go a-hunting
   For fear of little men;
Wee folk, good folk,
   Trooping all together;
Green jacket, red cap,
   And white owl's feather!

Down along the rocky shore
   Some make their home,
They live on crispy pancakes
   Of yellow tide-foam;
Some in the reeds
   Of the black mountain-lake,
With frogs for their watch-dogs,
   All night awake.
High on the hill-top
   The old King sits;
He is now so old and gray
   He's nigh lost his wits.

With a bridge of white mist
   Columbkill he crosses,
On his stately journeys
   From Slieveleague to Rosses;
Or going up with music
   On cold starry nights,
To sup with the Queen
   Of the gay Northern Lights.

They stole little Bridget
   For seven years long;

When she came down again
  Her friends were all gone.
They took her lightly back,
  Between the night and morrow,

They thought that she was fast asleep,
  But she was dead with sorrow.
They have kept her ever since
  Deep within the lake,
On a bed of flag-leaves,
  Watching till she wake.

By the craggy hill-side,
  Through the mosses bare,
They have planted thorn-trees
  For pleasure here and there.
Is any man so daring
  As to dig one up in spite,
He shall find the thornies set
  In his bed at night.

Up the airy mountain,
  Down the rushy glen,
We daren't go a-hunting
  For fear of little men;
Wee folk, good folk,
  Trooping all together;
Green jacket, red cap,
  And white owl's feather!

WILLIAM ALLINGHAM

134. *Overheard on a Saltmarsh*

Nymph, nymph, what are your beads?

Green glass, goblin. Why do you stare at them?

Give them me.
              No.

Give them me. Give them me.
                      No.

Then I will howl all night in the reeds,
Lie in the mud and howl for them.

Goblin, why do you love them so?
They are better than stars or water,
Better than voices of winds that sing,
Better than any man's fair daughter,
Your green glass beads on a silver ring.

Hush, I stole them out of the moon.

Give me your beads, I want them.
                          No.

I will howl in a deep lagoon
For your green glass beads, I love them so.
Give them me. Give them.

              No.

                    HAROLD MONRO

135. *The Fairy Thorn*

'Get up, our Anna dear, from the weary spinning wheel;
    For your father's on the hill, and your mother is asleep:
Come up above the crags, and we'll dance a highland reel
        Around the fairy thorn on the steep.'

At Anna Grace's door 'twas thus the maidens cried,
  Three merry maidens fair in kirtles of the green;
And Anna laid the rock[1] and the weary wheel aside,
    The fairest of the four, I ween.

They're glancing through the glimmer of the quiet eve,
  Away in milky wavings of neck and ankle bare;
The heavy-sliding stream in its sleep song they leave,
    And the crags in the ghostly air.

And linking hand and hand, and singing as they go,
  The maids along the hill-side have ta'en their fearless way,
Till they come to where the rowan trees in lonely beauty grow
    Beside the Fairy Hawthorn grey.

The hawthorn stands between the ashes tall and slim,
  Like matron with her twin grand-daughters at her knee;
The rowan berries cluster o'er her low head grey and dim
    In ruddy kisses sweet to see.

The merry maidens four have ranged them in a row,
  Between each lovely couple a stately rowan stem,
And away in mazes wavy, like skimming birds they go,
    Oh, never carolled bird like them!

But solemn is the silence of the silvery haze
  That drinks away their voices in echoless repose,
And dreamily the evening has stilled the haunted braes,
    And dreamier the gloaming grows.

And sinking one by one, like lark-notes from the sky
  When the falcon's shadow saileth across the open shaw,
Are hushed the maidens' voices, as cowering down they lie
    In the flutter of their sudden awe.

1. Distaff

For, from the air above, and the grassy ground beneath,
    And from the mountain-ashes and the old Whitethorn between,
A power of faint enchantment doth through their beings breathe,
      And they sink down together on the green.

They sink together silent, and stealing side to side,
    They fling their lovely arms o'er their drooping necks so fair.
Then vainly strive again their naked arms to hide,
      For their shrinking necks again are bare.

Thus clasped and prostrate all, with their heads together bowed,
    Soft o'er their bosom's beating – the only human sound –
They hear the silky footsteps of the silent fairy crowd,
      Like a river in the air, gliding round.

Nor scream can any raise, nor prayer can any say,
    But wild, wild, the terror of the speechless three –
For they feel fair Anna Grace drawn silently away,
      By whom they dare not look to see.

They feel their tresses twine with her parting locks of gold,
    And the curls elastic falling, as her head withdraws;
They feel her sliding arms from their trancèd arms unfold,
      But they dare not look to see the cause:

For heavy on their senses the faint enchantment lies
    Through all that night of anguish and perilous amaze;
And neither fear nor wonder can ope their quivering eyes
      Or their limbs from the cold ground raise,

Till out of Night the Earth has tolled her dewy side,
    With every haunted mountain and streamy vale below;
When, as the mist dissolves in the yellow morning-tide,
      The maidens' trance dissolveth so.

Then fly the ghastly three as swiftly as they may,
    And tell their tale of sorrow to anxious friends in vain –
They pined away and died within the year and day,
    And ne'er was Anna Grace seen again.

SAMUEL FERGUSON

136. *Thomas Rymer*

True Thomas lay oer yond grassy bank,
    And he beheld a ladie gay,
A ladie that was brisk and bold,
    Come riding oer the fernie brae.

Her skirt was of the grass-green silk,
    Her mantel of the velvet fine,
At ilka tett of her horse's mane
    Hung fifty silver bells and nine.

True Thomas he took off his hat,
    And bowed him low down till his knee:
'All hail, thou mighty Queen of Heaven!
    For your peer on earth I never did see.'

'O no, O no, True Thomas,' she says,
    'That name does not belong to me;
I am but the queen of fair Elfland,
    And I'm come here for to visit thee. . . .

'But ye maun go wi me now, Thomas,
    True Thomas, ye maun go wi me,
For ye maun serve me seven years,
    Thro weel or wae as may chance to be,

'Then harp and carp, Thomas,' she said,
    'Then harp and carp, alang wi me;
But it will be seven years and a day
    Till ye win back to yere ain countrie.'

She turned about her milk-white steed,
   And took True Thomas up behind,
And aye wheneer her bridle rang,
   The steed flew swifter than the wind.

For forty days and forty nights
   He wade thro blude to the knee,
And he saw neither sun nor moon,
   But heard the roaring of the sea.

O they rade on, and further on,
   Until they came to a garden green:
'Light down, light down, ye laddie free,
   Some of that fruit let me pull to thee.'

'O no, O no, True Thomas,' she says,
   'That fruit maun not be touched by thee,
For a' the plagues that are in hell
   Light on the fruit of this countrie.

'But I have a loaf here in my lap,
   Likewise a bottle of claret wine,
And now ere we go farther on,
   We'll rest a while, and ye may dine.'

When he had eaten and drunk his fill: —
   'Lay down your head upon my knee,'
The lady sayd, 'ere we climb yon hill
   And I will show you fairlies three.

'O see not ye yon narrow road,
   So thick beset wi thorns and briers?
That is the path of righteousness,
   Tho after it but few enquires.

'And see not ye that braid braid road,
   That lies across yon lillie leven?
That is the path of wickedness,
   Tho some call it the road to heaven.

'And see not ye that bonny road,
    Which winds about the fernie brae?
That is the road to fair Elfland,
    Where you and I this night maun gae.

'But Thomas, ye maun hold your tongue,
    Whatever you may hear or see,
For gin ae word you should chance to speak,
    You will neer get back to your ain countrie.'

He has gotten a coat of the even cloth,
    And a pair of shoes of velvet green,
And till seven years were past and gone
    True Thomas on earth was never seen.

137. *La Belle Dame sans Merci*

O, what can ail thee, knight at arms,
    Alone and palely loitering;
The sedge has withered from the lake,
    And no birds sing.

O, what can ail thee, knight at arms,
    So haggard and so woe-begone?
The squirrel's granary is full,
    And the harvest's done.

I see a lilly on thy brow
    With anguish moist and fever-dew,
And on thy cheeks a fading rose
    Fast withereth too.

I met a lady in the meads,
    Full beautiful – a faery's child,
Her hair was long, her foot was light,
    And her eyes were wild.

I made a garland for her head,
    And bracelets too, and fragrant zone,
She looked at me as she did love,
    And made sweet moan.

I set her on my pacing steed
    And nothing else saw all day long;
For sideways would she lean, and sing
    A faery's song.

She found me roots of relish sweet,
    And honey wild and manna dew;
And sure in language strange she said —
    I love thee true.

She took me to her elfin grot,
    And there she gazed and sighed full sore:
And there I shut her wild wild eyes
    With kisses four.

And there she lullèd me asleep,
    And there I dreamed, ah woe betide,
The latest dream I ever dreamed
    On the cold hill side.

I saw pale kings and princes too,
    Pale warriors, death-pale were they all:
They cry'd — 'La belle Dame sans Merci
    Hath thee in thrall!'

I saw their starved lips in the gloam
    With horrid warning gapèd wide,
And I awoke, and found me here
    On the cold hill side.

And this is why I sojourn here
   Alone and palely loitering,
Though the sedge is withered from the lake,
   And no birds sing.

JOHN KEATS

138. *Sabrina*

'Sabrina fair
   Listen where thou art sitting
Under the glassie, cool, translucent wave,
   In twisted braids of Lillies knitting
The loose train of thy amber-dropping hair,
   Listen for dear honour's sake,
   Goddess of the silver lake,
       Listen and save! . . .

'By all the *Nymphs* that nightly dance
Upon thy streams with wily[1] glance,
Rise, rise, and heave thy rosie head
From thy coral-pav'n bed,
And bridle in thy headlong wave,
Till thou our summons answered have.
       Listen and save!'

'By the rushy-fringèd bank
Where grows the Willow and the Osier dank,
   My sliding Chariot stayes,
Thick set with Agat, and the azurn sheen
Of Turkis blew, and Emrauld green
   That in the channel strayes,
Whilst from off the waters fleet
Thus I set my printless feet

1. Wile-full, beguiling

O're the Cowslips Velvet head,
   That bends not as I tread,
Gentle swain at thy request
       I am here.'

JOHN MILTON

139. *Now the Hungry Lion Roars*

Now the hungry Lyon rores,
And the Wolfe behowls the Moone:
Whilst the heavy ploughman snores,
All with weary taske fordone.
Now the wasted brands doe glow,
Whil'st the scritch-owle scritching loud,
Puts the wretch that lies in woe
In remembrance of a shrowd.
Now it is the time of night
That the graves, all gaping wide,
Every one lets forth his spright,
In the Church-way paths to glide.
And we Fairies, that do runne
By the triple *Hecate*'s teame,
From the presence of the Sunne,
Following darkness like a dreame,
Now are frollicke; not a Mouse
Shall disturbe this hallowed house.
I am sent with broome before,
To sweep the dust behinde the doore.

Through the house give glimmering light,
By the dead and drowsie fier;
Everie Elfe and Fairie spright
Hop as light as bird from brier! . . .

WILLIAM SHAKESPEARE

140. *The Fairies Feast*

. . . *Awn.*	Who feasts tonight?
Some Elves.	Prince Olbin is troth-plight To Rosalind, daughter of the Faery Queen.
Other Elves.	She's a mannikin changeling; her name shows it.
Other Elves.	We have heard tell; that she as dream is fair.
Awn.	I've heard old Paigle say, fays gave for her To humans, in the cradle, Moonsheen bright.
Other Elves.	And Eglantine should wedded be this night, To Ivytwine, in the laughing full moon.
Moth.	I was there and saw it: on hoar roots, All gnarled and knotty, of an antique oak, . . . Crowned, some with plighted frets of violets sweet; Other, with flower-cups many-hewed, had dight Their locks of gold; the gentle faeries sate: All in their watchet cloaks: were dainty mats Spread under them, of dwarve-wives rushen work: And primroses were strewed before their feet. They at banquet sate, from dim of after-noon . . . *(Enter more elves running.)*
Howt.	Whence come ye foothot?
One of the new-come Elves.	O Awn, O Howt! Not past a league from hence, lies close-cropped plot, Where purple milkworts blow, which conies haunt, haunt, Amidst the windy heath. We saw gnomes dance dance

There; that not bigger been than harvest mice.
Some of their heads were deckt, as seemed to us,
With moonbeams bright; and those to-night hold
    feast:
Though in them there none utterance is of speech.

Be those our mother's cousins, dainty of grace:
But seld now, in a moonlight, are they seen.
They live not longer than do humble been.

Elves.   We saw of living herb, intressed with moss,
Their small wrought cabins open on the grass.

Awn.   Other, in gossamer bowers, wonne underclod.

Elves.   And each gnome held in hand a looking glass;
Wherein he keeked, and kissed oft the Moons face.

Awn.   Are they a faery offspring, without sex,
Of the stars' rays.

Elves.   They'd wings on their flit feet;
That seemed, in their oft shining, glancing drops
Of rain, which beat on bosom of the grass:
Wherein be some congealed as adamant.

We stooped to gaze (a neighbour tussock hid us),
On sight so fair: their beauty being such,
That seemed us it all living thought did pass.
Yet were we spied! for looked down full upon us.
Disclosing then murk skies, Moons clear still face.
    In that they shrunk back, and clapped tó their
      doors. . .

CHARLES M. DOUGHTY

SUMMER: GREENWOOD: SOLITUDE

141. *The Hunt Is Up*

The hunt is up, the hunt is up,
    And it is well nigh day;
And Harry our King is gone hunting
    To bring his deer to bay.

The east is bright with morning light,
    And darkness it is fled;
And the merry horn wakes up the morn
    To leave his idle bed.

Behold the skies with golden dyes
    Are glowing all around;
The grass is green, and so are the treen
    All laughing at the sound.

The horses snort to be at sport,
    The dogs are running free,
The woods rejoice at the merry noise
    Of *Hey tantara tee ree!*

The sun is glad to see us clad
    All in our lusty green,
And smiles in the sky as he riseth high
    To see and to be seen.

Awake all men, I say again,
    Be merry as you may;
For Harry our King is gone hunting,
    To bring his deer to bay.

142. *The Cheerful Horn*

The cheerful arn he blaws in the marn,
And we'll a-'untin' goo;
The cheerful arn he blaws in the marn,
 And we'll a-'untin' goo,
  And we'll a-'untin' goo,
  And we'll a-'untin' goo . . .

  Var all my vancy dwells upon Nancy,
   And I'll zing Tally ho!
  Var all my vancy dwells upon Nancy,
   And I'll zing Tally ho!

The vox jumps awer the 'edge zo 'igh,
 An' the 'ouns all atter un goo;
  Var all my vancy dwells upon Nancy,
   And I'll zing Tally ho!

Then never despoise the soldjer lod,
 Thof 'is ztaition be boot low;
  Var all my vancy dwells upon Nancy,
   And I'll zing Tally ho!

Then push about the coop, my bwoys,
 An' we will wumwards goo,
  Var all my vancy dwells upon Nancy,
   And I'll zing Tally ho!

If you áx me the zénze of this zóng vur to téll,
 Or the reäzon vur to zhow;
Woy, I doän't exacaly knoo,
 Woy, I doän't exacaly knoo:
  Var all my vancy dwells upon Nancy,
   And I'll zing Tally ho!
  Var all my vancy dwells upon Nancy,
   And I'll zing Tally ho!

143. *John Peel*

D'ye ken John Peel with his coat so gay?
D'ye ken John Peel at the break of the day?
D'ye ken John Peel when he's far, far away,
With his hounds and his horn in the morning?

 'Twas the sound of his horn called me from my bed,
 And the cry of his hounds has me oft-times led,
 For Peel's *View-hollo* would waken the dead,
 Or a fox from his lair in the morning.

D'ye ken that bitch whose tongue is death?
D'ye ken her sons of peerless faith?
D'ye ken that a fox with his last breath
Cursed them all as he died in the morning?

Yes, I ken John Peel and Ruby too
Ranter and Royal and Bellman as true;
From the drag to the chase, from the chase to a view,
From a view to the death in the morning.

And I've followed John Peel both often and far
O'er the rasper-fence and the gate and the bar,
From Low Denton Holme up to Scratchmere Scar,
When we vied for the brush in the morning.

Then here's to John Peel with my heart and soul,
Come fill – fill to him another strong bowl:
And we'll follow John Peel through fair and through foul,
While we're waked by his horn in the morning.
 'Twas the sound of his horn called me from my bed,
 And the cry of his hounds has me oft-times led,
 For Peel's *View-hollo* would waken the dead
 Or a fox from his lair in the morning.

JOHN WOODCOCK GRAVES

144. *The Schoolboy*

I love to rise in a summer morn
When the birds sing on every tree;
The distant huntsman winds his horn,
And the skylark sings with me.
O! what sweet company.

But to go to school in a summer morn,
Oh! it drives all joy away:
Under a cruel eye outworn,
The little ones spend the day
In sighing and dismay.

Ah! then at times I drooping sit,
And spend many an anxious hour,
Nor in my book can I take delight,
Nor sit in learning's bower,
Worn thro' with the dreary shower.

How can the bird that is born for joy
Sit in a cage and sing?
How can a child, when fears annoy,
But droop his tender wing,
And forget his youthful spring?

O! father and mother, if buds are nipped,
And blossoms blown away,
And if the tender plants are stripped
Of their joy in the springing day,
By sorrow and care's dismay,

How shall the summer arise in joy,
Or the summer fruits appear?
Or how shall we gather what griefs destroy,
Or bless the mellowing year,
When the blasts of winter appear?

WILLIAM BLAKE

145. *A Boy's Song*

Where the pools are bright and deep,
Where the grey trout lies asleep,
Up the river and over the lea,
That's the way for Billy and me.

Where the blackbird sings the latest,
Where the hawthorn blooms the sweetest,
Where the nestlings chirp and flee,
That's the way for Billy and me.

Where the mowers mow the cleanest,
Where the hay lies thick and greenest,
There to track the homeward bee,
That's the way for Billy and me.

Where the hazel bank is steepest,
Where the shadow falls the deepest,
Where the clustering nuts fall free,
That's the way for Billy and me.

Why the boys should drive away
Little sweet maidens from their play,
Or love to banter and fight so well,
That's the thing I never could tell.

But this I know, I love to play
Through the meadow, among the hay;
Up the water and over the lea,
That's the way for Billy and me.

JAMES HOGG

146. *Market Day*

Who'll walk the fields with us to town,
In an old coat and a faded gown?
We take our roots and country sweets,
Where high walls shade the steep old streets,
And golden bells and silver chimes
Ring up and down the sleepy times.
The morning mountains smoke like fires;
The sun spreads out his shining wires;
The mower in the half-mown lezza
Sips his tea and takes his pleasure.
Along the lane slow waggons amble.
The sad-eyed calves awake and gamble;
The foal that lay so sorrowful
Is playing in the grasses cool.
By slanting ways, in slanting sun,
Through startled lapwings now we run
Along the pale green hazel-path,
Through April's lingering aftermath
Of lady's smock and lady's slipper;
We stay to watch a nesting dipper.
The rabbits eye us while we pass,
Out of the sorrel-crimson grass;
The blackbird sings, without a fear,
Where honeysuckle horns blow clear –
Cool ivory stained with true vermilion,
And here, within a silk pavilion,
Small caterpillars lie at ease.
The endless shadows of the trees
Are painted purple and cobalt;
Grandiloquent, the rook-files halt,
Each one aware of you and me,
And full of conscious dignity.
Our shoes are golden as we pass
With pollen from the pansied grass.

Beneath an elder — set anew
With large clean plates to catch the dew —
On fine white cheese and bread we dine.
The clear brook-water tastes like wine.
If all folk lived with labour sweet
Of their own busy hands and feet,
Such marketing, it seems to me,
Would make an end of poverty.

MARY WEBB

147. *Under the Greenwood Tree*

Under the greenewood tree,
Who loves to lye with me,
And turne his merrie Note
Unto the sweet Bird's throte:
Come hither, come hither, come hither,
Heere shall he see no enemie
But Winter and rough Weather.

Who doth ambition shunne
And loves to live i' the Sunne,
Seeking the food he eates
And pleased with what he gets:
Come hither, come hither, come hither,
Heere shall he see no enemie
But Winter and rough Weather.

WILLIAM SHAKESPEARE

148. *In Summer*

In somer when the shawes be sheyne,[1]
   And leves be large and long,
Hit[2] is full merry in feyre foreste
   To here the foulys[3] song.

To se the dere draw to the dale
   And leve the hillès hee,
And shadow him in the levès grene
   Under the green-woode tree.

Hit befell on Whitsontide
   Early in a May mornyng,
The Sonne up faire gan shyne,
   And the briddis mery gan syng.

'This is a mery mornyng,' said Litulle Johne,
   'By Hym that dyed on tree;
A more mery man than I am one
   Lyves not in Christiante.

'Pluk up thi hert, my dere mayster,'
   Litulle Johne can say,
'And thynk hit is a fulle fayre tyme
   In a mornynge of May.'

149. *Lubber Breeze*

   The four sails of the mill
   Like stocks stand still;
   Their lantern-length is white
   On blue more bright.

1. When the woods are fresh and fair   3. Small birds'
2. It

Unruffled is the mead,
Where lambkins feed
And sheep and cattle browse
And donkeys drowse.

Never the least breeze will
The wet thumb chill
That the anxious miller lifts,
Till the vane shifts.

The breeze in the great flour-bin
Is snug tucked in;
The lubber, while rats thieve,
Laughs in his sleeve.

T. STURGE MOORE

150. *A Summer's Day*

The ample heaven of fabrik sure,
  In cleannes dois surpas
The chrystall and the silver pure,
  Or clearest poleist[1] glas.

The shadow of the earth anon
  Removes and drawès by,
Sine in the east, when it is gon,
  Appears a clearer sky.

Quhilk sune[2] perceives the little larks,
  The lapwing and the snyp,
And tune their sangs, like Nature's clarks
  Our medow, mure and stryp.[3]

1. Polished   3. O'er meadow, moor and stream
2. Which soon

The time sa tranquil is and still,
    Than na where sall ye find,
Saife on ane high and barren hill,
    Ane aire of peeping wind.

All trees and simples⁴ great and small,
    That balmie liefe do beir,
Nor thay were painted on a wall,
    Na mair they move or steir⁵. . .

                    ALEXANDER HUME

151. *Leisure*

What is this life if, full of care,
We have no time to stand and stare?

No time to stand beneath the boughs
And stare as long as sheep or cows.

No time to see, when woods we pass,
Where squirrels hide their nuts in grass.

No time to see, in broad daylight,
Streams full of stars, like skies at night.

No time to turn at Beauty's glance,
And watch her feet, how they can dance.

No time to wait till her mouth can
Enrich that smile her eyes began.

A poor life this if, full of care,
We have no time to stand and stare.

                    WILLIAM H. DAVIES

    4. Herbs, wild flowers   5. Stir

152. *The Happy Countryman*

Who can live in heart so glad
As the merry country lad?
Who upon a fair green balk[1]
May at pleasure sit and walk,
And amid the azure skies
See the morning sun arise, –
While he hears in every spring
How the birds do chirp and sing:
Or before the hounds in cry
See the hare go stealing by:
Or along the shallow brook,
Angling with a baited hook,
See the fishes leap and play
In a blessèd sunny day:
Or to hear the partridge call,
Till she have her covey all:
Or to see the subtle fox,
How the villain plies the box:
After feeding on his prey,
How he closely sneaks away,
Through the hedge and down the furrow
Till he gets into his burrow:
Then the bee to gather honey,
And the little black-haired coney,
On a bank for sunny place,
With her forefeet wash her face:
Are not these, with thousands moe[2]
Than the courts of kings do know,
The true pleasing spirit's sights
That may breed love's delights? . . .

NICHOLAS BRETON

1. A green bank left in ploughing   2. More

153. *O for a Booke*

O for a Booke and a shadie nooke,
  eyther in-a-doore or out;
With the grene leaves whispering overhede,
  or the Streete cryes all about.
Where I maie Reade all at my ease,
  both of the Newe and Olde;
For a jollie goode Booke whereon to looke,
  is better to me than Golde.

154. *Green Broom*

There was an old man lived out in the wood,
  His trade was a-cutting of Broom, green Broom;
He had but one son without thrift, without good,
  Who lay in his bed till 'twas noon, bright noon.

The old man awoke, one morning and spoke,
  He swore he would fire the room, that room,
If his John would not rise and open his eyes,
  And away to the wood to cut Broom, green Broom,

So Johnny arose, and he slipped on his clothes,
  And away to the wood to cut Broom, green Broom,
He sharpened his knives, for once he contrives
  To cut a great bundle of Broom, green Broom.

When Johnny passed under a lady's fine house,
  Passed under a lady's fine room, fine room,
She called to her maid, 'Go fetch me,' she said,
  'Go fetch me the boy that sells Broom, green Broom.'

When Johnny came in to the lady's fine house,
　　And stood in the lady's fine room, fine room;
'Young Johnny,' she said, 'Will you give up your trade,
　　And marry a lady in bloom, full bloom?'

Johnny gave his consent, and to church they both went,
　　And he wedded the lady in bloom, full bloom,
At market and fair, all folks do declare,
　　There is none like the Boy that sold Broom, green Broom.

155. *The Twelve Oxen*

I have twelfè oxen that be faire and brown,
And they go a grasing down by the town.
　　With hey! with how! with hoy!
Saweste not you mine oxen, you litill prety boy?

I have twelfè oxen, and they be faire and white,
And they go a grasing down by the dyke.
　　With hey! with how! with hoy!
Saweste not you mine oxen, you litill prety boy?

I have twelfè oxen, and they be faire and blak,
And they go a grasing down by the lake.
　　With hey! with how! with hoy!
Saweste not you mine oxen, you litill prety boy?

I have twelfè oxen, and they be faire and rede,
And they go a grasing down by the mede.
　　With hey! with how! with hoy!
Saweste not you mine oxen, you litill prety boy?

156. *Lavender's Blue*

Lavender's blue, dilly dilly, lavender's green,
When I am king, dilly dilly, you shall be queen.
Who told you so, dilly dilly, who told you so?
'Twas mine own heart, dilly dilly, that told me so.

Call up your men, dilly dilly, set them to work,
Some with a rake, dilly dilly, some with a fork,
Some to make hay, dilly dilly, some to thresh corn,
Whilst you and I, dilly dilly, keep ourselves warm . . .

157. *The Garden*

. . . What wondrous life is this I lead!
Ripe apples drop about my head;
The luscious clusters of the vine
Upon my mouth do crush their wine;
The nectarine and curious peach
Into my hands themselves do reach;
Stumbling on melons, as I pass,
Ensnared with flowers, I fall on grass.

Meanwhile the mind, from pleasure less,
Withdraws into its happiness;
The mind, that ocean where each kind
Does straight its own resemblance find;
Yet it creates, transcending these,
Far other worlds and other seas,
Annihilating all that's made
To a green thought in a green shade.

Here at the fountain's sliding foot
Or at some fruit-tree's mossy root,

Casting the body's vest aside
My soul into the boughs does glide:
There, like a bird, it sits and sings,
Then whets[1] and claps its silver wings,
And, till prepared for longer flight,
Waves in its plumes the various light. . . .

Such was the happy Garden-state
While man there walked without a mate:
After a place so pure and sweet,
What other help could yet be meet!
But 'twas beyond a mortal's share
To wander solitary there:
Two paradises 'twere in one,
To live in Paradise alone. . . .

ANDREW MARVELL

158. *Cherry Ripe*

Cherrie Ripe, Ripe, Ripe, I cry,
Full and faire ones; come and buy:
If so be you ask me where
They doe grow? I answer, There,
Where my *Julia*'s lips doe smile;
There's the Land, or Cherrie Ile:
Whose Plantations fully show
All the yeare, where Cherries grow.

ROBERT HERRICK

1. Preens

159. *Cherry Ripe*

There is a Garden in her face
Where Roses and white Lillies grow;
   A heav'nly paradice is that place,
Wherein all pleasant fruits doe flow.
   There Cherries grow, which none may buy,
   Till *Cherry Ripe* themselves doe cry.

Those Cherries fayrely doe enclose
Of Orient Pearle a double row,
   Which when her lovely laughter showes,
They look like Rose-buds filled with snow.
   Yet them nor Peere nor Prince can buy,
   Till *Cherry Ripe* themselves doe cry.

Her Eyes like Angels watch them still;
Her Browes like bended bowes doe stand,
   Threat'ning with piercing frownes to kill
All that approach with eye or hand
   These sacred Cherries to come nigh,
   Till *Cherry Ripe* themselves doe cry.

THOMAS CAMPION

160. *Song*

What is there hid in the heart of a rose,
     Mother-mine?
Ah, who knows, who knows, who knows?
A Man that died on a lonely hill
May tell you, perhaps, but none other will,
     Little child.

What does it take to make a rose,
                    Mother-mine?
The God that died to make it knows
It takes the world's eternal wars,
It takes the moon and all the stars
It takes the might of heaven and hell
And the everlasting Love as well,
                    Little child.

ALFRED NOYES

161. *The Mystery*

He came and took me by the hand
    Up to a red rose tree,
He kept His meaning to Himself
    But gave a rose to me.
I did not pray Him to lay bare
    The mystery to me,
Enough the rose was Heaven to smell,
    And His own face to see.

RALPH HODGSON

162. *The Rose*

A Rose, as fair as ever saw the North,
Grew in a little garden all alone;
A sweeter flower did Nature ne'er put forth,
Nor fairer garden yet was never known:

The maidens danced about it morn and noon,
And learnèd bards of it their ditties made;
The nimble fairies by the pale-faced moon
Watered the root and kissed her pretty shade.

But well-a-day! – the gardener careless grew;
The maids and fairies both were kept away,
And in a drought the caterpillars threw
Themselves upon the bud and every spray.
God shield the stock! If heaven send no supplies,
The fairest blossom of the garden dies.

WILLIAM BROWNE

163. *Song*

Ask me no more, where Jove bestows
When June is past the fading rose;
For in your beauty's orient deep
These flowers, as in their causes, sleep.

Ask me no more, whither do stray
The golden atoms of the day;
For in pure love heaven did prepare
Those powders to enrich your hair.

Ask me no more, whither doth haste
The nightingale when May is past;
For in your sweet dividing throat
She winters and keeps warm her note.

Ask me no more, where those stars light[1]
That downwards fall in dead of night;
For in your eyes they sit and there
Fixèd become as in their sphere.

Ask me no more if east or west
The Phœnix builds her spicy nest;
For unto you at last she flies,
And in your fragrant bosom dies.

THOMAS CAREW

1. Stay

164. *The Bower of Bliss*

(The 'daintie Paradise of the Enchauntresse' whereinto the
Palmer brought Sir Guyon.)

. . . And in the midst of all, a fountaine stood,
   Of richest substaunce that on earth might bee,
   So pure and shiny, that the silver flood
   Through every channell running, one might see;
   Most goodly it with pure imageree
   Was over-wrought, and shapes of naked boyes,
   Of which some seemed with lively jolitee
   To fly about, playing their wanton toyes,
Whiles others did them selves embay in liquid joyes.

And over all, of purest gold was spred
   A trayle of yvie in his native hew:
   For the rich mettall was so colourèd,
   That wight, who did not well-advised it vew,
   Would surely deeme it to be yvie true.
   Lowe his lascivious arms adown did creep,
   That themselves dipping in the silver dew,
   Their fleecy flowres they tenderly did steepe,
Which drops of Cristall seemed for wantonnes to weepe.

Infinit streames continually did well
   Out of this fountaine, sweet and faire to see,
   The which into an ample laver fell,
   And shortly grew to so great quantitie,
   That like a little lake it seemed to bee;
   Whose depth exceeded not three cubits hight,
   That through the waves one might the bottom see,
   All paved beneath with Jaspar shining bright
That seemd the fountains in that sea did sayle upright.

And all the margent round about was set
  With shady lawrell-trees, thence to defend
  The sunny beames, which on the billows bet,
  And those which therein bathèd, mote[1] offend . . .

Eftsoones they heard a most melodious sound,
  Of all that mote delight a daintie eare,
  Such as att once might not on living ground,
  Save in this Paradise, be heard elsewhere:
  Right hard it was, for wight, which did it heare,
  To read, what manner musicke that mote bee:
  For all that pleasing is to living eare,
  Was there consorted in one harmonie,
Birdes, voyces, instruments, windes, waters, all agree.

The joyous birdes, shrouded in cheareful shade,
  Their notes unto the voice attempred sweet;
  Th' Angelicall soft trembling voyces made
  To th' instruments divine respondence meet:
  The silver sounding instruments did meet;
  With the base murmure of the waters fall:
  The waters fall with difference discreet,
  Now soft, now loud, unto the wind did call:
The gentle warbling wind low answerèd to all.

                              EDMUND SPENSER

165. *Small Fountains*

  . . . Jarring the air with rumour cool,
  Small fountains played into a pool
  With sound as soft as the barley's hiss
  When its beard just sprouting is;
  Whence a young stream, that trod on moss,
  Prettily rimpled the court across.
  And in the pool's clear idleness,
  Moving like dreams through happiness,

                    1. Might

188

Shoals of small bright fishes were;
In and out weed-thickets bent
Perch and carp, and sauntering went
With mounching jaws and eyes a-stare;
Or on a lotus leaf would crawl,
A brinded loach to bask and sprawl,
Tasting the warm sun ere it dipt
Into the water; but quick as fear
Back his shining brown head slipt
To crouch on the gravel of his lair,
Where the cooled sunbeams broke in wrack,
Spilt shattered gold about his back. . . .

LASCELLES ABERCROMBIE

166. *The Invitation, to Jane*

Best and brightest, come away!
Fairer far than this fair Day,
Which, like thee to those in sorrow,
Comes to bid a sweet good-morrow
To the rough Year just awake
In its cradle on the brake.
The brightest hour of unborn Spring,
Through the winter wandering,
Found, it seems, the halcyon Morn
To hoar February born;
Bending from Heaven, in azure mirth,
It kissed the forehead of the Earth,
And smiled upon the silent sea,
And bade the frozen streams be free,
And waked to music all their fountains,
And breathed upon the frozen mountains,
And like a prophetess of May
Strewed flowers upon the barren way,

Making the wintry world appear
Like one on whom thou smilest, dear. . . .

Radiant Sister of the Day,
Awake! arise! and come away!
To the wild woods and the plains,
And the pools where winter rains
Image all their roof of leaves,
Where the pine its garland weaves
Of sapless green and ivy dun
Round stems that never kiss the sun;
Where the lawns and pastures be,
And the sand-hills of the sea; —
Where the melting hoar-frost wets
The daisy-star that never sets,
The wind-flowers, and violets,
Which yet join not scent to hue,
Crown the pale year weak and new;
When the night is left behind
In the deep east, dun and blind,
And the blue noon is over us,
And the multitudinous
Billows murmur at our feet,
Where the earth and ocean meet,
And all things seem only one
In the universal sun.

PERCY BYSSHE SHELLEY

167. *The Recollection*

. . . We wandered to the Pine Forest
    That skirts the Ocean's foam;
The lightest wind was in its nest,
    The tempest in its home.
The whispering waves were half asleep,
    The clouds were gone to play,

And on the bosom of the deep
    The smile of Heaven lay;
It seemed as if the hour were one
    Sent from beyond the skies,
Which scattered from above the sun
    A light of Paradise.

We paused amid the pines that stood
    The giants of the waste,
Tortured by storms to shapes as rude
    As serpents interlaced;
And soothed by every azure breath,
    That under Heaven is blown,
To harmonies and hues beneath,
    As tender as its own;
Now all the tree-tops lay asleep,
    Like green waves on the sea,
As still as in the silent deep
    The ocean woods may be.

How calm it was! – the silence there
    By such a chain was bound
That even the busy woodpecker
    Made stiller with her sound
The inviolable quietness;
    The breath of peace we drew
With its soft motion made not less
    The calm that round us grew.
There seemed from the remotest seat
    Of the white mountain waste,
To the soft flower beneath our feet,
    A magic circle traced, –

A spirit interfused around,
    A thrilling, silent life,
To momentary peace it bound
    Our mortal nature's strife;

And still I felt the centre of
   The magic circle there
Was one fair form that filled with love
   The lifeless atmosphere. . . .

PERCY BYSSHE SHELLEY

168. *The Goat Paths*

The crooked paths go every way
   Upon the hill – they wind about
   Through the heather in and out
Of the quiet sunniness.
And there the goats, day after day,
   Stray in sunny quietness,

Cropping here and cropping there,
   As they pause and turn and pass,
Now a bit of heather spray,
   Now a mouthful of the grass.

In the deeper sunniness,
   In the place where nothing stirs,
Quietly in quietness,
   In the quiet of the furze,
For a time they come and lie
Staring on the roving sky.

If you approach they run away,
   They leap and stare, away they bound,
   With a sudden angry sound,
To the sunny quietude;
   Crouching down where nothing stirs
   In the silence of the furze,
Couching down again to brood
In the sunny solitude.

If I were as wise as they,
   I would stray apart and brood,
I would beat a hidden way
Through the quiet heather spray
   To a sunny solitude;

And should you come I'd run away,
   I would make an angry sound,
   I would stare and turn and bound
To the deeper quietude,
   To the place where nothing stirs
   In the silence of the furze.

In that airy quietness
   I would think as long as they;
Through the quiet sunniness
   I would stray away to brood
By a hidden beaten way
   In a sunny solitude,
I would think until I found
   Something I can never find,
Something lying on the ground,
   In the bottom of my mind.

JAMES STEPHENS

169. *Under a Wiltshire Apple Tree*

Some folks as can afford,
So I've heard say,
Set up a sort of cross
Right in the garden way
To mind 'em of the Lord.
But I, when I do see
Thik[1] apple tree

   1. This

193

An' stoopin' limb
All spread wi' moss,
I think of Him
And how He talks wi' me.
I think of God

And how He trod
That garden long ago;
He walked, I reckon, to and fro
And then sat down
Upon the groun'
Or some low limb
What suited Him,
Such as you see
On many a tree,
And on thik very one
Where I at set o' sun
Do sit and talk wi' He.

And, mornings, too, I rise and come
An' sit down where the branch be low;
A bird do sing, a bee do hum,
The flowers in the border blow,
And all my heart's so glad and clear
As pools be when the sun do peer,
As pools a-laughing in the light
When mornin' air is swep' an' bright,
As pools what got all Heaven in sight,
So's my heart's cheer
When He be near.

He never pushed the garden door,
He left no foot mark on the floor;
I never heard 'Un stir nor tread
And yet His Hand do bless my head,
And when 'tis time for work to start
I takes Him with me in my heart.

And when I die, pray God I see
At very last thik apple tree
An' stoopin' limb,
And think of Him
And all He been to me.

ANNA DE BARY

170. *Wonder*

How like an Angel came I down!
    How bright were all things here!
When first among His works I did appear
    O how their Glory me did crown!
The world resembled His ETERNITY,
    In which my soul did walk;
    And every thing that I did see
        Did with me talk.

The skies in their magnificence,
    The lively, lovely air,
Oh how divine, how soft, how sweet, how fair!
    The stars did entertain my sense,
And all the works of God, so bright and pure,
    So rich and great did seem,
    As if they ever must endure
        In my esteem. . . .

The streets were paved with golden stones,
    The boys and girls were mine,
Oh how did all their lovely faces shine!
    The sons of men were holy ones,
In joy and beauty they appeared to me,
    And every thing which here I found,
    While like an Angel I did see,
        Adorned the ground.

Rich diamond and pearl and gold
    In every place was seen;
Rare splendours, yellow, blue, red, white and green,
    Mine eyes did everywhere behold.
Great wonders clothed with glory did appear,
      Amazement was my bliss,
    That and my wealth was everywhere;
          No joy to this! . . .

THOMAS TRAHERNE

171. *Song*

How sweet I roamed from field to field
And tasted all the summer's pride,
Till I the Prince of Love beheld
Who in the sunny beams did glide!

He showed me lilies for my hair,
And blushing roses for my brow;
He led me through his gardens fair
Where all his golden pleasures grow.

With sweet May dews my wings were wet,
And Phoebus fired my vocal rage;
He caught me in his silken net,
And shut me in his golden cage.

He loves to sit and hear me sing,
Then, laughing, sports and plays with me;
Then stretches out my golden wing,
And mocks my loss of liberty.

WILLIAM BLAKE

172. *The Book*

Of this fair volume which we World do name
If we the sheets and leaves could turn with care,
Of Him who it corrects and did it frame,
We clear might read the art and wisdom rare:

Find out His power which wildest powers doth tame,
His providence extending everywhere,
His justice which proud rebels doth not spare,
In every page, no period of the same.

But silly we, like foolish children, rest
Well pleased with coloured vellum, leaves of gold,
Fair dangling ribbands, leaving what is best,
On the great Writer's sense ne'er taking hold;

Or, if by chance we stay our minds on aught,
It is some picture on the margin wrought.

WILLIAM DRUMMOND

173. *Tethy's Festival*

Are they shadows that we see?
And can shadows pleasures give?
    Pleasures only shadows be,
    Cast by bodies we conceive;
    And are made the things we deem
    In those figures which they seem.

But those pleasures vanish fast,
Which by shadows are exprest;
    Pleasures are not, if they last;
    In their passing is their best:
    Glory is more bright and gay
    In a flash, and so away.

Feed apace then, greedy eyes,
On the wonder you behold:
    Take it sudden, as it flies,
    Though you take it not to hold.
    When your eyes have done their part
    Thought must length'n it in the heart.

SAMUEL DANIEL

WAR

174. *A War Song to Englishmen*

Prepare, prepare the iron helm of War,
Bring forth the lots, cast in the spacious orb;
The Angel of Fate turns them with mighty hands,
And casts them out upon the darkened earth!
　　　　　　　　　Prepare, prepare!

Prepare your hearts for Death's cold hand! prepare
Your souls for flight, your bodies for the earth;
Prepare your arms for glorious victory;
Prepare your eyes to meet a holy God!
　　　　　　　　　Prepare, prepare!

Whose fatal scroll is that? Methinks 'tis mine!
Why sinks my heart, why faltereth my tongue?
Had I three lives, I'd die in such a cause,
And rise, with ghosts, over the well-fought field.
　　　　　　　　　Prepare, prepare!

The arrows of Almighty God are drawn!
Angels of Death stand in the lowering heavens!
Thousands of souls must seek the realms of light,
And walk together on the clouds of heaven!
　　　　　　　　　Prepare, prepare!

Soldiers, prepare! Our cause is Heaven's cause;
Soldiers, prepare! Be worthy of our cause:
Prepare to meet our father's in the sky:
Prepare, O troops, that are to fall to-day!
　　　　　　　　　Prepare, prepare!

Alfred shall smile, and make his harp rejoice;
The Norman William, and the learnèd Clerk,
And Lion Heart, and black-browed Edward, with
His loyal Queen, shall rise, and welcome us!
                              Prepare, prepare!

                    WILLIAM BLAKE

175. *For Soldiers*

Ye buds of Brutus' land, courageous youths, now play your parts;
Unto your tackle stand, abide the brunt with valiant hearts.
For news is carried to and fro, that we must forth to warfare go:
Men muster now in every place, and soldiers are prest forth apace.
            Faint not, spend blood,
        To do your Queen and country good;
            Fair words, good pay,
        Will make men cast all care away.

The time of war is come, prepare your corslet, spear and shield;
Methinks I hear the drum strike doleful marches to the field;
Tantarâ, tantarâ, ye trumpets sound, which makes our hearts with
    joy abound.
The roaring guns are heard afar, and everything denounceth war.
            Serve God; stand stout;
        Bold courage brings this gear about.
            Fear not; fate run;[1]
        Faint heart fair lady never won.

Ye curious[2] carpet-knights, that spend the time in sport and play;
Abroad and see new sights, your country's cause calls you away;
Do not to make your ladies' game, bring blemish to your worthy
    name.
Away to field and win renown, with courage beat your enemies
    down.

            1. Risk, hazard, dare   2. Dainty; luxurious

Stout hearts gain praise,
When dastards sail in Slander's seas;
Hap what hap shall,
We sure shall die but once for all.

Alarm methinks they cry, Be packing, mates, begone with speed;
Our foes are very nigh; shame have that man that shrinks at need!
Unto it boldly let us stand, God will give Right the upper hand.
Our cause is good, we need not doubt, in sign of coming give a
    shout.

March forth, be strong,
Good hap will come ere it be long.
Shrink not, fight well,
For lusty lads must bear the bell.

All you that will shun evil, must dwell in warfare every day;
The world, the flesh, and devil, always do seek our soul's decay;
Strive with these foes with all your might, so shall you fight a
    worthy fight.
That conquest doth deserve most praise, where vice do yield to
    virtue's ways.

Beat down foul sin,
A worthy crown then shall ye win;
If ye live well,
In heaven with Christ our souls shall dwell.

HUMPHREY GIFFORD

176. *Battle Hymn of the Republic*

Mine eyes have seen the glory of the coming of the Lord;
He is trampling out the vintage where the grapes of wrath are
    stored;
He hath loosed the fateful lightning of His terrible swift sword;
His truth is marching on.

I have seen Him in the watch-fires of a hundred circling camps;
They have builded Him an altar in the evening dews and damps;
I can read his righteous sentence by the dim and flaring lamps;
        His day is marching on.

I have read a fiery gospel, writ in burnished rows of steel:
'As ye deal with my contemners, so with you my grace shall deal;
Let the Hero, born of woman, crush the serpent with his heel,
        Since God is marching on.'

He has sounded forth the trumpet that shall never call retreat;
He is sifting out the hearts of men before His judgment-seat;
Oh, be swift, my soul, to answer Him! be jubilant, my feet!
        Our God is marching on.

In the beauty of the lilies Christ was born across the sea,
With a glory in His bosom that transfigures you and me:
As He died to make men holy, let us die to make men free,
        While God is marching on.

                JULIA WARD HOWE

177. *I Heard a Soldier*

    I heard a soldier sing some trifle
      Out in the sun-dried veldt alone:
    He lay and cleaned his grimy rifle
      Idly, behind a stone.

    'If after death, love, comes a waking,
      And in their camp so dark and still
    The men of dust hear bugles, breaking
      Their halt upon the hill,

'To me the slow, the silver pealing
 That then the last high trumpet pours
Shall softer than the dawn come stealing,
 For, with its call, comes yours!'

What grief of love had he to stifle,
 Basking so idly by his stone,
That grimy soldier with his rifle
 Out in the veldt, alone?

HERBERT TRENCH

178. *The Dug-out*

Why do you lie with your legs ungainly huddled,
And one arm bent across your sullen cold
Exhausted face? It hurts my heart to watch you,
Deep-shadowed from the candle's guttering gold;
And you wonder why I shake you by the shoulder;
Drowsy, you mumble and sigh and turn your head . . .
You are too young to fall asleep for ever;
And when you sleep you remind me of the dead.

SIEGFRIED SASSOON

179. *Nocturne*

Be thou at peace this night
 Wherever be thy bed,
Thy slumbering be light,
 The fearful dreams be dead
 Within thy lovely head;
God keep thee in His sight.

No hint of love molest
    Thy quiet mind again;
Night fold thee to her breast
    And hush thy crying pain;
    Let memory in vain
Conspire against thy rest.

So may thy thoughts be lost
    In the full hush of sleep.
Lest any sight accost
    Thine eyes to make them weep,
    In darkness buried deep
    For ever be my ghost.

EDWARD L. DAVISON

180. *The Dead*

These hearts were woven of human joys and cares,
    Washed marvellously with sorrow, swift to mirth.
The years had given them kindness. Dawn was theirs,
    And sunset, and the colours of the earth.

These had seen movement, and heard music; known
    Slumber and waking; loved; gone proudly friended;
Felt the quick stir of wonder; sat alone;
    Touched flowers and furs and cheeks. All this is ended.

There are waters blown by changing winds to laughter
And lit by the rich skies, all day. And after,
    Frost, with a gesture, stays the waves that dance
And wandering loveliness. He leaves a white
    Unbroken glory, a gathered radiance,
A width, a shining peace, under the night.

RUPERT BROOKE

181. *The End*

After the blast of lightning from the east,
The flourish of loud clouds, the Chariot throne;
After the drums of time have rolled and ceased,
And, from the bronze west, long retreat is blown —

Shall Life renew these bodies? Of a truth
All death will he annul, all tears assuage? —
Or fill these void veins full again with youth,
And wash, with an immortal water, Age?

When I do ask white Age, he saith, 'Not so:
My head hangs weighed with snow.'
And when I hearken to the Earth, she saith:
'My fiery heart sinks aching. It is death.
Mine ancient scars shall not be glorified.
Nor my titanic tears, the seas, be dried.'

WILFRED OWEN

182. *The Crowns*

Cherry and pear are white,
Their snows lie sprinkled on the land like light
On darkness shed.
Far off and near
The orchards toss their crowns of delight,
And the sun casts down
Another shining crown.

The wind tears and throws down
Petal by petal the crown
Of cherry and pear till the earth is white,

And all the brightness is shed
In the orchards far off and near,
That tossed by the road and under the green hill;
And the wind is fled.

Far, far off the wind
Has shaken down
A brightness that was as the brightness of cherry or pear
When the orchards shine in the sun.
– Oh there is no more fairness
Since this rareness,
The radiant blossom of English earth – is dead!

JOHN FREEMAN

183. *Coronach*[1]

He is gone on the mountain,
    He is lost to the forest,
Like a summer-dried fountain,
    When our need was the sorest.
The font, reappearing,
    From the rain-drops shall borrow,
But to us comes no cheering,
    To Duncan no morrow!

The hand of the reaper
    Takes the ears that are hoary,
But the voice of the weeper
    Wails manhood in glory.
The autumn winds rushing
    Waft the leaves that are serest,
But our flower was in flushing,
    When blighting was nearest.

1. Dirge, lament

Fleet foot on the correi,[1]
   Sage counsel in cumber,[2]
Red hand in the foray,
   How sound is thy slumber!
Like the dew on the mountain,
   Like the foam on the river,
Like the bubble on the fountain,
   Thou art gone, and for ever.

SIR WALTER SCOTT

184. *The Children's Bells*

Where are your Oranges?
Where are your Lemons?
What, are you silent now,
Bells of St Clement's?[3]
You, of all bells that rang
Once in old London,
You, of all bells that sang,
Utterly undone?
You whom all children know
Ere they know letters,
Making Big Ben himself
Call you his betters?
Where are your lovely tones
Fruitful and mellow,
Full-flavoured orange-gold,
Clear lemon-yellow?
Ring again, sing again,
Bells of St Clement's!
Call as you swing again,
'Oranges! Lemons!'

1. Vast hill-hollow   2. Danger or defeat
3. When the half-muffled City Bells rang in commemoration of the Bell-Ringers who fell in the First World War, the bells of St Clement Danes could not take part owing to a defect in the framework.

Fatherless children
Are listening near you –
Sing for the children,
The fathers will hear you.

ELEANOR FARJEON

185. *Men Who March Away*

We be the King's men, hale and hearty,
Marching to meet one Buonaparty;
If he won't sail, lest the wind should blow,
We shall have marched for nothing, O!
          Right fol-lol!

We be the King's men, hale and hearty,
Marching to meet one Buonaparty;
If he be sea-sick, says 'No, no!'
We shall have marched for nothing, O!
          Right fol-lol!

We be the King's men, hale and hearty,
Marching to meet one Buonaparty;
Never mind, mates; we'll be merry, though
We may have marched for nothing, O!
          Right fol-lol!

THOMAS HARDY

186. *Budmouth Dears*

When we lay where Budmouth Beach is,
O, the girls were fresh as peaches,
With their tall and tossing figures and their eyes of blue and brown!
      And our hearts would ache with longing
      As we paced from our sing-songing,
With a smart *Clink! Clink!* up the Esplanade and down.

They distracted and delayed us
By the pleasant pranks they played us,
And what marvel, then, if troopers, even of regiments of renown,
On whom flashed those eyes divine, O,
Should forget the countersign, O,
As we tore *Clink! Clink!* back to camp above the town.

Do they miss us much, I wonder,
Now that war has swept us sunder,
And we roam from where the faces smile to where the faces frown?
And no more behold the features
Of the fair fantastic creatures,
And no more *Clink! Clink!* past the parlours of the town?

Shall we once again there meet them?
Falter fond attempts to greet them?
Will the gay sling-jacket glow again beside the muslin gown?
Will they archly quiz and con us
With a sideway glance upon us,
While our spurs *Clink! Clink!* up the Esplanade and down?

THOMAS HARDY

187. *Trafalgar*

In the wild October night-time, when the wind raved round the
land,
And the Back-sea met the Front-sea, and our doors were blocked
with sand,
And we heard the drub of Dead-man's Bay, where bones of thousands are,
We knew not what the day had done for us at Trafalgár.
                    (*All*) Had done,
                            Had done,
                    For us at Trafalgar!

'Pull hard, and make the Nothe, or down we go!' one says, says he.
We pulled; and bedtime brought the storm; but snug at home slept
   we.
Yet all the while our gallants after fighting through the day,
Were beating up and down the dark, sou'-west of Cadiz Bay.

The dark,

The dark,

Sou'-west of Cadiz Bay!

The victors and the vanquished then the storm it tossed and tore,
As hard they strove, those worn-out men, upon that surly shore;
Dead Nelson and his half-dead crew, his foes from near and far,
Were rolled together on the deep that night at Trafalgar!

The deep,

The deep,

That night at Trafalgar!

THOMAS HARDY

188. *Messmates*

He gave us all a good-bye cheerily
   At the first dawn of day;
We dropped him down the side full drearily
   When the light died away.
It's a dead dark watch that he's a-keeping there,
And a long, long night that lags a-creeping there,
Where the Trades and the tides roll over him
   And the great ships go by.

He's there alone with green sea rocking him
   For a thousand miles round;
He's there alone with dumb things mocking him,
   And we're homeward bound.

It's a long, lone watch that he's a-keeping there,
And a dead cold night that lags a-creeping there,
While the months and the years roll over him
    And the great ships go by.

I wonder if the tramps come near enough
    As they thrash to and fro,
And the battle-ships' bells ring clear enough
    To be heard down below;
If through all the lone watch that he's a-keeping there,
And the long, cold night that lags a-creeping there,
The voices of the sailor-men shall comfort him
    When the great ships go by.

HENRY NEWBOLT

189. *Song for All Seas, All Ships*

To-day a rude brief recitative,
Of ships sailing the seas, each with its special flag or ship-signal,
Of unnamed heroes in the ships – of waves spreading and spreading
    far as the eye can reach,
Of dashing spray, and the winds piping and blowing,
And out of these a chant for the sailors of all nations.
Fitful, like a surge.
Of sea-captains young or old, and the mates, and of all intrepid
    sailors,
Of the few, very choice, taciturn, whom fate can never surprise nor
    death dismay,
Picked sparingly without noise by thee, old ocean, chosen by thee,
Thou sea that pickest and cullest the race in time, and unitest
    nations,
Suckled by thee, old husky nurse, embodying thee,
Indomitable, untamed as thee. . . .

Flaunt out, O sea, your separate flags of nations!
Flaunt out visible as ever the various ship-signals!
But do you reserve especially for yourself and for the soul of man
    one flag above all the rest,
A spiritual woven signal for all nations, emblem of man elate above
    death,
Token of all brave captains and all intrepid sailors and mates,
And all that went down doing their duty,
Reminiscent of them, twined from all intrepid captains young or
    old,
A pennant universal, subtly waving all time, o'er all, brave sailors,
All seas, all ships.

WALT WHITMAN

190. *Hohenlinden*

On Linden, when the sun was low,
All bloodless lay the untrodden snow;
And dark as winter was the flow
    Of Iser, rolling rapidly.

But Linden saw another sight,
When the drum beat at dead of night
Commanding fires of death to light
    The darkness of her scenery.

By torch and trumpet fast arrayed
Each horseman drew his battle-blade,
And furious every charger neighed
    To join the dreadful revelry.

Then shook the hills with thunder riven;
Then rushed the steed, to battle driven;
And louder than the bolts of Heaven
    Far flashed the red artillery.

But redder yet that light shall glow
On Linden's hills of stainèd snow;
And bloodier yet the torrent flow
    Of Iser, rolling rapidly.

'Tis morn; but scarce yon level sun
Can pierce the war-clouds, rolling dun,
Where furious Frank and fiery Hun
    Shout in their sulphurous canopy.

The combat deepens. On, ye Brave,
Who rush to glory or the grave!
Wave, Munich! all thy banners wave,
    And charge with all thy chivalry!

Few, few shall part, where many meet!
The snow shall be their winding-sheet,
And every turf beneath their feet
    Shall be a soldier's sepulchre.

THOMAS CAMPBELL

191. *Hame, Hame, Hame*

Hame, hame, hame, hame, fain wad I be:
O hame, hame, hame, to my ain countrie!

When the flower is in the bud, and the leaf is on the tree,
The lark shall sing me hame to my ain countrie.
Hame, hame, hame! O hame fain wad I be!
O hame, hame, hame to my ain countrie!

The green leaf o' loyalty's beginning now to fa';
The bonnie white rose it is withering an' a';
But we'll water it with the blude of usurping tyrannie,
And fresh it shall blaw in my ain countrie!

O, there's nocht now frae ruin my countrie can save,
But the keys o' kind heaven, to open the grave,
That a' the noble martyrs wha died for loyaltie
May rise again and fight for their ain countrie.

The great now are gane, who attempted to save;
The green grass is growing abune their grave;
Yet the sun through the mirk seems to promise to me –
I'll shine on ye yet in your ain countrie.

Hame, hame, hame, hame, fain wad I be;
O hame, hame, hame to my ain countrie!

ALLAN CUNNINGHAM

192. *Dark Rosaleen*

O my dark Rosaleen,
    Do not sigh, do not weep!
The priests are on the ocean green,
    They march along the deep.
There's wine from the royal Pope
    Upon the ocean green,
And Spanish ale shall give you hope,
    My dark Rosaleen!
    My own Rosaleen!
Shall glad your heart, shall give you hope,
Shall give you health, and help, and hope,
    My dark Rosaleen!

Over hills and through dales
    Have I roamed for your sake;
All yesterday I sailed the sails
    On river and on lake.

The Erne, at its highest flood,
   I dashed across unseen,
For there was lightning in my blood,
   My dark Rosaleen!
   My own Rosaleen!
Oh! there was lightning in my blood,
Red lightning lightened through my blood,
   My dark Rosaleen!

All day long, in unrest,
   To and fro do I move.
The very soul within my breast
   Is wasted for you, love!
The heart in my bosom faints
   To think of you, my Queen,
My life of life, my saint of saints,
   My dark Rosaleen!
   My own Rosaleen!
To hear your sweet and sad complaints,
My life, my love, my saint of saints,
   My dark Rosaleen!

Woe and pain, pain and woe,
   Are my lot, night and noon,
To see your bright face clouded so,
   Like to the mournful moon.
But yet will I rear your throne
   Again in golden sheen;
'Tis you shall reign, shall reign alone
   My dark Rosaleen!
   My own Rosaleen!
'Tis you shall have the golden throne,
'Tis you shall reign, and reign alone,
   My dark Rosaleen!

Over dews, over sands,
   Will I fly for your weal:
Your holy delicate white hands
   Shall girdle me with steel.

At home, in your emerald bowers,
   From morning's dawn till e'en
You'll pray for me, my flower of flowers,
   My dark Rosaleen!
   My fond Rosaleen!
You'll think of me through daylight hours,
My virgin flower, my flower of flowers,
   My dark Rosaleen!

I could scale the blue air,
   I could plough the high hills,
Oh, I could kneel all night in prayer,
   To heal your many ills!
And one beamy smile from you
   Would float like light between
My toils and me, my own, my true,
   My dark Rosaleen!
   My fond Rosaleen!
Would give me life and soul anew,
A second life, a soul anew,
   My dark Rosaleen!

Oh! the Erne shall run red
   With redundance of blood,
The earth shall rock beneath our tread,
   And flames wrap hill and wood,
And gun-peal and slogan-cry
   Wake many a glen serene,
Ere you shall fade, ere you shall die,
   My dark Rosaleen!
   My own Rosaleen!
The Judgment Hour must first be nigh,
Ere you shall fade, ere you can die,
   My dark Rosaleen!

JAMES CLARENCE MANGAN

193. *My Luve's in Germany*

'My Luve's in Germany;
   Send him hame, send him hame;
My Luve's in Germany,
   Send him hame:
My Luve's in Germany;
Fighting for Royalty;
He may ne'er his Jeanie see;
   Send him hame, send him hame;
He may ne'er his Jeanie see,
   Send him hame.

'He's brave as brave can be,
   Send him hame, send him hame;
He's brave as brave can be,
   Send him hame.
He's brave as brave can be,
He wad rather fa' than flee;
But his life is dear to me,
   Send him hame, send him hame;
Oh! his life is dear to me,
   Send him hame.

'Our faes are ten to three,
   Send him hame, send him hame;
Our faes are ten to three,
   Send him hame.
Our faes are ten to three.
He maun either fa' or flee,
In the cause o' Loyalty;
   Send him hame, send him hame;
In the cause o' Loyalty,
   Send him hame.'

'Your luve ne'er learnt to flee,
  Bonnie Dame, winsome Dame;
Your luve ne'er learnt to flee,
  Winsome Dame.
Your luve ne'er learnt to flee,
But he fell in Germany,
Fighting brave for Loyalty,
  Mournfu' Dame, bonnie Dame,
Fighting brave for Loyalty,
  Mournfu' Dame!'

'He'll ne'er come owre the sea,
  Willie's slain, Willie's slain;
He'll ne'er come owre the sea,
  Willie's gane!
He'll ne'er come owre the sea,
To his Love and ain Countrie —
This warld's nae mair for me,
  Willie's gane, Willie's gane!
This warld's nae mair for me
  Willie's slain!'

194. *A Weary Lot Is Thine*

'A weary lot is thine, fair maid,
  A weary lot is thine!
To pull the thorn thy brow to braid,
  And press the rue for wine.
A lightsome eye, a soldier's mien,
  A feather of the blue,
A doublet of the Lincoln green —
  No more of me you knew,
          My love!
No more of me you knew.

'This morn is merry June, I trow,
 The rose is budding fain;
But she shall bloom in winter snow
 Ere we two meet again.'
He turned his charger as he spake
 Upon the river shore,
He gave the bridle-reins a shake,
 Said, 'Adieu for evermore,
 My love!
And adieu for evermore.'

SIR WALTER SCOTT

195. *Charlie He's My Darling*

An' Charlie he's my darling,
 My darling, my darling!
Charlie he's my darling,
 The young Chevalier!

'Twas on a Monday morning,
 Right early in the year,
That Charlie cam' to our town,
 The young Chevalier!

As he was walking up the street,
 The city for to view,
O, there he spied a bonnie lass
 The window lookin' through.

Sae light's he jimpèd up the stair,
 An' tirlèd at the pin;
An' wha sae ready as hersel
 To let the laddie in?

221

He set his Jenny on his knee,
  A' in his Highland dress;
For brawlie weel he keened the way
  To please a lassie best.

It's up yon heathery mountain,
  An' down yon scroggy glen,
We daur na gang a-milking
  For Charlie an' his men!

    An' Charlie he's my darling,
    My darling, my darling!
    Charlie he's my darling,
    The young Chevalier!

196. *The Farewell*

It was a' for our rightfu' king
  We left fair Scotland's strand;
It was a' for our rightfu' king
  We e'er saw Irish land,
      My dear,
  We e'er saw Irish land.

Now a' is done that man can do,
  And a' is done in vain;
My love, and native land, farewell,
  For I maun cross the main,
      My dear,
  For I maun cross the main.

He turned him right and round about
  Upon the Irish shore;
And gae his bridle-reins a shake,
  With Adieu for evermore,
      My dear,
  Adieu for evermore.

The sodger frae the wars returns,
　　The sailor frae the main;
But I hae parted frae my love,
　　Never to meet again.
　　　　My dear,
　　Never to meet again.

When day is gane, and night is come,
　　And a' folks bound to sleep;
I think on him that's far awa',
The lee-lang night, and weep,
　　　　My dear,
The lee-lang night, and weep.

ROBERT BURNS

197. *The Flowers of the Forest*

I've heard them lilting at our ewe-milking,
Lasses a-lilting before the dawn of day;
But now they are moaning on ilka green loaning: –
The Flowers of the Forest are a' wede away.

At bughts in the morning nae blythe lads are scorning;
The lasses are lanely, and dowie, and wae;
Nae daffing, nae gabbing, but sighing and sabbing,
Ilk ane lifts her leglin, and hies her away.

In hairst, at the shearing, nae youths now are jeering:
The bandsters are lyart, and runkled, and gray.
At fair or at preaching, nae wooing, nae fleeching –
The Flowers of the Forest are a' wede away.

At e'en, in the gloaming, nae swankies are roaming
'Bout stacks wi' the lasses at bogle to play;
But ilk ane sits drearie, lamenting her dearie –
The Flowers of the Forest are a' wede away.

Dool and wae for the order sent our lads to the Border!
The English, for ance, be guile wan the day;
The Flowers of the Forest, that fought aye the foremost,
The prime of our land, lie cauld in the clay.

We'll hear nae mair lilting at our ewe-milking;
Women and bairns are heartless and wae,
Sighing and moaning on ilka green loaning;
The Flowers of the Forest are a' wede away.

JEAN ELLIOT

198. *As I Was Going*

As I was going by Charing Cross,
I saw a black man upon a black horse;
They told me it was King Charles the First;
Oh dear, my heart was ready to burst!

199. *Of the Great and Famous*

EVER TO BE HONOURED KNIGHT, SIR FRANCIS DRAKE,
AND OF MY LITTLE-LITTLE SELFE.

The Dragon that our Seas did raise his Crest
And brought back heapes of gold unto his nest,
Unto his Foes more terrible than Thunder,
Glory of his age, After-ages' wonder,
Excelling all those that excelled before;
It's feared we shall have none such any more;
Effecting all he sole did undertake,
Valiant, just, wise, milde, honest, Godly *Drake*.

This man when I was little I did meete
As he was walking up Totnes' long street.
He asked me whose I was? I answered him.
He asked me if his good friend were within?
A faire red Orange in his hand he had,
He gave it me whereof I was right glad,
Takes and kist me, and prayes *God blesse my boy*:
Which I record *with comfort* to this day.
Could he on me have breathèd with his breath,
His gifts, Elias-like, after his death,
Then had I beene enabled for to doe
Many brave things I have a heart unto.
I have as great desire as e're had *hee*
To joy, annoy, friends, foes; but 'twill not be.

ROBERT HAYMAN

200. *A Lamentation*

All looks be pale, hearts cold as stone,
For Hally now is dead and gone.
    Hally in whose sight,
      Most sweet sight,
All the earth late took delight.
    Every eye, weep with me,
    Joys drowned in tears must be.

His ivory skin, his comely hair,
His rosy cheeks so clear and fair,
    Eyes that once did grace
      His bright face,
Now in him all want their place.
    Eyes and hearts, weep with me,
    For who so kind as he?

His youth was like an April flower,
Adorned with beauty, love, and power.
Glory strewed his way,
Whose wreaths gay
Now all are turnèd to decay.
Then, again, weep with me,
None feel more cause than we.

No more may his wished sight return.
His golden lamp no more can burn,
Quenched is all his flame,
His hoped fame
Now hath left him nought but name.
For him all weep with me,
Since more him none shall see.

THOMAS CAMPION

201. *What If Some Little Paine the Passage Have*

. . . What if some little paine the passage have,
That makes fraile flesh to feare the bitter wave?
Is not short paine well borne, that brings long ease,
And layes the soule to sleepe in quiet grave?
Sleep after toyle, port after stormie seas,
Ease after warre, death after live does greatly please . . .

EDMUND SPENSER

202. *Henry before Agincourt:*

OCTOBER 25, 1415

. . . Our King went up upon a hill high
And looked down to the valleys low:
He saw where the Frenchmen came hastily
As thick as ever did hail or snow.
Then kneeled our King down, in that stound,[1]
And all his men on every side:
Every man made a cross and kissed the ground,
And on their feet fast gan abide.
Our King said, 'Sirs, what time of the day?'
'My Liege,' they said, 'it is nigh Prime.'
'Then go we to our journey,
By the grace of JESU, it is good time:
For saints that lie in their shrine
To GOD for us be praying.
All the Religious of England, in this time,
Ora pro nobis for us they sing.'
ST GEORGE was seen over the host:
Of very truth this sight men did see.
Down was he sent by the HOLY GHOST,
To give our King the victory . . .

JOHN LYDGATE

203. *Alexander the Great*

Four men stood by the grave of a man,
The grave of Alexander the Proud:
They sang words without falsehood
Over the prince from fair Greece.

1. For a moment

227

Said the first man of them:
'Yesterday there were around the king
The men of the world – a sad gathering!
Though to-day he is alone.'

'Yesterday the king of the brown world
Rode upon the heavy earth:
Though to-day it is the earth
That rides upon his neck.'

'Yesterday,' said the third wise author,
'Philip's son owned the whole world:
To-day he has nought
Save seven feet of earth.'

'Alexander the liberal and great
Was wont to bestow silver and gold:
To-day,' said the fourth man,
'The gold is here, and it is nought.'

Thus truly spoke the wise men
Around the grave of the high-king:
It was not foolish women's talk
What those four sang.

204. *The Myrtle Bush Grew Shady*

'The myrtle bush grew shady
    Down by the ford.' –
'Is it even so?' said my lady.
    'Even so!' said my lord.
'The leaves are set too thick together
    For the point of a sword.'
'The arras in your room hangs close,
    No light between!

228

You wedded one of those
   That see unseen.' –
'Is it even so?' said the King's Majesty.
  'Even so!' said the Queen.

                MARY COLERIDGE

205. *The Fort of Rathangan*

The fort over against the oak-wood,
Once it was Bruidge's, it was Cathal's,
It was Aed's, it was Ailill's,
It was Conaing's, it was Cuiline's,
And it was Maelduin's;
The fort remains after each in his turn –
And the kings asleep in the ground.

DANCE, MUSIC, AND BELLS

206. *A Piper*

A piper in the streets to-day
Set up, and tuned, and started to play,
And away, away, away on the tide
Of his music we started; on every side
Doors and windows were opened wide,
And men left down their work and came,
And women with petticoats coloured like flame.
And little bare feet that were blue with cold,
Went dancing back to the age of gold,
And all the world went gay, went gay,
For half an hour in the street to-day.

SEUMAS O'SULLIVAN

207. *The Little Dancers*

Lonely, save for a few faint stars, the sky
Dreams; and lonely, below, the little street
Into its gloom retires, secluded and shy.
Scarcely the dumb roar enters this soft retreat;
And all is dark, save where come flooding rays
From a tavern window: there, to the brisk measure
Of an organ that down in an alley merrily plays,
Two children, all alone and no one by,
Holding their tattered frocks, through an airy maze
Of motion, lightly threaded with nimble feet,
Dance sedately: face to face they gaze,
Their eyes shining, grave with a perfect pleasure.

LAURENCE BINYON

208. *Two Nut Trees*

i

I had a little nut tree,
   Nothing would it bear,
But a silver nutmeg,
   And a golden pear.
The King of Spain's daughter
   Came to visit me,
And all was because of
   My little nut tree.
I skipped over water
   I danced over sea,
And all the birds in the air
   Could not catch me.

THOMAS ANON

ii

The King of China's daughter
So beautiful to see
With her face like yellow water, left
Her nutmeg tree.
Her little rope for skipping
She kissed and gave it me –
Made of painted notes of singing-birds
Among the fields of tea.
I skipped across the nutmeg grove, –
I skipped across the sea;
But neither sun nor moon, my dear,
Has yet caught me.

The King of China's daughter,
She never would love me,
Though I hung my cap and bells upon
Her nutmeg tree.

234

For oranges and lemons,
The stars in bright blue air,
(I stole them long ago, my dear)
Were dangling there.
The Moon did give me silver pence,
The Sun did give me gold,
And both together softly blew
And made my porridge cold;
But the King of China's daughter
Pretended not to see
Where I hung my cap and bells upon
The nutmeg tree.

EDITH SITWELL

209. *When the Green Woods Laugh*

When the green woods laugh with the voice of joy,
And the dimpling stream runs laughing by;
When the air does laugh with our merry wit,
And the green hill laughs with the noise of it;

When the meadows laugh with lively green,
And the grasshopper laughs in the merry scene,
When Mary and Susan and Emily
With their sweet round mouths sing 'Ha, Ha, He!'

When the painted birds laugh in the shade,
Where our table with cherries and nuts is spread,
Come live, and be merry, and join with me,
To sing the sweet chorus of 'Ha, Ha, He!'

WILLIAM BLAKE

210. *Fa La La*

My mistress frowns when she should play;
I'll please her with a *Fa la la*.
Sometimes she chides, but I straightway
Present her with a *Fa la la*.

You lovers that have loves astray
May win them with a *Fa la la*.
Quick music's best, for still they say
None pleaseth like your *Fa la la*.

211. *It Was a Lover*

It was a Lover, and his lasse,
    With a hey, and a ho, and a hey nonino,
That ore the greene corne-field did passe,
    In spring time, the onely pretty ring time,
When Birds do sing, *hey ding a ding, ding:*
Sweet Lovers love the spring.

Between the acres of the Rie,
    With a hey, and a ho, and a hey nonino,
These prettie Country folks would lie,
    In spring time, the onely pretty ring time,
When Birds do sing, *hey ding a ding, ding:*
Sweet Lovers love the spring.

This Carroll they began that houre,
    With a hey, and a ho, and a hey nonino;
How that a life was but a Flower,
    In spring time, the onely pretty ring time,
When Birds do sing, *hey ding a ding, ding:*
Sweet Lovers love the spring.

And therefore take the present time,
 With a hey, and a ho, and a hey nonino;
For love is crownèd with the prime
 In spring time, the onely pretty ring time,
When Birds do sing, *hey ding a ding, ding:*
Sweet Lovers love the spring.

WILLIAM SHAKESPEARE

212. *Hey, Nonny No!*

Hey, nonny no!
Men are fools that wish to die!
Is't not fine to dance and sing
When the bells of death do ring?
Is't not fine to swim in wine,
And turn upon the toe,
And sing *Hey, nonny no!*

When the winds blow and the seas flow?
 Hey, nonny no!

213. *Tarantella*

Do you remember an Inn,
Miranda?
Do you remember an Inn?
And the tedding and the spreading
Of the straw for a bedding,
And the fleas that tease in the High Pyrenees,
And the wine that tasted of the tar?
And the cheers and the jeers of the young muleteers
(Under the dark of the vine verandah)?
Do you remember an Inn, Miranda,

Do you remember an Inn?
And the cheers and the jeers of the young muleteers
Who hadn't got a penny,
And who weren't paying any,
And the hammer at the doors and the Din?
And the Hip! Hop! Hap!
Of the clap
Of the hands to the twirl and the swirl
Of the girl gone chancing,
Glancing,
Dancing,
Backing and advancing,
Snapping of the clapper to the spin
Out and in —
And the Ting, Tong, Tang of the guitar!
Do you remember an Inn,
Miranda?
Do you remember an Inn?
Never more;
Miranda,
Never more.
Only the high peaks hoar:
And Aragon a torrent at the door.
No sound
In the walls of the Halls where falls
The tread
Of the feet of the dead to the ground.
No sound:
Only the boom
Of the far Waterfall like Doom.

HILAIRE BELLOC

214. *I Loved a Lass*

I loved a lass, a fair one,
  As fair as e'er was seen;
She was indeed a rare one,
  Another Sheba Queen:
But, fool as then I was,
  I thought she loved me too:
But now, alas! she has left me,
  Falero, lero, loo! . . .

And as abroad we walkèd
  As lovers' fashion is,
Oft as we sweetly talkèd
  The sun would steal a kiss.
The wind upon her lips
  Likewise most sweetly blew;
But now, alas! she has left me,
  Falero, lero, loo!

Many a merry meeting
  My love and I have had;
She was my only sweeting,
  She made my heart full glad;
The tears stood in her eyes
  Like to the morning dew:
But now, alas! she has left me,
  Falero, lero, loo!

Her cheeks were like the cherry,
  Her skin was white as snow;
When she was blithe and merry
  She angel-like did show;
Her waist exceeding small,
  The fives did fit her shoe:
But now, alas! she's left me,
  Falero, lero, loo!

In summer time or winter
   She had her heart's desire;
I still did scorn to stint her
   From sugar, sack, or fire;
The world went round about,
   No cares we ever knew:
But now, alas! she's left me,
   Falero, lero loo! . . .

No riches now can raise me,
   No want make me despair;
No misery amaze me,
   Nor yet for want I care.
I have lost a world itself,
   My earthly heaven, adieu,
Since she, alas! hath left me,
   Falero, lero, loo . . .

GEORGE WITHER

215. *Green Grass*

A dis, a dis, a green grass,
   A dis, a dis, a dis;
Come all you pretty fair maids
   And dance along with us.

For we are going roving,
   A roving in this land;
We take this pretty fair maid,
   We take her by the hand.

She shall get a duke, my dear,
   As duck do get a drake;
And she shall have a young prince,
   For her own fair sake.

And if this young prince chance to die,
 She shall get another;
The bells will ring, and the birds will sing,
 And we clap hands together.

216. *The Lincolnshire Poacher*

When I was bound apprentice in famous Lincolnshire,
Full well I served my master for more than seven year,
Till I took úp to poaching – as you shall quickly hear:
  Oh, 'tis my delight on a shining night
  In the season of the year!

As mé and my cómrade were setting of a snare,
Twas then we spied the gamekeeper, for him we did not care,
For we can wrestle and fight, my boys, and jump o'er anywhere:
  Oh, 'tis my delight on a shining night
  In the season of the year!

As me and my comrade were setting four or five,
And taking on 'em up again we caught a hare alive,
We took the hare alive, my boys, and through the woods did
 steer:
  Oh, 'tis my delight on a shining night
  In the season of the year!

I threw him on my shoulder, and then we trudged home,
We took him to a neighbour's house and sold him for a crown
We sold him for a crown, my boys, but I did not tell you where:
  Oh, 'tis my delight on a shining night
  In the season of the year!

Success to every gentleman that lives in Lincolnshire,
Success to every poacher that wants to sell a hare,
Bad luck to every gamekeeper that will not sell his deer:[1]
      Oh, 'tis my delight on a shining night
      In the season of the year!

217. *The Men of Gotham*

Seamen three! What men be ye?
Gotham's three wise men we be.
Whither in your bowl so free?
To rake the moon from out the sea.
The bowl goes trim. The moon doth shine.
And our ballast is old wine —
And your ballast is old wine.

Who art thóu, so fast adrift?
I am he they call Old Care.
Here on board we will thee lift.
No: I may not enter there.
Wherefore so? 'Tis Jove's decree,
In a bowl Care may not be —
In a bowl Care may not be.

Fear ye not the waves that roll?
No; in charmèd bowl we swim.
What the charm that floats the bowl?
Water may not pass the brim.
The bowl goes trim. The moon doth shine.
And our ballast is old wine —
And your ballast is old wine.

            THOMAS LOVE PEACOCK

      1. Game

218. *Early Morning Meadow Song*

Now some may drink old vintage wine
    To ladies gowned with rustling silk,
But we will drink to dairymaids,
    And drink to them in rum and milk –
O, it's up in the morning early,
    When the dew is on the grass,
And St John's bell rings for matins,
    And St Mary's rings for mass!

The merry skylarks soar and sing,
    And seem to Heaven very near –
Who knows what blessed inns they see,
    What holy drinking songs they hear?
O, it's up in the morning early,
    When the dew is on the grass,
And St John's bell rings for matins,
    And St Mary's rings for mass!

The mushrooms may be priceless pearls
    A queen has lost beside the stream;
But rum is melted rubies when
    It turns the milk to golden cream!
O, it's up in the morning early,
    When the dew is on the grass,
And St John's bell rings for matins,
    And St Mary's rings for mass!

CHARLES DALMON

219. *Dabbling in the Dew*

Oh, where are you going to, my pretty little dear
With your red rosy cheeks and your coal-black hair?
I'm going a-milking, kind sir, she answered me:
And it's dabbling in the dew makes the milkmaids fair!

Suppose I were to clothe you, my pretty little dear,
In a green silken gown and the amethyst rare?
O no, sir, O no, sir, kind sir, she answered me,
For it's dabbling in the dew makes the milkmaids fair!

Suppose I were to carry you, my pretty little dear,
In a chariot with horses, a grey gallant pair?
O no, sir, O no, sir, kind sir, she answered me,
For it's dabbling in the dew makes the milkmaids fair!

Suppose I were to feast you, my pretty little dear,
With dainties on silver, the whole of the year?
O no, sir, O no, sir, kind sir, she answered me,
For it's dabbling in the dew makes the milkmaids fair!

O but London's a city, my pretty little dear,
And all men are gallant and brave that are there –
O no, sir, O no, sir, kind sir, she answered me,
For it's dabbling in the dew makes the milkmaids fair!

O fine clothes and dainties and carriages so rare
Bring grey to the cheeks and silver to the hair;
What's a ring on the finger if rings are round the eye?
But it's dabbling in the dew makes the milkmaids fair!

220. *Bonny Lassie O!*

O the evening's for the fair, bonny lassie O!
To meet the cooler air and walk an angel there,
   With the dark dishevelled hair,
      Bonny lassie O!

The bloom's on the brere, bonnie lassie O!
Oak apples on the tree; and wilt thou gang to see
   The shed I've made for thee,
      Bonny lassie O!

'Tis agen the running brook, bonnie lassie O!
In a grassy nook hard by, with a little patch of sky,
    And a bush to keep us dry,
        Bonny lassie O!

There's the daisy all the year, bonny lassie O!
There's the king-cup bright as gold, and the speedwell never cold,
    And the arum leaves unrolled,
        Bonny lassie O!

O meet me at the shed, bonny lassie O!
With the woodbine peeping in, and the roses like thy skin
    Blushing, thy praise to win,
        Bonny lassie O!

I will meet thee there at e'en, bonny lassie O!
When the bee sips in the bean, and grey willow branches lean,
    And the moonbeam looks between,
        Bonny lassie O!

JOHN CLARE

221. *The Mad Maid's Song*

Good-morrow to the Day so fair,
    Good-morning, Sir, to you:
Good-morrow to mine own torn hair,
    Bedabled with the dew.

Good-morning to this Prim-rose too,
    Good-morrow to each maid,
That will with flowers the *Tomb* bestrew
    Wherein my Love is laid.

Ah! woe is me, woe, woe is me,
    Alack and welladay!
For pitty, Sir, find out that Bee
    Which bore my Love away.

Ile seek him in your Bonnet brave,
　　Ile seek him in your eyes;
Nay, now, I think they've made his grave
　　I' the bed of strawburies.

Ile seek him there; I know, ere this,
　　The cold, cold Earth doth shake him;
But I will go, or send a kiss
　　By you, Sir, to awake him.

Pray hurt him not, though he be dead,
　　He knowes well who do love him,
And who with green-turfes reare his head,
　　And who do rudely move him.

He's soft and tender (Pray take heed);
　　With bands of Cowslips bind him,
And bring him home – but 'tis decreed
　　That I shall never find him.

ROBERT HERRICK

222. *Tell Me Where Is Fancie Bred*

Tell me where is Fancie bred,
Or in the heart or in the head?
How begot, how nourishèd?
　　　　Replie, replie!
It is engendered in the eyes,
With gazing fed; and Fancy dies
In the cradle where it lies,
Let us all ring Fancie's knell:
Ile begin it:
　　　　Ding, dong, bell.
All.　　　　*Ding, dong, bell.*

WILLIAM SHAKESPEARE

223. *Music*

Music, when soft voices die,
Vibrates in the memory –
Odours, when sweet violets sicken,
Live within the sense they quicken.

Rose leaves, when the rose is dead,
Are heaped for the belovèd's bed;
And so thy thoughts, when thou art gone,
Love itself shall slumber on.

PERCY BYSSHE SHELLEY

224. *The Bells of Shandon*

With deep affection and recollection
I often think of the Shandon bells,
Whose sounds so wild would, in the days of childhood,
Fling around my cradle their magic spells.
On this I ponder where'er I wander,
And thus grow fonder, sweet Cork, of thee;
 With thy bells of Shandon,
 That sounds so grand on
The pleasant waters of the river Lee.

I've heard bells chiming full many a clime in,
Tolling sublime in cathedral shrine,
While at a glib rate brass tongues would vibrate;
But all their music spoke naught to thine;
For memory, dwelling on each proud swelling
Of thy belfry, knelling its bold notes free,
 Made the bells of Shandon
 Sound more grand on
The pleasant waters of the river Lee.

I've heard bells tolling old 'Adrian's Mole' in,
Their thunder rolling from the Vatican,
And cymbals glorious, swinging uproarious
In the gorgeous turrets of Notre Dame;
But thy sounds were sweeter than the dome of Peter
Flings o'er the Tiber, pealing solemnly.
    O! the bells of Shandon
    Sound far more grand on
The pleasant waters of the river Lee.

There's a bell in Moscow; while on Tower and Kiosk, O!
In St Sophia the Turkman gets,
And loud in air, calls men to prayer,
From the tapering summit of tall minarets.
Such empty phantom I freely grant them;
But there is an anthem more dear to me, –
    'Tis the bells of Shandon,
    That sound so grand on
The pleasant waters of the river Lee.

FRANCIS MAHONY (FATHER PROUT)

225. *Upon a Ring of Bells*

Bells have wide mouths and tongues, but are too weak,
    Have they not help, to sing, or talk or speak.
But if you move them they will mak't appear,
By speaking they'l make all the Town to hear.
    When Ringers handle them with Art and Skill,
They then the ears of their Observers fill,
With such brave Notes, they ting and tang so well
As to out strip all with their ding, dong, Bell.

Comparison

These Bells are like the Powers of my Soul;
Their Clappers to the Passions of my mind;

The Ropes by which my Bells are made to tole,
Are Promises (I by experience find).
  My body is the Steeple where they hang,
  My graces they which do ring ev'ry Bell;
Nor is there any thing given such a tang,
When by these Ropes these Ringers ring them well.

  Let not my Bells these Ringers want, nor Ropes;
Yea let them have room for to swing and sway:
To toss themselves deny them not their Scopes.
Lord! in my Steeple give them room to play.
If they do tole, ring out, or chime all in,
They drown the tempting tinckling Voice of Vice:
Lord! when my Bells have gone, my Soul has bin
As 'twere a tumbling in this Paradice!

  Or if these Ringers do the Changes ring,
Upon my Bells, they do such Musick make,
My Soul then (Lord) cannot but bounce and sing,
So greatly her they with their Musick take.
But Boys (my Lusts) into my Belfry go,
And pull these Ropes, but do no Musick make;
They rather turn my Bells by what they do,
Or by disorder make my Steeple shake.

  Then, Lord! I pray thee keep my Belfry Key,
Let none but Graces meddle with these Ropes:
And when these naughty Boys come, say them Nay.
From such Ringers of Musick there's no hopes.

  O Lord! If thy poor Child might have his will,
And might his meaning freely to thee tell;
He never of this Musick has his fill,
There's nothing to him like thy ding, dong, Bell.

JOHN BUNYAN

226. *The Belfry*

Dark is the stair, and humid the old walls
Wherein it winds, on worn stones, up the tower.
Only by loophole chinks at intervals
Pierces the late glow of this August hour.

Two truant children climb the stairway dark,
With joined hands, half in glee and half in fear,
The boy mounts brisk, the girl hangs back to hark
If the gruff sexton their light footsteps hear.

Dazzled at last they gain the belfry-room.
Barred rays through shutters hover across the floor
Dancing in dust; so fresh they come from gloom
That breathless they pause wondering at the door.

How hushed it is! what smell of timbers old
From cobwebbed beams! The warm light here and there
Edging a darkness, sleeps in pools of gold,
Or weaves fantastic shadows through the air.

How motionless the huge bell! Straight and stiff,
Ropes through the floor rise to the rafters dim.
The shadowy round of metal hangs, as if
No force could ever lift its gleamy rim.

A child's awe, a child's wonder, who shall trace
What dumb thoughts on its waxen softness write
In such a spell-brimmed, time-forgotten place,
Bright in that strangeness of approaching night?

As these two gaze, their fingers tighter press;
For suddenly the slow bell upward heaves
Its vast mouth, the cords quiver at the stress,
And ere the heart prepare, the ear receives

Full on its delicate sense the plangent stroke
Of violent, iron, reverberating sound.
As if the tower in all its stones awoke,
Deep echoes tremble, again in clangour drowned,

That starts without a whir of frighted wings
And holds these young hearts shaken, hushed, and thrilled,
Like frail reeds in a rushing stream, like strings
Of music, or like trees with tempest filled,

And rolls in wide waves out o'er the lone land,
Tone following tone toward the far-setting sun,
Till where in fields long shadowed reapers stand
Bowed heads look up, and lo, the day is done . . .

LAURENCE BINYON

227. *Il Penseroso*

. . . Sweet bird that shunn'st the noise of folly,
Most musicall, most melancholy!
The chauntress of the Woods among
I woo to hear thy eeven-song;
And missing thee, I walk unseen
On the dry smooth-shaven green,
To behold the wandering moon
Riding near her highest noon,
Like one that had been led astray
Through the Heaven's wide pathles way,
And oft, as if her head she bowed,
Stooping through a fleecy cloud.

Oft on a Plat of rising ground,
I hear the far-off *Curfeu* sound
Over some wide-watered shoar,
Swinging slow with sullen roar:

Or if the Ayr will not permit,
Som still removèd place will fit,
Where glowing Embers through the room
Teach light to counterfeit a gloom,
Far from all resort of mirth,
Save the Cricket on the hearth,
Or the Belman's drousie charm
To bless the dores from nightly harm. . . .

JOHN MILTON

228. *Chimes*

Brief, on a flying night,
    From the shaken tower,
A flock of bells take flight,
    And go with the hour.

Like birds from the cote to the gales,
    Abrupt – O hark!
A fleet of bells set sails,
    And go to the dark.

Sudden the cold airs swing,
    Alone, aloud,
A verse of bells takes wing
    And flies with the cloud.

ALICE MEYNELL

229. *Cities Drowned*

Cities drowned in olden time
Keep, they say, a magic chime
Rolling up from far below
When the moon-led waters flow.

252

So within me, ocean deep,
Lies a sunken world asleep.
Lest its bells forget to ring,
Memory! set the tide a-swing!

HENRY NEWBOLT

230. *The Bell-Man*

From noise of Scare-fires rest ye free,
From Murders – *Benedicite*.
From all mischances, that may fright
Your pleasing slumbers in the night:
Mercie secure ye all, and keep
The Goblin from ye, while ye sleep.
Past one aclock, and almost two,
My Masters all, *Good day to you!*

ROBERT HERRICK

AUTUMN LEAVES:
WINTER SNOW

231. *To Meadows*

Ye have been fresh and green,
 Ye have been filled with flowers:
And ye the Walks have been
 Where maids have spent their houres.

Ye have beheld, how they
 With *Wicker Arks* did come
To kisse, and beare away
 The richer Couslips home.

Ye have heard them sweetly sing
 And seen them in a Round:
Each Virgin, like a Spring,
 With Hony-succles crowned.

But now, we see, none here,
 Whose silverie feet did tread,
And with dishevelled Haire,
 Adorned this smoother Mead.

Like Unthrifts, having spent,
 Your stock, and needy grown,
Ye are left here to lament
 Your poore estates, alone.

ROBERT HERRICK

232. *The Cottager to Her Infant*

The days are cold, the nights are long,
The North wind sings a doleful song;
Then hush again upon my breast;
All merry things are now at rest,
 Save thee, my pretty love!

The kitten sleeps upon the hearth,
The crickets long have ceased their mirth;
There's nothing stirring in the house
Save one wee, hungry, nibbling mouse,
    Then why so busy thou?
Nay! start not at the sparkling light;
'Tis but the moon that shines so bright
    On the window-pane
    Bedropped with rain:
Then, little darling! sleep again,
    And wake when it is day.

DOROTHY WORDSWORTH

233. *To Autumn*

Season of mists and mellow fruitfulness,
  Close bosom-friend of the maturing sun;
Conspiring with him how to load and bless
  With fruit the vines that round the thatch-eaves run;
To bend with apples the mossed cottage-trees,
  And fill all fruit with ripeness to the core;
    To swell the gourd, and plump the hazel shells
With a sweet kernel; to set budding more,
And still more, later flowers for the bees,
Until they think warm days will never cease,
    For Summer has o'er-brimmed their clammy cells—

Who hath not seen thee oft amid thy store?
  Sometimes whoever seeks abroad may find
Thee sitting careless on a granary floor,
  Thy hair soft-lifted by the winnowing wind;
Or on a half-reaped furrow sound asleep,
  Drowsed with the fume of poppies, while thy hook
    Spares the next swath and all its twinèd flowers:

And sometimes like a gleaner thou dost keep
   Steady thy laden head across a brook;
  Or by a cyder-press, with patient look,
    Thou watchest the last oozings hours by hours.

Where are the songs of Spring? Ay, where are they?
   Think not of them, thou hast thy music too, —
While barred clouds bloom the soft-dying day,
   And touch the stubble-plains with rosy hue;
Then in a wailful choir the small gnats mourn
   Among the river-sallows, borne aloft
    Or sinking as the light wind lives or dies;
And full-grown lambs loud bleat from hilly bourn;
   Hedge-crickets sing; and now with treble soft
   The red-breast whistles from a garden-croft;
    And gathering swallows twitter in the skies.

JOHN KEATS

234. *The Solitary Reaper*

Behold her, single in the field,
Yon solitary Highland Lass!
Reaping and singing by herself;
Stop here, or gently pass!
Alone she cuts and binds the grain,
And sings a melancholy strain;
O listen! for the vale profound
Is overflowing with the sound.

No nightingale did ever chaunt
More welcome notes to weary bands
Of travellers in some shady haunt,
Among Arabian sands:

A voice so thrilling ne'er was heard
In spring-time from the cuckoo bird,
Breaking the silence of the seas
Among the farthest Hebrides.

Will no one tell me what she sings?
Perhaps the plaintive numbers flow
For old, unhappy, far-off things,
And battles long ago;
Or is it some more humble lay,
Familiar matter of to-day?
Some natural sorrow, loss, or pain,
That has been, and may be again?

Whate'er the theme, the maiden sang
As if her song could have no ending;
I saw her singing at her work,
And o'er the sickle bending; –
I listened, motionless and still;
And, as I mounted up the hill,
The music in my heart I bore
Long after it was heard no more.

WILLIAM WORDSWORTH

235. *The Heaving Roses of the Hedge Are Stirred*

The heaving roses of the hedge are stirred
By the sweet breath of summer, and the bird
Makes from within his jocund voice be heard.

The winds that kiss the roses sweep the sea
Of uncut grass, whose billows rolling free
Half drown the hedges which part lea from lea.

But soon shall look the wondering roses down
Upon an empty field cut close and brown,
That lifts no more its height against their own.

And in a little while those roses bright,
Leaf after leaf, shall flutter from their height,
And on the reapèd fields lie pink and white.

And yet again the bird that sings so high
Shall ask the snow for alms with piteous cry;
Take fright in his bewildering bower, and die.

CANON DIXON

236. *Autumn*

A DIRGE

The warm sun is failing, the bleak wind is wailing,
The bare boughs are sighing, the pale flowers are dying;
      And the Year
On the earth her death-bed, in a shroud of leaves dead,
      Is lying.
   Come, Months, come away,
   From November to May,
   In your saddest array;
   Follow the bier
   Of the dead cold Year,
And like dim shadows watch by her sepulchre.

The chill rain is falling, the nipped worm is crawling,
The rivers are swelling, the thunder is knelling
      For the Year;
The blithe swallows are flown, and the lizards each gone
      To his dwelling.

Come, Months, come away;
Put on white, black, and grey;
Let your light sisters play –
Ye, follow the bier
Of the dead cold Year,
And make her grave green with tear on tear.

PERCY BYSSHE SHELLEY

237. *When That I Was and a Little Tiny Boy*

When that I was and a little tinie boy,
  With hey, ho, the winde and the raine:
A foolish thing was but a toy,
  For the raine it raineth every day.

But when I came to man's estate,
  With hey, ho, the winde and the raine:
'Gainst Knaves and Theeves men shut their gate,
  For the raine it raineth every day.

But when I came, alas, to wive,
  With hey, ho, the winde and the raine:
By swaggering could I never thrive,
  For the raine it raineth every day.

But when I came unto my beds,
  With hey, ho, the winde and the raine,
With tos-pottes still had drunken heades, –
  For the raine it raineth every day.

A great while ago the world begon,
  With hey, ho, the winde and the raine,
But that's all one, our Play is done,
  And we'll strive to please you every day.

WILLIAM SHAKESPEARE

238. *Song*

The feathers of the willow
Are half of them grown yellow
   Above the swelling stream;
And ragged are the bushes,
And rusty are the rushes
   And wild the clouded gleam.

The thistle now is older,
His stalk begins to moulder,
   His head is white as snow;
The branches all are barer,
The linet's song is rarer
   The robin pipeth now.

CANON DIXON

239. *Fall, Leaves, Fall*

Fall, leaves, fall; die, flowers, away;
Lengthen night and shorten day;
Every leaf speaks bliss to me,
Fluttering from the autumn tree.

I shall smile when wreaths of snow
Blossom where the rose should grow;
I shall sing when night's decay
Ushers in a drearier day.

EMILY BRONTË

240. *The Sands of Dee*

'O Mary, go and call the cattle home,
  And call the cattle home,
  And call the cattle home
 Across the sands of Dee';
The western wind was wild and dank with foam,
 And all alone went she.

The western tide crept up along the sand,
  And o'er and o'er the sand,
  And round and round the sand,
 As far as eye could see.
The rolling mist came down and hid the land:
 And never home came she.

'Oh! is it weed, or fish, or floating hair –
  A tress of golden hair,
  A drownèd maiden's hair
 Above the nets at sea?
Was never salmon yet that shone so fair
 Among the stakes on Dee.'

They rowed her in across the rolling foam,
  The cruel crawling foam,
  The cruel hungry foam,
 To her grave beside the sea:
But still the boatmen hear her call the cattle home
 Across the sands of Dee.

CHARLES KINGSLEY

241. *Break, Break, Break*

Break, break, break,
   On thy cold grey stones, O Sea!
And I would that my tongue could utter
   The thoughts that arise in me.

O well for the fisherman's boy,
   That he shouts with his sister at play!
O well for the sailor lad,
   That he sings in his boat on the bay!

And the stately ships go on
   To their haven under the hill;
But O for the touch of a vanished hand,
   And the sound of a voice that is still!

Break, break, break,
   At the foot of thy crags, O Sea!
But the tender grace of a day that is dead
   Will never come back to me.

       ALFRED, LORD TENNYSON

242. *Ode to the West Wind*

I

O, wild West Wind, thou breath of Autumn's being,
Thou, from whose unseen presence the leaves dead
Are driven, like ghosts from an enchanter fleeing,

Yellow, and black, and pale, and hectic red,
Pestilence-stricken multitudes: O, thou,
Who chariotest to their dark wintry bed

The wingèd seeds, where they lie cold and low,
Each like a corpse within its grave, until
Thine azure sister of the Spring shall blow

Her clarion o'er the dreaming earth, and fill
(Driving sweet buds like flocks to feed in air)
With living hues and odours plain and hill:

Wild Spirit, which art moving everywhere;
Destroyer and preserver; hear, O hear!

II

Thou on whose stream, mid the steep sky's commotion,
Loose clouds like earth's decaying leaves are shed,
Shook from the tangled boughs of Heaven and Ocean,

Angels of rain and lightning: there are spread
On the blue surface of thine aëry surge,
Like the bright hair uplifted from the head

Of some fierce Maenad, even from the dim verge
Of the horizon to the zenith's height
The locks of the approaching storm. Thou dirge

Of the dying year, to which this closing night
Will be the dome of a vast sepulchre,
Vaulted with all thy congregated might

Of vapours, from whose solid atmosphere
Black rain, and fire, and hail will burst: O hear!

III

Thou who didst waken from his summer dreams
The blue Mediterranean, where he lay,
Lulled by the coil of his crystàlline streams,

Beside a pumice isle in Baiae's bay,
And saw in sleep old palaces and towers
Quivering within the wave's intenser day,

All overgrown with azure moss and flowers
So sweet, the sense faints picturing them! Thou
For whose path the Atlantic's level powers

Cleave themselves into chasms, while far below
The sea-blooms and the oozy woods which wear
The sapless foliage of the ocean, know

Thy voice, and suddenly grow grey with fear,
And tremble and despoil themselves: O hear!

IV

If I were a dead leaf thou mightest bear;
If I were a swift cloud to fly with thee;
A wave to pant beneath thy power, and share

The impulse of thy strength, only less free
Than thou, O uncontrollable! If even
I were as in my boyhood, and could be

The comrade of thy wanderings over Heaven,
As then, when to outstrip thy skiey speed
Scarce seemed a vision; I would ne'er have striven

As thus with thee in prayer in my sore need.
Oh, lift me as a wave, a leaf, a cloud!
I fall upon the thorns of life! I bleed!

A heavy weight of hours has chained and bowed
One too like thee: tameless, and swift, and proud.

V

Make me thy lyre, even as the forest is:
What if my leaves are falling like its own!
The tumult of thy mighty harmonies

Will take from both a deep, autumnal tone,
Sweet though in sadness. Be thou, Spirit fierce,
My spirit! Be thou me, impetuous one!

Drive my dead thoughts over the universe
Like withered leaves to quicken a new birth!
And, by the incantation of this verse,

Scatter, as from an unextinguished hearth
Ashes and sparks, my words among mankind!
Be through my lips to unawakened earth

The trumpet of a prophecy! O, Wind,
If winter comes, can Spring be far behind?

PERCY BYSSHE SHELLEY

243. *That Wind*

That wind, I used to hear it swelling;
With joy divinely deep;
You might have seen my hot tears welling,
But rapture made me weep.

I used to love on winter nights
To lie and dream alone
Of all the rare and real delights
My lonely years had known;

And oh! – above the best – of those
That coming time should bear,
Like heaven's own glorious stars they rose,
Still beaming bright and fair.

EMILY BRONTË

244. *A Frosty Night*

Mother.   Alice, dear, what ails you,
           Dazed and white and shaken?
           Has the chill night numbed you?
           Is it fright you have taken?

Alice.   Mother I am very well,
           I felt never better;
           Mother, do not hold me so,
           Let me write my letter.

Mother.   Sweet, my dear, what ails you?
Alice.   No, but I am well.
           The night was cold and frosty,
           There's no more to tell.

Mother.   Ay, the night was frosty,
           Coldly gaped the moon,
           Yet the birds seemed twittering
           Through green boughs of June.

           Soft and thick the snow lay,
           Stars danced in the sky,
           Not all the lambs of May-day
           Skip so bold and high.

           Your feet were dancing, Alice,
           You seemed to dance on air,
           You looked a ghost or angel
           In the starlight there.

Your eyes were frosted starlight,
Your heart, fire and snow.
Who was it said 'I love you'?
Alice.   Mother, let me go!

ROBERT GRAVES

245. *In a Drear-Nighted December*

In a drear-nighted December,
    Too happy, happy tree,
Thy branches ne'er remember
    Their green felicity:
The north cannot undo them
With a sleety whistle through them;
Nor frozen thawings glue them
     From budding at the prime.

In a drear-nighted December,
    Too happy, happy brook,
Thy bubblings ne'er remember
    Apollo's summer look;
But with a sweet forgetting,
They stay their crystal fretting,
Never, never petting
     About the frozen time.

Ah! would 'twere so with many
    A gentle girl and boy!
But were there ever any
    Writhed not at passèd joy?
To know the change and feel it,
When there is none to heal it
Nor numbèd sense to steal it,
     Was never said in rhyme.

JOHN KEATS

246. *A Song of Winter*

Cold cold!
Cold to-night is broad Moylurg,
Higher the snow than the mountain-range,
The deer cannot get at their food.

Cold till Doom!
The storm has spread over all:
A river is each furrow upon the slope,
Each ford a full pool.

A great tidal sea is each loch,
A full loch is each pool:
Horses cannot get over the ford of Ross,
No more can two feet get there.

The fish of Ireland are a-roaming,
There is no strand which the wave does not pound,
Not a town there is in the land,
Not a bell is heard, no crane talks.

The wolves of Cuan-wood get
Neither rest nor sleep in their lair,
The little wren cannot find
Shelter in her nest on the slope of Lon.

Keen wind and cold ice
Has burst upon the little company of birds,
The blackbird cannot get a lee to her liking,
Shelter for its side in Cuan-wood.

Cosy our pot on its hook,
Crazy the hut on the slope of Lon:
The snow has crushed the wood here,
Toilsome to climb up Ben-bo.

Glenn Rye's ancient bird
From the bitter wind gets grief;
Great her misery and her pain,
The ice will get into her mouth.

From flock and from down to rise –
Take it to heart! – were folly for thee;
Ice in heaps on every ford –
That is why I say 'cold'!

247. *Cold Blows the Wind*

Cauld blows the wind frae north to south,
   And drift is driving sairly;
The sheep are couring[1] in the heugh,[2]
   Oh sirs; its winter fairly.
Now up in the morning's no' for me,
   Up in the morning early;
I'd rather gae supperless to my bed,
   Than rise in the morning early.

Loud rairs the blast amang the woods,
   The branches tirling barely,
Amang the chimley taps its thuds,
   And frost is nippin sairly,
Now up in the morning's no for me,
   Up in the morning early;
To sit a' night I'd rather agree,
   Than rise in the morning early.

The sun peeps o'er the southlan' hill,
   Like ony tim'rous carlie;[3]
Just blinks a wee, then sings again,
   And that we find severely.

      1. Cowering   3. Wee bit lassikin
      2. Glen

Now up in the morning's no' for me,
   Up in the morning early;
When snaw blaws into the chimley cheek,
   Wha'd rise in the morning early.

Nae linties[1] lilt on hedge or bush,
   Poor things, they suffer sairly;
In cauldrife[2] quarters a' the night,
   A' day they feed but sparely.
Now up in the morning's no' for me,
   Up in the morning early;
Nae fate can be waur,[3] in winter time,
   Than rise in the morning early.

JOHN HAMILTON

248. *Skating*

. . . So through the darkness and the cold we flew,
And not a voice was idle; with the din
Smitten, the precipices rang aloud;
The leafless trees and every icy crag
Tinkled like iron; while far distant hills
Into the tumult sent an alien sound
Of melancholy not unnoticed, while the stars
Eastward were sparkling clear, and in the west
The orange sky of evening died away.
Not seldom from the uproar I retired
Into a silent bay, or sportively
Glanced sideway, leaving the tumultuous throng,
To cut across the reflex of a star
That fled, and, flying still before me, gleamed
Upon the glassy plain; and oftentimes,

1. No linnets   2. Freezing   3. Worse

When we had given our bodies to the wind,
And all the shadowy banks on either side
Came sweeping through the darkness, spinning still
In rapid line of motion, then at once
Have I, reclining back upon my heels,
Stopped short; yet still the solitary cliffs
Wheeled by me – even as if the earth had rolled
With visible motion her diurnal round!
Behind me did they stretch in solemn train,
Feebler and feebler, and I stood and watched
Till all was tranquil as a dreamless sleep . . .

WILLIAM WORDSWORTH

249. *London Snow*

When men were all asleep the snow came flying,
In large white flakes falling on the city brown,
Stealthily and perpetually settling and loosely lying,
　Hushing the latest traffic of the drowsy town;
Deadening, muffling, stifling its murmurs failing;
Lazily and incessantly floating down and down;
　Silently sifting and veiling road, roof and railing;
Hiding difference, making unevenness even,
Into angles and crevices softly drifting and sailing.
　All night it fell, and when full inches seven
It lay in the depth of its uncompacted lightness,
The clouds blew off from a high and frosty heaven;
　And all woke earlier for the unaccustomed brightness
Of the winter dawning, the strange unheavenly glare:
The eye marvelled – marvelled at the dazzling whiteness;
　The ear hearkened to the stillness of the solemn air;
No sound of wheel rumbling nor of foot falling,
And the busy morning cries came thin and spare.
　Then boys I heard, as they went to school, calling,

They gathered up the crystal manna to freeze
Their tongues with tasting, their hands with snowballing;
　Or rioted in a drift, plunging up to the knees;
Or peering up from under the white-mossed wonder,
'O look at the trees!' they cried, 'O look at the trees!'
　With lessened load a few carts creak and blunder,
Following along the white deserted way,
A country company long dispersed asunder:
　When now already the sun, in pale display
Standing by Paul's high dome, spread forth below
His sparkling beams, and awoke the stir of the day.
　For now doors open, and war is waged with the snow;
And trains of sombre men, past tale of number,
Tread long brown paths, as toward their toil they go:
　But even for them awhile no cares encumber
Their minds diverted; the daily word is unspoken,
The daily thoughts of labour and sorrow slumber
At the sight of the beauty that greets them, for the charm they have
　broken.

ROBERT BRIDGES

250. *For Snow*

Oh the falling Snow!
Oh the falling Snow!
Where does it all come from?
Whither does it go?
Never never laughing,
Never never weeping,
Falling in its Sleep,
Forever ever sleeping –
From what Sleep of Heaven
Does it flow, and go
Into what Sleep of Earth,
The falling falling Snow?

ELEANOR FARJEON

251. *Velvet Shoes*

Let us walk in the white snow
  In a soundless space;
With footsteps quiet and slow,
  At a tranquil pace,
  Under veils of white lace.

I shall go shod in silk,
  And you in wool,
White as a white cow's milk,
  More beautiful
  Than the breast of a gull.

We shall walk through the still town
  In a windless peace;
We shall step upon white down,
  Upon silver fleece,
  Upon softer than these.

We shall walk in velvet shoes:
  Wherever we go
Silence will fall like dews
  On white silence below.
  We shall walk in the snow.

ELEANOR WYLIE

252. *Lucy Gray*

Oft I had heard of Lucy Gray:
And when I crossed the wild,
I chanced to see at break of day
The solitary child.

No mate, no comrade Lucy knew;
She dwelt on a wide moor,
The sweetest thing that ever grew
Beside a human door!

You yet may spy the fawn at play,
The hare upon the green;
But the sweet face of Lucy Gray
Will never more be seen.

'To-night will be a stormy night —
You to the town must go;
And take a lantern, Child, to light
Your mother through the snow.'

'That, Father! will I gladly do:
'Tis scarcely afternoon —
The minster-clock has just struck two,
And yonder is the moon!'

At this the father raised his hook,
And snapped a faggot-band;
He plied his work; — and Lucy took
The lantern in her hand.

Not blither is the mountain roe:
With many a wanton stroke
Her feet disperse the powdery snow,
That rises up like smoke.

The storm came on before its time:
She wandered up and down;
And many a hill did Lucy climb:
But never reached the town.

The wretched parents all that night
Went shouting far and wide;
But there was neither sound nor sight
To serve them for a guide.

At day-break on a hill they stood
That overlook'd the moor;
And thence they saw the bridge of wood
A furlong from their door.

They wept – and, turning homeward, cried
'In heaven we all shall meet!'
– When in the snow the mother spied
The print of Lucy's feet.

Then downwards from the steep hill's edge
They tracked the footmarks small;
And through the broken hawthorn hedge,
And by the long stone-wall:

And then an open field they crossed,
The marks were still the same;
They tracked them on, nor ever lost;
And to the bridge they came:

They followed from the snowy bank
Those footmarks, one by one,
Into the middle of the plank;
And further there were none!

– Yet some maintain that to this day
She is a living child;
That you may see sweet Lucy Gray
Upon the lonesome wild.

O'er rough and smooth she trips along,
And never looks behind;
And sings a solitary song
That whistles in the wind.

WILLIAM WORDSWORTH

253. *Gone Were But the Winter Cold*

Gane were but the winter cauld
    And gane were but the snaw,
I could sleep in the wild woods,
    Where primroses blaw.

Cauld's the snaw at my head,
    And cauld at my feet,
And the finger o' death is at my e'en
    Closing them to sleep,

Let nane tell my father,
    Or my mither sae dear;
I'll meet them baith in heaven
    At the Spring o' the year.

ALLAN CUNNINGHAM

254. *A Child's Winter Evening*

The smothering dark engulfs relentlessly
With nightmare tread approaching steadfastly;
All horrors thicken as the daylight fails
And, is it wind, or some lost ghost that wails?

Tongue cannot tell the stories that beset,
With livid pictures blackness dense as jet,
Or that wild questioning – whence we are; and why;
If death is darkness; and why I am I.

The children look through the uneven pane
Out to the world, to bring them joy again;
But only snowflakes melting into mire
Without, within the red glow of the fire.

They long for something wonderful to break
This long-drawn winter wistfulness, and take
Shape in the darkness; threatening like Fate
There comes a hell-like crackling from the grate.

But hand in hand they urge themselves anear
And watch the cities burning bright and clear;
Faces diabolical and cliffs and halls
And strangely-pinnacled, molten castle walls.

Tall figures flicker on the ceiling stark
Then grimly fade into one ominous dark;
Dream terrors iron-bound throng on them apace,
And dusk with fire, and flames with shadows race.

GWEN JOHN

255. *A Carol for Saint Stephen's Day*

Seynt Stevene was a clerk,
  In Kyng Herowdès halle,
And servyd him of bred and cloth,
  As every kyng befalle.

Stevyn out of Kechoun cam,
  With boris hed on honde,
He saw a sterr was fayr and bryght
  Over Bedlem stonde.

He kyst adoun the bores hed,
  And went into the halle:
'I forsake the, kyng Herowde,
  And thi werkès alle.

'I forsak the, kyng Herowde,
  And thi werkès alle:
Ther is a chyld, in Bedlem born,
  Is better than we alle.'

'Quhat eylyt the, Stevene?
  Quhat is the befalle?
Lakkyt the eyther mete or drynk
  In kyng Herowdès halle?'

'Lakyt me neyther mete ne drynk
  In kyng Herowdès halle;
Ther is a chyld, in Bedlem born,
  Is better than we alle.'

'Quhat eylyt the, Stevyn, art thu wod?
  Or thu gynnyst to brede?
'Lakkyt the eyther gold or fe,
  Or ony ryche wede?'

'Lakyt me neyther gold ne fe,
  Ne non rychè wede;
Ther is a chyld, in Bedlem born,
  Shal helpyn us at our nede.'

'That is al so soth, Stevyn,
  Al so soth, I wys,
As this capon crowè schel
  That lyth her in myn dych.'

That word was not so sonè seyd,
  That wordè in that halle,
The capon crew, *Christus natus est!*
  Among the lordès alle.

'Rysyt up, myn túrmentowres
  Be to and al be on,
And ledyt Stevyn out of this town,
  And stonyt hym wyth ston.'

Tokyn hem Stevene,
  And stonyd hym in the way:
And therfor is his evyn
  On Crystes owyn day.

256. *The Burning Babe*

As I in hoary winter's night
   Stood shivering in the snow,
Surprised I was with sudden heat,
   Which made my heart to glow;
And lifting up a fearful eye
   To view what fire was near,
A pretty babe all burning bright,
   Did in the air appear:
Who, scorchèd with excessive heat,
   Such floods of tears did shed,
As though his floods should quench his flames,
   Which with his tears were fed:
'Alas!' quoth he, 'but newly born,
   In fiery heats I fry,[1]
Yet none approach to warm their hearts
   Or feel my fire, but I!
My faultless breast the furnace is,
   The fuel wounding thorns;
Love is the fire, and sighs the smoke,
   The ashes shames and scorns;
The fuel Justice layeth on,
   And Mercy blows the coals;
The metal in this furnace wrought
   Are men's defilèd souls:
For which, as now on fire I am,
   To work them to their good,
So will I melt into a bath,
   To wash them in my blood.'
With this he vanished out of sight,
   And swiftly shrunk away,
And straight I called unto my mind
   That it was Christmas Day.

ROBERT SOUTHWELL

1. Burn

257. *The Holly and the Ivy*

The holly and the ivy,
  Now both are full-well grown,
Of all the trees that are in the wood,
  The holly bears the crown.
    O the rising of the sun,
      The running of the deer,
      The playing of the merry Organ,
      Sweet singing in the quire.
      Sweet singing in the quire.

The holly bears a blossom,
  As white as lily-flower;
And Mary bore sweet Jesus Christ,
  To be our sweet Saviour.
    O the rising of the sun, . . .

The holly bears a berry,
  As red as any blood;
And Mary bore sweet Jesus Christ,
  To do poor sinners good.
    O the rising of the sun, . . .

The holly bears a prickle,
  As sharp as any thorn;
And Mary bore sweet Jesus Christ,
  On Christmas Day in the morn.
    O the rising of the sun, . . .

The holly bears a bark,
  As bitter as any gall;
And Mary bore sweet Jesus Christ,
  For to redeem us all.
    O the rising of the sun, . . .

The holly and the ivy,
  Now both are full well grown,
Of all the tree that are in the wood,
  The holly bears the crown.

> *O the rising of the sun,*
>   *The running of the deer,*
> *The playing of the merry Organ,*
>   *Sweet singing in the quire.*
>   *Sweet singing in the quire.*

258. *Welcome Yule*

. . . Wolcum be thu, hevene kyng,
Wolcom, born in on morwenyng,
Wolcom for home[1] we shal syng,
  Wolcum yol.

Wolcum be ye Stefne and Jon,
Wolcum Innocentes everychon,
Wolcum Thomas martyr on,
  Wolcum yol.

Wolcum be ye, good newe yere,
Wolcum twelthe-day, bothe infer,[2]
Wolcum syentes lef[3] and der,
  Wolcum yol.

Wolcum be ye Candylmesse,
Wolcum be ye qwyn of blys,
Wolcum both to mor and lesse,
  Wolcum yol.

1. Him   2. Together   3. Loved

Wolcum be ye that arn her,[1]
Wolcum alle and mak good cher,
Wolcum alle another yer,
   Wolcum yol.

259. *Nay, Ivy, Nay*

Nay, Ivy, nay,
   Hyt shal not be, I wys;
Let Holy hafe the maystry,
   As the manner[2] ys.

Holy stond in the halle;
   Fayre to behold;
Ivy stond wythout the dore,
   She ys ful sore a-cold.
     Nay, Ivy, nay . . .

Holy and hys mery men,
   They dawnsyn and they syng;
Ivy and hur maydenys,
   They wepyn and they wryng.
     Nay, Ivy, nay . . .

Ivy hath a kybe,[3]
   She kaght yt wyth the colde,
So mot thay all haf ąe,
   That wyth Ivy hold.
     Nay, Ivy, nay . . .

Holy hath berys,
   As rede as any rose,
The foster[4] and the hunter
   Kepe hem[5] fro the doos.
     Nay, Ivy, nay . . .

1. Are here   3. Chilblain   4. Forester
2. Custom   5. Them

Ivy hath berys,
    As blake as any slo,
Ther come the oule,
    And ete hym as she goo.
        Nay, Ivy, nay . . .

Holy hath byrdys,
    A ful fayre flok,
The nyghtyngale, the poppynguy,
    The gayntyl lavyrok.
        Nay, Ivy, nay . . .

Gode Ivy [tell me]
    What byrdys ast thu?[1]
Non but the howlat,
    That kreye[2] how, how!

Nay, Ivy, nay.
    Hyt shal not be, I wys,
Let Holy hafe the maystry,
    As the maner ys.

260. *Tu-Whit To-Who*

When Isicles hang by the wall,
    And Dicke the shepheard blowes his naile,
And Tom beares Logges into the hall,
    And Milke comes frozen home in paile:
When blood is nipt, and waies be fowle,
Then nightly sings the staring Owle,
            Tu-whit to-who
        A merrie note,
While greasie Jone doth keele[3] the pot.

1. Hast Thou   2. Cries   3. Skim

286

When all aloud the winde doth blow,
    And coffing drownes the Parson's saw;
And birds sit brooding in the snow,
    And Marrian's nose lookes red and raw;
When roasted Crabs[1] hisse in the bowle,
Then nightly sings the staring Owle,
        Tu-whit to-who
        A merrie note,
While greasy Jone doth keele the pot.

                    WILLIAM SHAKESPEARE

261. *Blow, Blow, Thou Winter Wind*

Blow, blow, thou winter winde,
Thou art not so unkinde
        As man's ingratitude;
Thy tooth is not so keene,
Because thou art not seene,
        Although thy breath be rude.
Heigh ho! sing heigh ho, unto the green holly,
Most friendship is fayning, most Loving meere folly:
        Then heigh ho, the holly,
        This Life is most jolly.

Freize, freize, thou bitter skie,
That dost not bight so nigh
        As benefitts forgot;
Though thou the waters warpe,
Thy sting is not so sharpe,
        As friend remembered not.
Heigh ho! sing heigh ho, unto the green holly,
Most friendship is fayning, most Loving meere folly:
        Then heigh ho, the holly,
        This Life is most jolly.

                    WILLIAM SHAKESPEARE

1. Apples

ABOUT AND ROUNDABOUT

In the margins of Nahum Tarune's The Other Worlde *I found many things in his own handwriting about (and roundabout) the poems contained in it. Some of them I copied out at the time. Others of my own making were added afterwards. These were all included in the first edition of* Come Hither, *which appeared in 1923.*

Since its first publication many additions have been made to the notes, including new poems and rhymes, and always with the intention of carrying on the theme or meaning or of adding to the interest of the poems to which they refer in the earlier part of the book.

By the kindness and courtesy, too, of readers of the original edition I have now been able to put right a certain number of my first blunders and inaccuracies, though, it may be, others as flagrant still remain. Moreover, many entirely new notes have been added, with a fresh crop, I fear, of such weeds as disfigured the originals! For these I must ask to be as generously excused.

But why have taken any such risk? The fact is that in the making of notes – of which to some minds there should be no beginning – it is difficult to find an end. For many reasons. At every reading of a poem – though it may have been familiar from early childhood – some hitherto hidden delicacy of rhythm or intonation may be revealed; new shades of meaning show themselves; and even difficulties may become apparent which were before unheeded. Indeed what is read on the printed page is merely so many words; they may mean much or little to the reader, but in either case it is he alone who out of them can create a poem, *and therefore* his *poem. And this poem changes for him, as he himself changes with the years.*

A poem, too, is a blossoming in words of a language at a certain time in its history, and words stand for things, objects, actions, as well as ideas. It was the work also of one man living in a certain place and period and setting and state of being and often in a byegone century. Is it waste of pains, then, even when one is young, to attempt not only to realize this but to illustrate it in some degree, and so to cross again and again over the slender bridge between poetry and actuality, between the world of the imagination and the world without? There will not be less to be seen on either side by becoming familiar with both of them. And much, alas, that was of the very being of our early English poetry and particularly that of the folk, of the people, is rapidly vanishing away.

Still, it must be confessed that some of the pages that follow are not only without rhyme, but with very little detectable reason. An even larger number are, in fact, confessions of ignorance. For of all the boys in a school, it is the dunce who — if only he were encouraged — could ask the most questions. He may by no means be the best at answering them for himself: but the attempt to do so, even when it is made with so little method and so much at random as it has been here, is its own reward.

And last, owing to the pleasant custom of printing poetry so that, in intention at least, it cannot be mistaken for prose, any reader of the following pages who has a natural distaste for any annotator, can easily skip from rhyme to rhyme, dream on from poem to poem; and ignore everything else.

I

'This is the Key'

This jingle (like Nos. 15, 16 and others) is one of hundreds of nursery or dandling rhymes which I found in Mr Nahum's book. Compared with more formal poems they are like the least (and loveliest) of the wild flowers — pimpernel, eyebright, thyme, woodruff, and others even tinier, even quieter, but revealing their own private and complete little beauty if looked at closely. Who made them, how old they are; nobody knows. But when Noah's Ark stranded on the slopes of Mount Ararat, maybe a blossoming weed or two was nodding at the open third-storey window out of which over the waters of the flood the dove had followed the raven, and there, rejoicing in the sunshine and the green, sat Japheth's wife dandling little Magog on her lap, and crooning him some such lullaby.

3

On the one side is printed the old Scots, and on the other the best I can do to put it into the English of our own time. According to the dictionary the thistle-cock that cries shame on the sleepers still drowsing in their beds is the corn-bunting – a cousin of the yellow-hammer. He has a small harsh monotonous voice as if for the very purpose. Whereas the nightingale might seem to cry, 'Nay, nay: it is in dreams you wander. Happy ones! Sleep on; sleep on.'

But for most of us sleep keeps strangely to its hours; and though nearly all children of seven have spent about three long years abed, few of us have slept straight on even from one day's dark into another. Not so William Foxley. He was pot-maker in the Mint, then in the Tower of London. He fell asleep one day – the 27th of April, 1546 – and continued to sleep for fourteen days and nights. Not even a visit from Henry VIII and his royal physician stirred his slumbers. Having awakened at last, however, he returned to the busy world; and continued his pot-making for forty years after.

4

'*I passed by his garden*'

Whatever fate befell the Sluggard, I should like to have taken a walk in his *garden*, among those branching thistles, green thorns and briers. Maybe he sailed off at last to the Isle of Nightmare, or to the land where it is always afternoon, or was wrecked in Yawning Gap. He must, at any rate, have had an even heavier head than Dr Watts supposed if he never so much as lifted it from his pillow to brood awhile on that still, verdurous scene. And the birds!

Indeed, to lie, between sleep and wake, when daybreak is brightening of an April or a May morning, and so listen to the far-away singing of a thrush or to the whistling of a robin or a wren is to seem to be transported back into the garden of Eden. Dreamers, too, may call themselves travellers.

Mr Nahum's picture to this rhyme was of a man in rags looking into a small round mirror or looking-glass, but at what you couldn't see.

6

'The merchant bows'

– (as do the happy to the New Moon, for luck), for his merchandise is being wafted over the sea under the guidance of the Seaman's, or Ship, or Lode, or Pole Star. It shines in the constellation of the Little Bear, and 'is the cheefe marke whereby mariners governe their course in saylings by nyghte.' To find the 'marke', look towards the north some cloudless night for the constellation of Seven Stars called the Plough or the Dipper or Charles's Wain (or Waggon), which 'enclyneth his ravisshinge courses abouten the soverein heighte of the worlde' day and night throughout the year. Its hinder stars (Dubhe and Merak) are named 'the pointers', because if you follow the line of them with the eye into the empty skies, the next brightish star it will alight on *is* the Seaman's Star. Close beside the second of the seven is a mere speck of a star. And that is called by country people Jack-by-the-middle-horse. On this same star looked Shakespeare – as did the 1st Carrier in his *Henry IV*: 'Heigh-ho, an't be not foure by the day, Ile be hanged. Charles' waine is over the near Chimney, and yet our horse not packt'; and as did his 2nd Gentleman in *Othello:*

Montano.   What from the Cape can you discerne at Sea?
1st Gentleman. Nothing at all, it is a high-wrought Flood: I cannot 'twixt the Heaven, and the Maine Descry a Saile . . .
2nd Gentleman. . . . Do but stand upon the Foaming Shore,
The chidden Billow seemes to pelt the Clowds,
The wind-shaked-Surge, with high and monstrous Maine,
Seemes to cast water on the burning Beare,

And quench the Guards of the ever-fixèd Pole.
I never did like mollestation view
On the enchafèd Flood. . . .

Faintly shimmering, too, in the northern heavens is that other numerous starry cluster, known the world over as *Seven* – to us as the Seven Sisters or the Pleiades. A strange seven; for only six stars are now clearly visible to the naked eye, one having vanished, it would seem, within human memory. When? where? – none can tell. They play in light as close together as dewdrops in a cobweb hung from thorn to thorn, and near-by them, on winter's cold breast burns the most marvellous of the constellations – the huntsman Orion, the Dog-star at his heels.

'Seek him that maketh the Seven Stars and Orion, and turneth the shadow of death into the morning, and maketh the day dark with night . . .'

8

'*Bird, prune thy wing*'

It is as pleasant an occupation to watch a bird 'pruning' or preening its feathers – stretching out each delicately pinioned wing in turn – as it is to eye a cat washing his face. Assuredly no human nurse ever went so many times over the same ear of one of her charges (or used so little moisture) as he seems to do over one of his own. Forty-eight was my own black housecat's score when last I watched him at his toilet – and even then he looked no different! Preening (and cats nibble their fur as well as tongue it) is more than merely smoothing and rearranging, for it not only removes damaged feathers, but at the same time oils the sound ones.

9

'Bare Winter suddenly was changed to Spring'

In Marche, and in Aprill, from morning to night;
  In sowing and setting, good huswives delight.
To have in their garden, or some other plot:
  To trim up their house, and to furnish their pot . . .

At Spring (for the sommer) sowe garden ye shall,
  At harvest (for winter) or sowe not at all.
Oft digging, removing and weeding (ye see)
  Makes herbe the more holesome and greater to bee . . .

New set doo aske watering with pot or with dish,
  New sowne doo not so, if ye doo as I wish.
Though cunning with dible, rake, mattock and spade,
  By line and by leavell, trim garden is made.

Who soweth too lateward, hath seldom good seed,
  Who soweth too soone, little better shall speed.
Apt time and the season so divers to hit,
  Let aier and laier helpe practise and wit . . .

                              THOMAS TUSSER

'Like a child, half in tenderness and mirth'

At a first reading, perhaps, this line will not appear to flow so
smoothly as the rest. But linger an instant on the word *child*, and
you will have revealed to yourself one of Shelley's, and indeed one
of every poet's loveliest devices with words – to let the music of
his verse accord with its meaning, and at the same time to please
and charm the ear with a slight variation from the regular beat and
accent of the metre. So, too, in the middle lines of the next

stanza. This variation, which is called rhythm, is the very proof of its writer's sincerity. For if the sound of his verse (or of his voice) ring false, he cannot have completely realised what he was writing or saying. When a man says what he means, he says it *as if he meant it*. The *tune* of what he says sounds right. When a man does *not* mean what he says, he finds it all but impossible to say it as if he did. The *tune* goes wrong.

Just so with reading. One must catch the tune (the intonation) to ensure the meaning. Four brief rules from a gay and tiny *Compendious English Grammar* of 1780 may be of help:

'(1) ... Observe well the pauses, accents and emphases; and never stop but where the sense will admit of it.

'(2) Humor your voice a little, according to the subject. ...

'(3) Do not read too fast, lest [in lip or mind] you get a habit of stammering; adding or omitting words; and be sure that your understanding keep pace with your tongue.

'(4) In reading Verse, pronounce every word just as if it were prose, observing the stops with great exactness, and giving each word its proper accent; and if it be not harmonious, the Poet, and not the Reader, is to blame.'

This scrap of rhyme also contains sound advice: its 'each idle gait' meaning all lounging and laziness:

> Give your attention as you read,
>   And frequent pauses take.
> Think seriously; and take good heed
>   That you no dogs' ears make.
> Don't wet the fingers as you turn
>   The pages one by one;
> Never touch prints; observe; and learn
>   Each idle gait to shun.

But in general, if these rules are followed, there can be little danger of reading like a parrot, or like a small boy in his first breeches at a Dame's school. To *think* while one reads; that is the main thing: so that at last the eyes forget the words and fix themselves with a burning interest and delight upon the objects for which the words are music and symbol. That at least is not to be, as Sidney says, – just

> . . . like a child that some fair book doth find,
> With gilded leaves or coloured vellum plays,
> Or, at the most, on some fair pictures stays,
> But never heeds the fruit of writer's mind.

13

'Comes dancing from the East'

There is a story about this dancing in Mrs Wright's *Rustic Speech and Folklore*. It is the story of a woman who lived in a district called Hockley, in the parish of Broseley. She said that she had heard of such 'dancing' but did not believe it to be true, 'till on Easter morning last, I got up early, and then I saw the sun dance, and dance, and dance, three times, and I called to my husband and said, "*Rowland, Rowland, get up and see the sun dance!*" I used,' she said, 'not to believe it, but now I can never doubt more.' The neighbours agreed with her that the sun did dance on Easter morning, and that some of them had seen it. 'Seeing,' goes the old proverb, 'is believing' – which is true no less of the 'inward' than the outward eye. I once tried to comfort a little boy who was unhappy because there was a Bear under his bed. Candlestick in hand, I talked and talked, and *proved* that there wasn't a real bear for miles and miles around, except, of course, at the Zoological Gardens, and there – black, brown, sloth, spectacled, grizzly and polar alike – all of them, poor creatures, were cabined, cribbed and shut up in barred cages. He listened, tears still shining in his eyes, his small face sharp and clear. 'Why certainly, certainly *not*,' I ended, 'there can't be a real bear for miles around!' He smiled as if pitying me. 'Ah yes,' he answered with a die-away sob, 'but, you see, you's talking of *real* bears, and mine *isn't* real.'

14

'See the clear sun'

and here the motto on an old sun-dial:

Here stand I ever lonely amidst the flowers tall,
While o'er my figured bosom faint shadows slowly fall.
And to the busy world without whose life by hours I keep
I say, 'Tis time to rise: and then, 'Tis time to sleep.

'Us idle wenches'

It was a jolly bed in sooth,
  Of oak as strong as Babel.
And there slept Kit and Sall and Ruth
  As sound as maids are able.

Ay – three in one – and there they dreamed,
  Their bright young eyes hid under;
Nor hearkened when the tempest streamed
  Nor recked the rumbling thunder.

For marvellous regions strayed they in,
  Each moon-far from the other –
Ruth in her childhood, Kit in heaven,
  And Sall with ghost for lover.

But soon as ever sun shone sweet,
  And birds sang, Praise for rain, O –
Leapt out of bed three pair of feet
  And danced on earth again, O!

17

This, like No. 2, and the next song must be as old as the dewponds on the Downs. They were wont to be sung, I have read, by five or six men, with a fiddle, or flute, or clarionet accompaniment. When I was a boy I can remember one First of May seeing a Jack-in-the-Green in the street – a man in a kind of wicker cage hung about with flowers and leaves – with Maid Marian, Friar Tuck and the rest, dressed up, and dancing beside him. A great friend of mine, when she was a little girl of eight, was so frightened at sight of this leafy prancing creature on her way to school that she turned about and ran for a mile without stopping.

18

'*And gone to-morrow*'

Yesterday returneth not;
Perchance to-morrow cometh not;
There is to-day; misuse it not.

19

'*Daysies*'

There is far too little of Geoffrey Chaucer's – that most lovable, shrewd, compassionate, and natural of poets – in this book. There was much more of him, I noticed, in Mr Nahum's Tome II. At first sight his words look a little strange; but not for long; and if every dotted letter is made a syllable of, his rhythm will flow like water over bright green waterweed.

It is a curious, though little, thing, that while, among the one hundred and seventy varieties of flowers mentioned by Shakespeare, there are no less than about fifty-seven several references to the rose, twenty-one to the green grass, eighteen to the violet, and even to the serviceable but rank nettle a round dozen, he has but a scant five to Chaucer's beloved daisy. Flowers, it is true, as says Canon Ellacombe (who collected all such references into his delightful book, *Plant-lore and Garden-craft of Shakespeare*), never sweeten the Plays for their own sake alone, and foxgloves, snowdrops and forget-me-nots find no place there at all.

On reading this over again I began to wonder if any *other* reason than that given above could be found for the absence of all mention of these three familiar flowers in the *Plays*. With this result – which I owe chiefly to *British Flowering Plants*:

In none of the early English poets is mention made of the *Snowdrop*; and the wild snowdrop appears to be an escape, a runaway, from monastery gardens. About 180 years ago, it was recorded as flourishing at the foot of Herefordshire Beacon. The earliest reference to the flower in the Oxford English Dictionary is of 1664: 'Those purely white flowers that appear about the end of Winter, and are commonly call'd a Snow Drop.' Quite possibly, then, Shakespeare never set eyes on this frail green-flecked lovely thing, nid-nodding in the icy blasts of January.

Foxgloves, however, had been so called for at least seven centuries before he was born, and must have been a familiar flower in England in the late sixteenth century. But it has a rooted distaste for lime and chalk, and so is not found in north-east Gloucestershire. How about Stratford? I appealed to a friend, Miss Eleanor Doorly, living at Warwick, who very kindly made enquiries for me. It appears that foxgloves are to be found near Stratford, but only by the elect, so to speak, and in occasional clumps. There were foxgloves at Lapworth, for example, in the summer of last year [1927]. But none now grows on the bank that Oberon knew, with its thyme, oxlip, violet, musk rose and eglantine; and in South Warwickshire what foxgloves there are tend to disappear. They have been transplanted, maybe, and die of homesickness. It is possible, then, that Shakespeare when a child never saw a foxglove either; and it is what we see early in life that comes back easiest later. How else can we explain its absence, say, from *A Midsummer Night's Dream*? – its natural earthly paradise.

As for the *Forget-me-not*, it is only within the last hundred years or so that this name has been applied to the Great Water Scorpion Grass. There is a legend from the German to account for the name. A knight in armour and his Lady were straying beside a deep and rapid river. She espied a pretty pale flower growing in midstream, and entreated the Knight to pluck her a spray of it. He leapt in and perished, having adjured her with his last breath, as he flung the spray toward the bank, '*Vergeiss mein nicht*! ' – Forget me not!

But apart from the fact that this is the 'blue and bright-eyed floweret of the *brook*', and flourishes no more in deep water than a sailor does on land; to some tastes, Mouse-ear, which is all that *Myosotis* means, may seem a better name for it than the sentimental one borrowed from abroad.

Shakespeare, then, if he had referred to this particular flower, would not have so named it. None the less, there was a flower in his time with this name – it is mentioned in Gerard's *Herbal* – the ground-pine or 'herbe-ivie'. It is a sticky, hairy little plant with a pungent flavour of turpentine, and is never very happy far from chalk. Kent, then, might boast of its unforgettableness, but hardly South Warwickshire. So he never mentioned that either.

Having thus (joyfully) disposed of these three examples, it occurred to me to return to *Plant-lore* again, in case any other quite familiar flower had – poor soul – escaped Shakespeare's mention. And I found to my dismay that while honourable place has been given to the eryngo, to coloquintida and the pomegranate; while onions, pignuts, rhubarb, cabbage, potatoes, and turnips have won their niche (the last three in *The Merry Wives*); bindweed, corn-flower, dandelion, London Pride, buttercup, and *Sweet William* had bloomed for him in vain. The absence of the buttercup can be easily explained (though no explanation, of course, is *necessary*); but what of the others?

And now to return to Chaucer's *daisy*:

'A yellow cup, it hath,' says Pliny, 'and the same is crowned, as it were with a garland, consisting of five and fifty little leaves, set round about it in manner of fine pales. These be flowers of the meadow, and most of such are of no use at all.' No use at all – except only to make skylark of every heart whose owner has eyes in his head for a daisy's simple looks, its marvellous workmanship, and the sheer happiness of their multitudes wide open in the sun or round-headed and adrowse in the evening twilight.

But of all the daisies in poetry surely this from *The Second Brother*, by Thomas Beddoes, is not only the loveliest, but has the strangest setting:

> . . . I . . . say
>
> How thou art like the daisy in Noah's meadow,
> On which the foremost drop of rain fell warm
> And soft at evening; so the little flower
> Wrapped up its leaves, and shut the treacherous water
> Close to the golden welcome of its breast, –
> Delighting in the touch of that which led
> The shower of oceans, in whose billowy drops
> Tritons and lions of the sea were warring,
> And sometimes ships on fire sunk in the blood
> Of their own inmates; others were of ice,
> And some had islands rooted in their waves,
> Beasts on their rocks, and forest-powdering winds,
> And showers tumbling on their tumbling self, –
> And every sea of every ruined star
> Was but a drop in the world-melting flood . . .

Chaucer's painted portrait is well known. So is that in his own words in the *Canterbury Tales*. But here is another, less familiar, by Robert Greene – of 'Sir Jeffrey Chaucer', as he calls him. Water chamlet is a rich coloured silken plush, and a whittell is a knife:

> His stature was not very tall,
> Leane he was, his legs were small,
> Hosed within a stock of red
> A buttoned bonnet on his head,
> From under which did hang, I weene,
> Silver haires both bright and sheene,
> His beard was white, trimmèd round,
> His count'nance blithe and merry found,

A Sleevelesse Iacket large and wide,
With many pleights and skirts Side,
Of water Chamlet did he weare,
A whittell by his belt he beare,
His shooes were cornèd broad before,
His Inkhorne at his side he wore,
And in his hand he bore a booke,
Thus did this auntient Poet looke.

Few poets have been so much *delighted in* as Chaucer. He reminds one of the picture of Genius doffing his hat to Dame Nature in the MS. of *Roman de la Rose* in the British Museum, while the green things of Spring are enamelling the walled garden in which they meet; blue sky is over all, and the swallows are flying.

Caxton, his first printer, said that his poems were 'full of plesaunce'; Dryden, that 'he was a perpetual fountain of good sense'. Waller praised his 'matchless strain'. 'His words,' said Hazlitt, 'point as an index to the objects they refer to like the eye or finger' – alert, quick, direct.

Southey referred to him as 'Father Chaucer'; Denham and Akenside (meaning no less reverence), as 'old' Chaucer. Warton ventured (wisely) on 'immortal'. Addison spoke of the 'Merry Bard'; Spenser delighted in his 'merry tales' and Cowper in his 'merry page'. Tennyson called him 'the first warbler'; Wordsworth, the 'time-honoured'. Fenton chose 'sprightly' and Lowell 'vernal'. Byron (being Byron) dismissed him as 'obscene and contemptible'. Coleridge bubbled over with what he called his 'manly cheerfulness', Drayton said briefly, 'noble Chaucer'.

20

'*Brave prick-song*'

'Prick-song' is the music sung from notes written or *pricked* on the paper. It is the descant or melody warbled above the simple theme or plain-song which was sung from memory, and so formed its burden or undersong.

'The jolly cuckoos'

On a day when Jenkin
Did walk abroad to heare
    The birds rejoyce,
    With pleasant voyce;
In spring time of the yeare;
    Proudly and loudly
Her heard a bird then sing,
    Cuckoe, Cuckoe.
The cuckoe never lins [stays],
But still doth cry so merily,
And Cuckoe, cuckoe sings . . .

[1643]

In April, the koocoo can sing her song by rote,
In June – of tune – she cannot sing a note;
At first, *koo-coo, koo-coo*, sing still can she do,
At last, *kooke, kooke, kooke*; six *kookes* to one *koo*.

[1587]

21

'Cuckoo, jug, jug, pu we, to witta woo!'

Four birds, I suppose, have part in this: cuckoo, nightingale
(*yoog, yoog*), green-finch (?) and owl.

> I rose anon, and thought I wouldè gone
> Into the woods, to hear the birdis sing,
> When that the misty vapour was agone,
> And cleare and fairè was the morrowing;
> The dew, also, like silver in shining,
> Upon the leaves, as any baumè sweet.
>
> .   .   .   .

And in I went to hear the birdis sing,
Which on the branches, both in plain and vale,
So loudly y-sang, that all the wood y-rang,
Like as it should shiver in pieces smale;
And as me thoughten that the nightingale
With so great might her voice began out-wrest,
Right as her heart for love would all to-brest.

JOHN LYDGATE

22

'*And birds had drawn their valentines*'

To-morrow is St Valentine's day,
    All in the morning betime,
And I a Maid at your Window
    To be your Valentine!

For first thing in the early morning if you go out on St Valentine's Day, which is the 14th day of February, you will meet, if you meet anybody, your soon-to-be-loved one. So too the birds. In my young days, folks sent the daintiest pictures to their sweethearts on this day. So, too, in Pepys's time:

'This morning came up to my wife's bedside – I being up dressing myself – little Will Mercer to be her Valentine; and brought her name writ upon blue paper in gold letters, done by himself, very pretty . . .'

'*The jealous trout*'

Thou that desir'st to fish with line and hook,
Be it in pool, in river, or in brook,
To bless thy bait and make the fish to bite,
Lo, here's a means! if thou canst hit it right:

Take Gum of Life, fine beat, and laid in soak
In oil well drawn from that which kills the oak,
Fish where thou wilt, thou shalt have sport thy fill;
When twenty fail, thou shalt be sure to kill.

It's perfect and good,
If well understood;
Else not to be told
For silver or gold.

So advises Master Will. Lauson in the *Secrets of Angling*, which
was published in 1653; the ingredients (or *ingrediments* as I used to
say when I was a child) of his 'gum of life' being *Cocculus Juliæ*,
Assafoetida, Honey, and Wheat-flour. The 'that which kills the
oak', I suppose, is ivy. But it looks as if there may have been a wink
in his eye – to welcome the green in his reader's.

Here, on the same theme, are a few lines from a poem by Mr
Robert Bridges:

. . . Sometimes an angler comes, and drops his hook
Within its hidden depths, and, gainst a tree
Leaning his rod, reads in some pleasant book.
Forgetting soon his pride of fishery,
And dreams, or falls asleep,
While curious fishes peep
About his nibbled bait, or scornfully
Dart off and rise and leap . . .

And these are by J. Wolcot:

Why flyest thou away with fear?
Trust me there's naught of danger near,
I have no wicked hooke
All covered with a snaring bait,
Alas, to tempt thee to thy fate,
And dragge thee from the brooke . . .

Enjoy thy stream, O harmless fish;
And when an angler for his dish,
  Through gluttony's vile sin,
Attempts, a wretch, to pull thee out,
God give thee strength, O gentle trout,
  To pull the raskall in!

But to return to the 'line': 'For dyeing of your hairs,' says
Izaak Walton in *The Compleat Angler*, 'do it thus: Take a pint of
strong ale, half a pound of soot, and a little quantity of the juice of
walnut-tree leaves, and an equal quantity of alum; put these together, into a pot, pan, or pipkin, and boil them half an hour; and
having so done, let it cool; and being cold, put your hair into it,
and there let it lie; it will turn your hair to be a kind of water or
glass-colour or greenish; and the longer you let it lie, the deeper
coloured it will be. You might be taught to make many other
colours, but it is to little purpose; for doubtless the water-colour or
glass-coloured hair is the most choice and the most useful for an
angler, but let it not be too green.'

But there is a way of fishing without fly, hook or hairs, called
'tickling'. About 1277 Thomas of the Moor was charged with
taking fish in his Lord's pond. This was his defence:

'Sir, for God's sake do not take it ill of me if I tell the truth, how
the other evening I went along the bank of the pond, and saw the
fish playing in the water so lovely and bright, and for the great
craving I had for a perch I lay down on the bank of the pond and
with my hand only and quite simply took and carried away this
perch, and I will tell thee the cause of my covetous desire, my
companion, that is my wife had lain in bed a whole month . . . and
never eaten or drunk anything she could relish, and for the craving
to taste a perch she sent me to the bank of the pond to take one
perch only.'

' *Joan strokes a sillabub or twain* '

If you would make a Lemon Sillabub (as advised by Mrs Charlotte
Mason, 'a Professed Housekeeper, who from about 1740 had up-

wards of Thirty Years experience in Families of the First Fashion')
take 'a Pint of cream, a pint of white wine, the rind of two lemons
grated, and the juice. Sugar to the taste. Let it stand some time; mill
or whip it. Lay the froth on a sieve; put the remainder into glasses.
Lay on the froth.'

Or try this, the *Everlasting Sillabub*, from a cook book of 1790,
by 'the Principal Cook at the London Tavern', who gives four
others also – the *Solid*, the *under the Cows* the *Whipt* and the
Lemon.

'Take half a pint of Rhenish wine, half a pint of sack, with the
juice of two large Seville oranges, and put them into two pints and
a half of thick cream. Grate in just the yellow rind of three lemons,
and put in a pound of double-refined sugar well beaten and sifted.
Mix all together, with a spoonful of orange-flower water, and with
a whisk beat it well together for half an hour. Then, with a spoon,
take off the froth, and lay in on a sieve to drain, and then fill your
glasses.'

Mr Nahum must have had a fancy for Cookery Books; there
were dozens of them in his tower room. Indeed, the next best thing
to eating a good dish is to read how it is made; and somehow the
old 'cookbook' writers learned to write most appetising English.
Here is another 'May-Day' – from Pepys.

'*May 1st*, 1669. Up betimes. Called by my tailor, and there first
put on a summer suit this year; but it was not my fine one of
flowered tabby vest, and coloured camlet tunic, because it was too
fine with the gold lace at the bands, that I was afraid to be seen in
it; but put on the stuff suit I made the last year, which is now re-
paired; and so did go to the office in it, and sat all the morning, the
day looking as if it would be foul. At noon home to dinner, and
there find my wife extraordinary fine, with her flowered tabby gown
that she made two years ago, now laced exceeding pretty; and,
indeed, was fine all over; and mighty earnest to go, though the day
was very lowering; and she would have me put on my fine suit,
which I did. And so anon we went alone through the town with our
new liveries of serge, and the horses' manes and tails tied with red
ribbons, and the standards gilt with varnish, and all clean, and green
reins, that people did mightily look upon us; and, the truth is, I

did not see any coach more pretty, though more gay, than ours, all the day . . . [And] here was W. Batelier and his sister in a borrowed coach by themselves, and I took them and we to the lodge; and at the door did give them a sillabub, and other things, cost me 12s., and pretty merry. And so back to the coaches, and there till the evening, and then home.'

Here, from *Delightes for Ladies*, of 1608, is an ancient dainty that would eat uncommonly well with a sillabub: – '*To make a marchpane*. – Take two poundes of almonds being blanched, and dryed in a sieve over the fire, beate them in a stone mortar, and when they bee small mixe them with two pounde of sugar beeing finely beaten, adding two or three spoonefuls of rose-water, and that will keep your almonds from oiling: when your paste is beaten fine, drive it thin with a rowling pin, and so lay it on a bottom of wafers, then raise up a little edge on the side, and so bake it, then yce it with rose-water and sugar, then put it in the oven again, and when you see your yce is risen up and drie, then take it out of the oven and garnish it with pretie conceipts, as birdes and beasts being cast out of standing moldes. Sticke long comfits upright in it, cast biskets and carrowaies in it, and so serve it; guild it before you serve it: you may also print of this *marchpane* paste in your molds for banqueting dishes. And of this paste our confit makers at this day make their letters, knots, armes, escutcheons, beasts, birds, and other fancies.' Also pygmy castles and suchlike, for dessert, which the guests would demolish with sugar-plums.

'Good thou, save mee a piece of Marchpane, and as thou lovest me, let the Porter let in Susan Grindstone and Nell . . .'

Romeo and Juliet

It might be assumed that good dishes would long since have earned for themselves good names, but it is not so. Centuries ago Norfolk Dumplings, Gloucester Bag Puddings, Worchester Black Puddings and Devonshire White Pot Puddings were already famous, but I have never heard of their having positive Christian names. There are a few memorable examples in Mrs Glasse's famous cook-book – the book that does *not* prescribe for jugged hare with 'First catch your hare', but does angrily asseverate, 'I have heard of a [French] cook that used six pounds of butter to fry twelve eggs!'

But in general to browse over Mrs Glasse's pages is more likely to make the mouth water than to kindle the fancy. Here and there she succeeds in doing both: *e.g.*, Frangas incopades, Fricandillas, Oxford John, Bombarded Veal, Hottentot pie, a Bride's pie, a Thatch-house pie. There is Salmagundy, too, and Cowslip pudding, Florendine of Oranges, or Skirret pie. And could anything sound more soothing for the sick-room tea-tray than Panado, Brown Caudle, Buttered Water, Artificial Asses Milk, and Sago Tea!

With Steeple Cream and Moon-shine, however, we begin to recover, and with Mouse-trap at one end of the table and Carolina Snowballs or Hedgehog-in-Flummery at the other, there should certainly be Floating Island in between. And if, on returning from such a feast, you should chance to be bitten by a mad dog, Mrs Glasse will also see to *that*:

'Take of the herb called in Latin *lichen cinereus terrestris*, in English, ash-coloured ground liverwort, cleaned, dried, and powdered, half an ounce. Of black pepper, powdered, two drachms. Mix these well together, and divide the powder into four doses, one of which must be taken every morning fasting, for four mornings successively, in half a pint of cow's milk, warm. After these four doses are taken, the patient must go into the cold bath, or a cold spring or river every morning fasting for a month. He must be dipped all over, but not to stay in (with his head above water) longer than half a minute, if the water be very cold . . .

23

'*The Sun arising*'

'What other fire could be a better image of the fire which is there, than the fire which is here? Or what other earth than this, of the earth which is there?' So said Plotinus, and 'I know,' said Blake, 'that this world is a world of imagination and vision. I see everything I paint in this world, but everybody does not see alike. To the eye of a miser a guinea is far more beautiful than the sun, and a bag worn with the use of money has more beautiful proportions than a vine filled with grapes. The tree which moves some to tears of joy is in the eyes of others only a green thing which stands in the way . . . Some scarce see Nature at all. But to the eyes of the man of imagination, Nature is Imagination itself. As a man is, so he sees. As the eye is formed, such are its powers. You certainly mistake, when you say that the visions of fancy are not to be found in this world. To me this world is all one continued vision.' . . . Indeed, when Blake was a child, he saw on Peckham Rye a tree, full, not of birds, but of angels; and his poems show how marvellously clear were the eyes with which he looked at the things of Nature.

'In the year 1872, an old lady might have been seen driving across the Rye in her silvery carriage; and she came to where, under a flowering tree, sat a small boy – the locks of hair upon his head like sheaves of cowslips, his eyes like speedwells, and he in very bright clothes. And he was laughing up into the tree. She stopped her carriage and said to him almost as if she were more angry than happy, "What are you laughing at, child?" And he said, "At the sparrows, ma'am." "Mere sparrows!" says she, "but why?" "Because they were saying," says he, "here comes across the Rye a blind old horse, a blind old coachman, and a blind old woman." "But I am not blind," says she. "Nor are they not 'mere sparrows,'" said the child. And at that the old lady was looking out of her carriage at no child, but at a small bush, in bud, of gorse.'

24

'*And thank Him than*'

– as does Robert Herrick's child, in his 'Grace':

> Here a little child I stand,
> Heaving up my either hand;

Cold as Paddocks though they be,
Here I lift them up to Thee,
For a Benizon to fall
On our meat, and on us all. AMEN.

A paddock is a frog or a toad. To either small cold hand that child
had four cold fingers and a thumb; and in old times, says Halliwell,
our ancestors had names not only for each of the five fingers but
for each of the five toes. The fingers were called thumb, toucher,
longman, leche-man, little-man: leche-man being the ring-finger,
because in that 'there is a sinew very tender and small that reaches
to the heart.' In Essex they used to call them (and still may) – Tom
Thumbkin, Bess Bumpkin, Long Linkin, Bill Wilkin, and Little
Dick. In Scotland: Thumbkin, Lickpot, Langman, Berrybarn and
Pirlie Winkie. In (?) Lancashire and Cheshire, Tommy Thumbkin,
Billy Winkie, Long Duster, Jacky Molebar and Little Perky.

And here are some more from Dr Courtenay Dunn's *Natural
History of the Child* – a book which is graced with as handsome a
frontispiece as ever I've seen:

Thumb	- Tommy Tomkins	or Bill Milker.
Forefinger	- Billy Wilkins	” Tom Thumper.
Third finger	- Lond Larum	” Long Lazy.
Fourth finger	- Betsy Bedlam	” Cherry Bumper.
Little finger	- Little Bob	” Tippity, Tippity-Town-end.

Toes:

Big toe	- Tom Barker	or Toe Tipe.
Toe ii -	- Long Rachel	” Penny Wipe.
Toe iii -	- Minnie Wilkin	” Tommy Tistle.
Toe iv -	- Milly Larkin	” Billy Whistle.
Little Toe	- Little Dick	” Tripping-go.

So (if you wish) you can secretly name not only your fingers,
toes, rooms, chairs and tables, etc., but also the stars in their courses,

the trees in your orchard, and have your own privy countersign for the flowers you like best. 'Give a dog a bad name, and hang him,' says the old proverb. Give anything a *good* name, and it is yours for ever. There is the tale of the unhappy gardener in the Isle of Rumm who without ill intention called a snapdragon a scrofulariaceous antirrhinum. At which there arose out of the hillside a Monster named Zobj that reasoned with him in the manner of monsters. Doubtless the gardener meant well; but when he heard that Voice counting his last moments, not in common English, but in what Wensleydale Knitters still remember of the Norse – Yahn, Jyahn, Tether, Mether, Mumph, Hither, Lither, Auver, Dauver, Dic – well . . .

While we are on this subject here is a Face Rhyme:

> Bo Peeper
> Nose Dreeper
> Chin Chopper
> White Lopper
> Red Rag
> And Little Gap.

This is another:

> Here sits the Lord Mayor:
> Here sit his men;
> Here sits the cockadoodle;
> Here sits the hen;
> Here sits the little chickens;
> Here they run in;
> Chinchopper, chinchopper, chinchopper, chin.

The next three are foot rhymes, very soothing at times to fractious babies. The first is common in London, etc.:

> This little pig went to market;
> This little pig stayed at home;
> This little pig had roast beef;

This little pig had none;
This little pig cried *Wee-wee-wee-wee-wee!*
All the way home.

The second comes from the Isle of Wight:

This gurt pig zays, I wants meat;
T'other one zays, Where'll ye hay et?
This one zays, In gramfer's barn;
T'other one zays, Week! Week! I can't get over the
dreshel.

And this is from Scotland:

This ain biggit the baurn,
This ain stealit the corn,
This ain stood and saw,
This ain ran awa',
An' wee Pirlie Winkie paid for a'.

As for the 'gurt pig',

The cock sat in the yew tree,
The hen came chuckling by,
'I wish you all good morning, *and*
A good fat pig in the sty,
A *good fat pig* in the sty.'

And last; here is a Dance-babbie-on-knee (or This-is-the-way)
rhyme; also from Scotland:

The doggies gaed to the mill,
This way and that way;
They took a lick out o' *this* wife's poke
And they took a lick out o' *that* wife's poke,
And a loup in the lead, and a dip in the dam,
And gaed walloping, walloping, walloping, HAME.

And no doubt came to the conclusion expressed in the sixth stanza of Robert Herrick's *Ternary of Littles, upon a Pipkin of Jelly sent to a Lady*:

> A little Saint best fits a little Shrine,
> A little Prop best fits a little Vine,
> As my small Cruse best fits my little Wine.
>
> A little Seed best fits a little Soyle,
> A little Trade best fits a little Toyle,
> As my small Jarre best fits my little Oyle.
>
> A little Bin best fits a little Bread,
> A little Garland fits a little Head,
> As my small stuffe best fits my little Shed.
>
> A little Hearth best fits a little Fire,
> A little Chappell fits a little Quire,
> As my small Bell best fits my little Spire.
>
> A little streame best fits a little Boat,
> A little lead best fits a little Float,
> As my small Pipe best fits my little note.
>
> A little meat best fits a little bellie,
> As sweetly, Lady, give me leave to tell ye,
> This little Pipkin fits this little Jellie.

25

The spelling of this lovely and ancient little carol has been modernized; but here are its last four lines as they appear in a MS. of the early fifteenth century:

> Moder and maiden
> Was never non but sche;
> Well may swich a lady
> Godès moder be.

26

'Upon my lap my sovereign sits'

The 'animal' that Mary Wollstonecraft, the mother of Mary
Shelley, is telling her husband about in the following letter is *her*
'sovereign'; and how curiously (after the rest of the letter has been
read) this word reveals her entire adoration of the little creature.

PARIS, *January* 15*th*, 1795.

. . . My animal is well; I have not yet taught her to eat, but nature
is doing the business. I gave her a crust to assist the cutting of her
teeth; and now she has two she makes good use of them to gnaw
with . . . You would laugh to see her; she is just like a little squirrel;
she will guard a crust for two hours, and, after fixing her eyes on
an object for some time, dart on it with an aim as sure as a bird of
prey – nothing can equal her life and spirits . . . Adieu. Do not
forget to love us – and come soon to tell us that you do.

MARY

29

'Sleep stays not, though a monarch bids'

Why rather, sleep, liest thou in smoky cribs,
Upon uneasy pallets stretching thee,
And hushed with buzzing night-flies to thy slumber,
Than in the perfumed chambers of the great,
Under the canopies of costly state,
And lulled with sound of sweetest melody?
O thou dull god, why liest thou with the vile
In loathsome beds, and leavest the kingly couch
A watch-case or a common 'larum-bell?
Wilt thou upon the high and giddy mast
Seal up the ship-boy's eyes, and rock his brains

In cradle of the rude imperious surge,
And in the visitation of the winds,
Who take the ruffian billows by the top,
Curling their monstrous heads, and hanging them
With deafening clamour in the slippery clouds,
That, with the hurly, death itself awakes?
Canst thou, O partial sleep, give thy repose
To the wet sea-boy in an hour so rude;
And in the calmest and most stillest night,
With all appliances and means to boot,
Deny it to a king? Then happy low, lie down!
Uneasy lies the head that wears a crown.

Henry IV, Part ii.

30

'*I remember, I remember*'

On page 279 there is a reference to the tune or intonation in the reading of a poem – the rise and fall of the voice – which when too regularly repeated becomes a mere sing-song, and when carried to an extreme is what is sometimes called elocution. There are many ways of reading verse aloud – one of them being with little change of pitch, and resembling a spoken chaunt, or 'intoning'. This drowses the waking mind; and the words resemble an incantation.

· But whatever the best method may be, all poetry, unless its charm is to be wasted, should be *heard*, with the inward ear at least, if not with the outer; and the intonation, like the rhythm, is part and parcel of its meaning. Unless it be in accord with the thought and the feeling intended, it falsifies the poem. This is curiously true even of single words – that once were double. Stress lightly and raise the voice a little on the second or third syllable in each of the following words, and a meaning that may hitherto have been half-hidden slips up like a cuckoo out of a clock: gate*way*, lock*smith*,

highway*man*, hard*bake*, draw*back*, skin*flint*, dream*land*, cup*board*,
sea*worthy*, shoe*horn*.

No. 30 is a poem by Thomas Hood who (though *Alf* was denied
to Tennyson, and *Bob* to Browning, in spite of *Will* and *Kit* and
Ben before them) was affectionately known as *Tom*, and the first
line of this poem – one as long-endeared and familiar to thousands
of Englishmen as are wall-flowers, Sweet William and Old Man –
is a delicate case in point. Where in it precisely should the stress be,
and where the lift and cadence of the voice?

In some poems even the metre at first sight may be doubtful.
Take for example the first stanza of Drayton's sonorous and spirited
Agincourt:

> Fair stood the wind for France
> When we our sails advance,
> Nor now to prove our chance
>   Longer will tarry;
>
> But putting to the main
> At Caux the mouth of Seine,
> With all his martial train
>   Landed King Harry.

There are at least four ways of stressing the six longer lines. (1)
Fair *stood* the *wind* for *France*; (2) *Fair* stood the *wind* for France;
(3) *Fair stood* the *wind* for *France*; (4) *Fair* stood the *wind* for
France. (1) becomes a miserable sing-song. (2) mere capering. (3) is
stern, solemn, resolute. And (4) admits, I think, of the greatest
variety of rhythm and intonation. Perhaps the best way is to treat
each stanza as if it were composed of two metrical units – lines 1–4
and 5–8 – and then read these with as much and as little variation as
will provide the fullest meaning:

> *They* now to *fight* are *gone*
> *Ar-mour* on *armour shone*
> *Drum* now to *drum* did *groan*
>   *To hear* – was *wonder*;

That with the *cries*, they *make*
The *very earth* did *shake*:
Trumpet to *trum*pet *spake*,
Thun – der to *thun*der.

But complete tomes have been written on this subject; and the authors of them rarely agree. They add to one's knowledge, but not much to one's delight in the reading of poetry, and still less, I imagine, to the writing of it. In general, if you read a poem quietly over, first, to your head, then to your heart, most technical difficulties vanish like morning mist.

' *Those flowers made of light!* '

Hold up a flower between eye and sun, or even candle-flame, and it seems little but its own waxen hue and colour. Moonlight is too pale; the petals remain opaque. In the moon's light, indeed, blueness is scarcely distinguishable from shadowiness; red darkens but yellow pales, and the fairest flowers of all wake in her beams – jasmine, convolvulus, evening-primrose – as if they not only shared her radiance but returned a glow-wormlike fuminess of their own.

Once, long before I came to Thrae, having plucked for my mother a few convolvulus flowers, I remember when I was just about to give them into her hand I discovered that the beautiful cups of delight had enwreathed themselves together, and had returned as it were to the bud, never to reopen. I was but a child, and this odd little disappointment was so extreme that I burst out crying.

32

See page 297 and for proof of the curious obedience of words to any bidden rhythm it is interesting to compare this poem – which seems as if it had been spoken in ordinary talk and yet is of a singular beauty – with its neighbours. Mr Frost's colt is called 'a little Morgan', because he is of a famous breed of horses of that name which are the pride of the State of Vermont.

Autumn Evening

The shadows flickering, the daylight dying,
And I upon the old red sofa lying,
The great brown shadows leaping up the wall,
The sparrows twittering; and that is all.

I thought to send my soul to far-off lands,
Where fairies scamper on the windy sands,
Or where the autumn rain comes drumming down
On huddled roofs in an enchanted town.

But O my sleepy soul, it will not roam,
It is too happy and too warm at home:
With just the shadows leaping up the wall,
The sparrows twittering; and that is all.

FRANCES CORNFORD

35

Only a single copy of the old play, *Mundus et Infans*, from which this fragment is taken, is known to be in existence. It was printed by Wynkyn de Worde in 1522; and was written round-about 1500.

The lines need a slow reading to get the run and lilt of them: and even at that they jog and creak like an old farm-cart. But the boy, Dalyaunce, if one take a little pains, will come gradually out of them as clear to the eye as if you had met him in the street to-day, on his way to 'schole' for yet another 'docking'.

Clothes, houses, customs, food a little, thoughts a little, knowledge, too – all change as the years and centuries go by, but Dalyaunce under a thousand names lives on. It never occurred to me when I was young to think that the children in Rome talked Latin at their games, and that Solomon and Caesar, Prester John and the Grand Khan knew in their young days what it means to be homesick and none too easy to sit down. Yet there are knucklebones and dolls in London that the infant subjects of the Pharaohs played with, and at Stratford Grammar School, for all to see, is Shakespeare's school desk. As for Dalyaunce, 'dockings' are not nowadays so harsh as once they were.

In proof of this, there is a passage from a book, telling of his own life as a small boy, written by Guibert de Nogent. He is speaking of his childhood, about the year when William the Conqueror landed at Hastings:

'So, after a few of the evening hours had been passed in that study, during which I had been beaten even beyond my deserts, I came and sat at my mother's knees. She, according to her wont, asked whether I had been beaten that day; and I, unwillingly to betray my master, denied it; whereupon, whether I would or no, she threw back my inner garment (such as men call shirt), and found my little ribs black with the strokes of the osier, and rising everywhere into weals. Then, grieving in her inmost bowels at this punishment so excessive for my tender years, troubled and boiling with anger, and with brimming eyes, she cried, "Never now shalt thou become a clerk, nor shalt thou be thus tortured again to learn thy letters!" Whereupon, gazing upon her with all the seriousness that I could call to my face, I replied, "Nay, even though I should die under the rod, I will not desist from learning my letters and becoming a clerk."'

But there were more merciful schoolmasters than Guibert de Nogent's, even in days harsh as his; as this further extract from Mr G. G. Coulton's enticing *Medieval Garner* shows:

'One day, when a certain Abbot, much reputed for his piety, spake with Anselm concerning divers points of Monastic Religion, and conversed among other things of the boys that were brought up in the cloister, he added: "What, pray, can we do with them? They are perverse and incorrigible; day and night we cease not to chastise them, yet they grow daily worse and worse."

'Whereat Anselm marvelled, and said, "Ye cease not to beat them? And when they are grown to manhood, of what sort are they then?" "They are dull and brutish," said the other.

'Then said Anselm, "With what good profit do ye expend your substance in nurturing human beings till they become brute beasts? ... But I prithee tell me, for God's sake, wherefore ye are so set against them? Are they not human, sharing in the same nature as yourselves? Would ye wish to be so handled as ye handle them? Ye will say, 'Yes, if we were as they are.' So be it, then; yet is there no way but that of stripes and scourges for shaping them to good? Did ye ever see a goldsmith shape his gold or silver plate into a fair image by blows alone? I trow not. What then? That he may give the plate its proper shape, he will first press it gently and tap it with his tools; then again he will more softly raise it with discreet pressure from below, and caress it into shape. So ye also, if ye would see your boys adorned with fair manners, ye should not only beat them down with stripes, but also raise their spirits and support them with fatherly kindness and pity." . . .'

In 1530 – about thirty years, that is, after *Mundus et Infans* was written – the Headmaster of Eton at the time, Richard Cox, wrote an account of the 'order' of the school:

'They [the boys] assembled in school at six of the Clock in the morning; they say *Deus misereatur* with a Collect; at nine they say *De profundis* and go to breakfast. Within a quarter of an hour come again and tarry (until) eleven and then to dinner; at five to supper, before an Anthem and *De profundis* . . .

'When they go home two and two in order, [there is] a monitor to see that they do so till they come at their house door.

'Also privy monitors how many the Master will.

'Prepositors in the field when they play, for fighting, rent clothes, blue eyes, or such like.

'Prepositors for ill kept heads, unwashed faces, foul clothes and such other . . .

'When any do come new, the master doth inquire from whence he comes, what friends he hath, whether there be any plague. No man goeth out of the school, nor home to his friends, without the master's licence. If there be any dullard the master giveth his friends warning and putteth him away, that he slander not the school.'

I have seen an old woodcut showing a boy in the middle ages being whipped in a kind of machine (something like a roasting-jack), and a schoolmaster standing by, nicely smiling, in a gown. When Coleridge was a bluecoat boy at Christ's Hospital with

Charles Lamb, he had a headmaster of this kind: ' "Boy!" I remember Bowyer saying to me once when I was crying the first day after my return after the holidays, – "Boy! the school is your father! Boy! the school is your mother! Boy! the school is your brother! the school is your sister! the school is your first cousin, and your second cousin, and all the rest of your relations! Let's have no more crying." ...

'Mrs Bowyer was no comforter, either. Val. Le Grice and I were once going to be flogged for some domestic misdeed, and Bowyer was thundering away at us, by way of prologue, when Mrs B. looked in and said, "Flog them soundly, sir, I beg!" This saved us. Bowyer was so nettled at the interruption that he growled out, "Away, woman, away!" and we were let off.'

Charles Lamb also remembered his school-days: 'I was a hypochondriac lad; and the sight of a boy in fetters, upon the day of my first putting on the blue clothes, was not exactly fitted to assuage the natural terrors of initiation. I was of tender years, barely turned of seven; and had only read of such things in books, or seen them but in dreams. I was told he had *run away*. This was the punishment for the first offence. As a novice I was soon after taken to see the dungeons. These were little, square, Bedlam cells, where a boy could just lie at his length upon straw and a blanket – a mattress, I think, was afterwards substituted – with a peep of light, let in askance, from a prison-orifice at top, barely enough to read by. Here the poor boy was locked in by himself all day, without sight of any but the porter who brought him his bread and water – who *might not speak to him*; or of the beadle, who came twice a week to call him out to receive his periodical chastisement, which was almost welcome, because it separated him for a brief interval from solitude: and here he was shut up by himself of *nights*, out of the reach of any sound, to suffer whatever horrors the weak nerves, and superstition incident to his time of life, might subject him to. This was the penalty for the *second* offence. Wouldst thou like, reader, to see what became of him in the next degree?

'The culprit, who had been a third time an offender, and whose expulsion was at this time deemed irreversible, was brought forth, as at some solemn *auto da fé*, arrayed in uncouth and most appalling attire ... a jacket resembling those which London lamplighters formerly delighted in, with a cap of the same ... In this disguise-ment he was brought into the hall where awaited him the whole number of his schoolfellows, whose joint lessons and sports he was thenceforth to share no more ... The scourging was, after the old Roman fashion, long and stately. The lictor accompanied the criminal quite round the hall ... After scourging, he was made over, in his *San Benito*, to his friends, if he had any (but commonly such poor runagates were friendless), or to his parish officer, who, to enhance the effect of the scene, had his station allotted to him on the outside of the hall gate.' So the poor friendless wretch, having proved his misery in *Christ's Hospital* by three times endeavouring to escape from it, was at last flogged into the streets again for good and all.

In 1821, when Charles Lamb was 46 and Coleridge 49, a tale was published entitled ' *Young Wilfred; or, the Punishment of Falsehood: a Tale of Truth and Caution for the Benefit of the Rising Generation*, by W. F. Sullivan, A. M., Teacher of Elocution and Belles Lettres.' In this we get a close view – and one probably pretty true to the facts – of a similar ceremony in 'a private academy'. The Head-master (and we get a close view of this unsightly, ungrammatical 'folio', also), before the assembled school, addresses the miserable culprit thus:

' "Thou unparalleled, ungrateful hypocrite; thou prince of liars! – before I send you back to your unfortunate parents, as a disgrace to them and to human nature, I will endeavour, with God's blessing, to expel the evil spirit out of thy little body; for if ever mortal being was possessed with a devil thou art he. Hand those two letters round the school. You see here, young gentlemen, a little monster of deceit, fraud, falsehood, treachery and cunning. During the twenty-five years I have kept school, and the many hundred pupils who have passed through my hands, I have never met even the shadow of his resemblance. Who would have thought so small a duodecimo could have contained such a folio of atrocious lies? I am truly shocked; I feel for your unhappy parents, and your miserable mother who must curse the hour in which she brought you into the world. I foresee, with pain I say it, unless a miracle work a speedy reformation, you inevitably must come to an untimely end. As it is, it is my duty to make you remember this day as long as you live."

'On this the serving-man entered with a new birch-broom, which the Doctor opened and gave a sprig to every boy in the school: the culprit was now fastened to a desk, and each young gentleman advanced in rotation and inflicted a stripe, till the number of 200 was unsparingly bestowed. When taken down his wounds were dressed, and he was confined in a dark room, and no longer admitted among the boys ... On his quitting the academy he was saluted with the groans and hisses of the whole school assembled; and had they not been strictly prohibited, they would have pelted him to the imminent danger of his life.'

Coleridge tells of yet another schoolmaster, whose name, like Bowyer and birch, also began with a B: 'Busby was the father of the English public school system. He was headmaster of Westminster through the reign of Charles I, the Civil War, the Protectorate, the reign of Charles II, and the Revolution of 1688. Under him Westminster became the first school in the kingdom. When Charles II visited the school, Busby stalked before the King with his hat upon his head, whilst his most sacred majesty meekly followed him. In private Busby explained that his conduct was due to the fact that he could not allow, for discipline's sake, the boys to imagine there could be a greater man than himself alive.' Quite rightly, of course.

There is, too, the story of the little Lion that went to school to the Bear. Being, though of royal blood, a good deal of a dunce, Master Lion bore many sound duffings from Dr Bruin on the road to learning, and found it hot and dusty. After such administrations, he would sometimes sit in the sun under a window, learning his task and brooding on a day when he would return to the school and revenge himself upon the Doctor for having treated him so sore. But Master Lion was all this time growing up, and so many were the cares of the State when he had left his books and become a Prince and Heir Apparent, that for a time he had no thought for his old school. Being, however, in the Royal Gardens one sunny morning, and seeing bees busy about their hive, he remembered an old saying on the sweetness of knowledge and wisdom, and this once more reminded him of his old Master. Bidding his servants sling upon a rod half a dozen of the hives, he set out to visit Dr Bruin. The hives were taken into his study, and the bees, being unused to flitting within walls out of the sunshine, angrily sang and droned about the head of the old schoolmaster as he sat as his desk. Their stings were of little account against his thick hide, but their molestation was a fret, and he presently cried aloud, 'Would that the Prince had kept his gifts to himself!' The Prince, who was standing outside the door, listening and smiling to himself, there-upon cried out: 'Ah! Dr Bruin, when I was under your charge, you often heavily smit and cuffed me with those long-clawed paws of yours. Now I am older, and have learned how sweet and worthy is the knowledge they instilled. This too will be your experience. My bees may fret and buzz and sting a little now, but you will think of me more kindly when you shall be tasting their rich honey in the Winter that is soon upon us.' And Dr Bruin, peering out at the Prince from amid the cloud of the bees, when he heard him thus call Tit for Tat, couldn't help but laugh.

But to return to Coleridge once more – who, in the bad old days, so far as food goes, never 'had a belly full' at Christ's Hospital, and whose appetite was only 'damped, never satisfied', – here is one of his earliest letters (to his elder brother George), which *may* have an (indirect) reference to Dr Bowyer's birch:

Dear Brother, – You will excuse me for reminding you that, as our holidays commence next week, and I shall go out a good deal, a good pair of breeches will be no inconsiderable accession to my appearance. For though my present pair are excellent for the purpose of drawing mathematical figures on them, and though a walking thought, sonnet or epigram would appear in them in very *splendid* type, yet they art not altogether so well adapted for a female eye – not to mention that I should have the charge of vanity brought against me for wearing a looking-glass. I hope you have got rid of your cold – and I am

Your affectionate brother,

SAMUEL TAYLOR COLERIDGE

And now for a pinch of sugar and spice after all these snips and snails, this being a letter home from school from Marjorie Fleming who was in her eighth (and last) year when she wrote it:

October 12*th*, 1811.

My Dear Mother, – You will think that I entirely forgot you, but I assure you that you are greatly mistaken. I think of you always and often sigh to think of the distance between us two loving creatures of nature. We have regular hours for all our occupations, first at 7 o'clock we go to the dancing and come home at 8, we then read our Bible and get our repeating and then play till ten then we get our music till 11 when we get our writing and accounts we sew from 12 till 1, after which I get my gramer and then work till five. At 7 we come and knit till 8 when we don't go to the dancing. This is an exact description. I must take a hasty farewell to her whom I love, reverence and doat on, and whom I hope thinks the same of

MARJORIE FLEMING

P.S. – An old pack of cards would be very exeptible.

And last, for companion pieces, here, first, is a letter (the original being in the Bodleian Library), written in Greek on papyrus in the second or third century A.D. from a small boy to his father:

Theon to his father Theon, greeting. It was a fine thing of you not to take me with you to town. If you won't take me with you to Alexandria, I won't write you a letter or speak to you . . . Mother said to Archelaus, 'He upsets me. Take him away.' . . . So send for me, I implore you. If you won't send, I won't eat, I won't drink; there now! Farewell.

About fifteen centuries after Theon's ultimatum was dispatched, a small girl, (and 'dutiful daughter'), sent her mother a loving little epistle stitched in on a piece of canvas. It runs – the commas being mine:

DEAR MOTHER, MY DUTY REMEMBER UNTO THE, AND MY DEAR LOVE UNTO MY SISTER. WHEN I

SAW MY FATHER LAST HIS LOVE WAS TO THE, BUT
I THOUGHT IT LONG BEFORE I SAW THE BUT I DID
MY INDEAVOUR TO RITE UNTO THE NO MORE BUT
THEY DUTYFULL DAFTER S F
                    FROM WANSTEAD 1693 THE
25 OF THE 5 MONTH.

But what exactly S.F. meant by the words between her first 'but'
and her third, I can't be certain.

Eighty-five years after this, and on May Day, one Debby wrote
to another in the same fashion, but added a pretty wandering border
of flowers for a frame:

Dear Debby
I love you sincerely
My heart retains a grateful sense
of your past kindness
When will the hours of our
Separation be at an end
Preserve in your bosom a Remembrance
of your Affectionate
Deborah Jane Berkin
Bristol.

May 1st.   1778.

But enough:

F for Francis, **I** for Iancis, **N** for Nickley Boney,
I for Ihon the Waterman, and **S** for Signey Coney.

40

This too should go to the lilt of its verbal music, as then the accents
would come clearly. I think, in the reading of it, there should be
four stressed syllables to the first, second and fifth lines in each
stanza: 'Whâr hae ye bêen a' day, mỳ boy Tâmmy'; and 'The wêe
thing gi'es her hând, and says, Therē, gâng and ask my Mâmmy.' A
line of verse like this resembles a piece of elastic; if you leave it very

slack you will get no music out of it at all; stretch it a little too far, it snaps.

41

This little jingle and Nos. 15, 16, 68, 75, etc., are Singing Game Rhymes, of which scores have been collected from the mouths of children near and far from all over the kingdom, and are now to be found in print in Lady Gomme's two stout engrossing volumes entitled *Traditional Games*. In these more than seven hundred games are described, including Rakes and Roans, Rockety Row, Sally Go Round the Moon, Shuttle-feather, Spannims, Tods and Lambs, Whigmeleerie, Allicomgreenaie, Bob-Cherry, Oranges and Lemons, Cherry Pit, Thumble-bones, Lady on Yandor Hill, Hechefragy, and Snail Creep.

A good many of these games have singing rhymes to them. And the words of them vary in different places. For the children in each of twenty or more villages and towns may have their own particular version of the same rhyme. As for the original from which all such versions must once have come – *that* may be centuries old. Like the Nursery Rhymes, they were most of them in the world ages before our great-great-great-grand-dams were babies in their cradles. The noble game of Hop Scotch, for instance, Lady Gomme tells us, was in favour before the year 1, and in case its champions are fewer than they were, it may be as well to mention that there are two varieties: Great Marelle and Little Marelle (the Little only fit for infants). 'You trace one long square with four divisions in it. A semicircle is drawn above the narrowest end, and in it a St Andrew's cross. Where the lines intersect, make a little round, called the copper, and in the last triangle to the right, a key.' The stone is called a quoit, and the rules are as various as they should be famous.

The most mysterious game-rhymes of all are said to refer to ancient tribal customs, rites and ceremonies – betrothals, harvest-homes, sowings, reapings, well-blessings, dirges, divinations, battles, hunting and exorcisings – before even London was else than a few hovels by its river's side. Rhymes such as these having been passed on from age to age and from one piping throat to another, have become worn and battered of course, and queerly changed in their words.

These from Mr Nahum's book have their own differences too. He seems to have liked best those that make a picture, or sound racy, gay and sweet and so carry the fancy away. Any little fytte or jingle or jargon of words that manages *that* is like a charm or a talisman, and to make new ones is as hard as to spin silk out of straw, or to turn beech leaves into fairy money. When one thinks, too, of the myriad young voices that generation after generation have carolled these rhymes into the evening air, and now are still – well, it's a thought no less sorrowful for being strange, and no less strange for the fact that our own voices too will some day be as silent.

> Summer's pleasures they are gone like to visions every one,
> And the cloudy days of autumn and of winter cometh on.
> I tried to call them back, but unbidden they are gone
> Far away from heart and eye and for ever far away.
> Dear heart, and can it be that such raptures meet decay?
> I thought them all eternal when by Langley Bush I lay,
> I thought them joys eternal when I used to shout and play
> On its bank at 'clink and brandy', 'chock' and 'taw' and
>   'ducking stone',
> Where silence sitteth now on the wild heath as her own
> Like a ruin of the past all alone . . .

JOHN CLARE

42

The loveliest and gayest song of praise and sweetness to a 'young thing' I have ever seen. It is taken from a poem entitled *The Garland of Laurell*, and the headlong, twice-laureate poet who wrote it was described to Henry VIII by Erasmus as *Britannicarum Literarum Lumen et Decus*!

'Ieloffer' – gelofer, gelofre, gillofre, gelevor, gillyvor, gillofer, jerefloure, gerraflour – all these are ways of spelling Gillyflower, gelofre coming nearest to its original French; *giroflée* – meaning spiced like the clove. There were of old, I find, three kinds of gilly-flowers: the clove, the stock and the wall. It was the first of these kinds that was meant in the earlier writers by the small clove carnation (or Coronation, because it was made into chaplets or garlands). Its Greek name was dianthus (the flower divine); and its twin sister is the Pink, so called because its edges are pinked, that is, jagged, notched, scalloped. Country names for it are Sweet John, Pagiants, Blunket and Sops-in-Wine, for it spices what it floats in, and used to be candied for a sweetmeat. Blossoming in July, the Gillyflower suggests July-flower, and if Julia is one's sweetheart, it may also be a Julie-flower. So one name may carry many echoes. It has been truly described as a gimp and gallant flower, and, says Parkinson, who wrote *Paradisus Terrestris*, it was the chiefest of account in Tudor gardens. There was a garden in Westminster in his own time belonging to a Master Ralph Tuggie, famous all London over for the beauty and variety of its gillyflowers; *e.g.*, 'Master Tuggie his Princesse', 'Master Bradshaw his daintie Ladie', 'The Red Hulo', 'The Fair Maid of Kent', 'Lustie Gallant', 'The Speckled Tawny', and 'Ruffling Robin'.

By 1700 there were 360 kinds and four classes of clove gilly-flower – the Flake, the Bizarre, the Piquette or picotte (*picotée* or pricketed), and the Painted Lady, the last now gone. Its ancestor, the dianthus, seems to have crossed the Channel with the Normans, for it flourishes on the battlements of Falaise, the Conqueror's birthplace, and crowns the walls of many a Norman Castle – Dover, Ludlow, Rochester, Deal – to this day.

43

'*Pygsnye*'

which means Piggie's eye, Tiny-eye or Twinkle eye – a loveword in use long before Chaucer – just as we nowadays call a child or loved-one Goosikins, or Pussikins, or Lambkin Pie, or Bunch-of-Roses, or Chickabiddy, or Come-kiss-me-quick, or (further north), wee bit lassikie, *i.e.*, wee, small, tiny *little* wee lass. *Minion*, too, means anything small, minikin, delicate dainty, darling. Look close for example, at the grown-green florets of a stalk of mignonette.

44

'A worm's light'

Many years ago I had the curious pleasure of reading a little book – and one in small print too (Alice Meynell's lovely *Flower of the Mind*) – by *English* glowworm light. The worm was lifting its green beam in the grasses of a cliff by the sea, and shone the clearer the while because it was during an eclipse of the moon.

49

'Reader,' pleaded Charles Lamb, 'if thou meetest one of these small gentry in thy early rambles, it is good to give him a penny. It is better to give him two-pence. Better still – a basin of saloop, of which the chief ingredient is Sassafras; for it is a composition sur-prisingly gratifying to the palate of a young chimney-sweeper.'

> Oh! sweep chimney, sweep!
> You maidens shake off sleep
> If you my cry can follow.
> I climb the chimney top,
> Without ladder, without rope;
> Aye and there! aye and there! aye and there you shall hear my
> halloo!
>
> Arise! maids, arise!
> Unseal and rub your eyes,
> Arise and do your duty.
> I summon yet again
> And do not me disdain,
> That my call, that my call, that my calling's poor and sooty.

Behold! here I stand!
With brush and scrape in hand,
As a soldier that stands on his sentry.
I work for the better sort,
And well they pay me for't.
O I work, O I work, O I work for the best of the gentry.

Oh! sweep chimney, sweep!
The hours onward creep.
As the lark I am alert, I
Clear away, and take
The smut that others make.
O I clean, O I clean, O I clean what others dirty.

50

'*But never cam' he*'

. . . 'O wha will shoe my bonny foot?
And wha will glove my hand?
And wha will lace my middle jimp,
Wi' a lang, lang linen band?

'O who will kame my yellow hair,
With a haw bayberry kame?
And wha will be my babe's father,
Till Gregory come hame?'

'Thy father, he will shoe thy foot,
Thy brother will glove thy hand,
Thy mother will bind thy middle jimp
Wi' a lang, lang linen band!

'Thy sister will kame thy yellow hair,
Wi' a haw bayberry kame;
The Almighty will be thy babe's father,
Till Gregory come hame.'

ANON

334

There's nane o' my ain to care,
　　There's nane to mind me now,
There's nane o' my ain to comb my hair,
　　There's nane to sponge my mou'.

There's nane o' my ain to care,
　　Strange han's sall straighten me,
Strangers sall fauld about my limbs
　　The claes o' my deid body.

WILLIAM OGILVIE

Rock well, my cradle,
And *bee-baa*, my son;
You shall have a new gown
When ye lord comes home.
Oh! still my child, Orange!
Still him with a bell;
I can't still him, ladie,
Till you come down yoursel'.

'Haw' is an old English word meaning (?) blue or braw, and
bayberry is the all-spice tree, in the light of whose flames sat
Alexander Selkirk in his solitude on Juan Fernandez, surrounded
by his 'hundreds' of cats. So this sad one's yellow hair had for
comb an uncommonly charming thing. In another version the
comb is of 'new silver', and in a third it is a 'red river kame', which,
thinks Child, may be a corruption of red *ivory*. And then, too, there
is

　　　. . . fair Ligea's *golden* comb,
Wherewith she sits on diamond rocks
Sleeking her soft alluring locks.

5 1

'The first sense of sorrow I ever knew,' wrote Richard Steele, 'was
upon the death of my father, at which time I was not quite five years

of age; but was rather amazed at what all the house meant than possessed with a real understanding why nobody was willing to play with me. I remember I went into the room where his body lay, and my mother sat weeping alone by it. I had my battledore in my hand, and fell a-beating the coffin, and calling, papa; for, I know not how, I had some slight idea that he was locked up there. My mother catched me in her arms, and transported beyond all patience of the silent grief she was before in, she almost smothered me in her embraces; and told me in a flood of tears, "Papa could not hear me, and would play with me no more, for they were going to put him under ground, whence he could never come to us again."'

'*I had a little bird*'

'My second child, but eldest daughter, like M[argaret] is between two and three weeks less than two years old ... About three weeks since ... in the earlier half of May, some of our neighbours gave [her] a little bird ... The present was less splendid than it seemed. For the bird was wounded; though not in a way that made the wound apparent; and ... as the evening wore away it drooped ...

'At length sunset arrived, which was the signal for M.'s departure to bed. She came therefore as usual to me, threw her arms round my neck and went through her prayers ... As she was moving off to bed, [she] whispered to me that I was to "mend" the bird with "yoddonum" ... For her satisfaction, I placed a little diluted laudanum near to the bird; and she then departed to bed, though with uneasy looks reverting to her sick little pet.

'Occupied with some point of study, it happened that I sat up through the whole night: and long before seven o'clock in the morning she had summoned Barbara [her nurse] to dress her, and soon I heard the impatient little foot descending the stairs to my study. As the morning was one of heavenly splendour, I proposed that we should improve the bird's chances by taking it out-of-doors into the little orchard at the foot of Fairfield – out loftiest Grasmere mountain. Thither moved at once Barbara, little M., myself, and the poor languishing bird.

'By that time in May, in any far southern county, perhaps the birds would be ceasing to sing; but not so with us dilatory people in Westmoreland. Suddenly, as we all stood around the little perch on which the bird rested, one thrilling song, louder than the rest, arose from a neighbouring hedge. Immediately the bird's eye, previously dull, kindled into momentary fire: the bird rose on its perch, struggled for an instant, seemed to be expanding its wings, made one aspiring movement upwards, in doing so fell back, and in another moment was dead . . .'

THOMAS DE QUINCEY

53

The first and third stanzas of this poem were (and are) my particular favourites, and especially the second line in each. Such poems are like wayside pools, or little well-springs of water. It does not matter how many wayfarers come thither to quench their thirst, there is abundance for all.

The *craftsmanship* of the poem seems simplicity itself. But the closer we examine it the more clearly we see the intricate devices that are responsible for its triumph. To express truth, and to express one's heart, need extreme care and skill – though the intense wish to do so may supply them almost without effort.

Listen here to the lingering chime of the vowels: 'Nor *Ouse* on his *bosom*,' 'The poplars are *felled*; *farewell*'; to the echoings of *retreat*, *screen*, *heat*, *scene*, *sweet* of the third stanza. How delightful throughout is the ease to throat and ear, to mind and spirit, effected by the interweaving alliteration of the f's and v's – *felled*, *farewell*, *faint*, *field*, *fled*, *afford*, *before*, *fugitive*, fading away at last in *turf*, *if*, *life*, *grove* and *even*. The z's too and the m's – *melody charmed me* – and finally the *dream* and *durable* in the last stanza.

Not that this particular poem is either profound, subtle, or elaborate. It is simple, homely, true and tender. But it could not have proved itself so (and particularly in this particular metre) if the words, which are its all, had been clumsily put together, ill-matched, and art-less.

' *The perishing pleasures of man* '

And for yet another look behind, I cannot leave out this close-packed little rhyme from William Allingham, who made one of the happiest of all anthologies, 'Nightingale Valley':

> Four ducks on a pond,
> A grass-bank beyond,
> A blue sky of spring,
> White clouds on the wing;
> What a little thing
> To remember for years –
> To remember with tears.

Or this lovely scrap from the Scots:

> O Alva hills is bonny,
>   Dalycoutry hills is fair,
> But to think on the braes of Menstrie
>   It maks my heart fu' sair.

57

> . . . Ill fares the land, to hastening ills a prey,
>   Where wealth accumulates, and men decay;
>   Princes and lords may flourish, or may fade;
>   A breath can make them, as a breath has made;
>   But a bold peasantry, their country's pride,
>   When once destroyed, can never be supplied . . .

Oliver Goldsmith, when he wrote these lines was thinking of Ireland. But what of England now?

60

Edward Thomas, who wrote this poem, knew by heart most of the villages, streams, high roads, by-roads, hills, forests, woods and dales of the southern counties of England and came so to know them by the slowest but best of all methods – walking; and, when so inclined, sitting down by the wayside or leaning over a farm or field gate to gaze and muse and day-dream. Here is another poem of his, fresh and sweet with country flowers:

> If I should ever by chance grow rich
> I'll buy Codham, Cockridden, and Childerditch,
> Roses, Pyrgo, and Lapwater,
> And let them all to my elder daughter.
> The rent I shall ask of her will be only
> Each year's first violets, white and lonely,
> The first primroses and orchises –
> She must find them before I do, that is.
> But if she finds a blossom on furze –
> Without rent they shall all for ever be hers,
> Codham, Cockridden, and Childerditch,
> Roses, Pyrgo and Lapwater, –
> I shall give them all to my elder daughter.

Not, of course, to find a blossom on furze or gorse as soon as any sun is in the new year's sky, is the rare feat; and if in wanderings over the hills and far away you should chance on secret hidden-away Pyrgo or Childerditch, sweet with its fragrance, then enquire for the beautiful, happy young Lady of the Manor. As a matter of fact, the scent of the furze-blossoms is not exactly sweet, but nutlike and aromatic.

'The gorse is most fragrant at noon, when the sun shines brightest and hottest. At such an hour when I approach a thicket of furze, the wind blowing from it, I am always tempted to cast myself down on the grass to lie for an hour drinking in the odour. The effect is to make me languid; to wish to lie till I sleep and live again in dreams in another world in a vast open-air cathedral where a great festival of ceremony is perpetually in progress, and acolytes, in scores and hundreds with beautiful bright faces, in flame yellow and orange surplices, are ever and ever coming toward me, swinging their censers until I am ready to swoon in that heavenly incense!' ...

W. H. HUDSON

'A stoat'

It is the gentle custom of gamekeepers to slaughter at sight so-called *vermin*, *i.e.*, 'worms of earth' – the little preying beasts and birds of the woodlands – owls, hawks, crows, jays, stoats, weasels, and the like. They then nail up their carcases to a shed side, or to a barn door or on a field-gate, leaving them to rot in the wind for a warning to their mates. Foxes, otters, badgers are 'hunted' to death. It is said they enjoy the fun.

61

'The howes of the silent vanished races'

are, I suppose, the mounds, barrows, tumuli or Fairies' Hills, some of them round, some of them long, some of them chambered, beneath which the ancient races of Britain, centuries before the coming of the Saxons and the Danes, buried their dead. So once slept the mummied Pharaohs beneath their prodigious Pyramids. Age hangs densely over these solitary mounds, as over the Dolmens and the Cromlechs – Stonehenge, the Whispering Knights – and the single gigantic Menhirs – the Tingle Stone, the Whittle Stone, and Bair-down-Man and the demoniac Hoar Stone.

These were ancient and unintelligible marvels even when the monk Ranulph Higden wrote his *Polychronicon* in 1352: The second wonder, he says, is at Stonehenge beside Salisbury. There great stones marvellously huge, be a-reared up on high, as it were gates, so that there seemeth gates to be set up upon other gates. Nevertheless it is not clearly known nor perceived how and to what end they be so a-reared up, and 'so wonderlych yhonged'. And yet, what are they but as falling apple-blossom compared with the age of the world and the antiquity of the Universe:

1st Gravedigger.   Come my spade; there is no ancient Gentlemen
but Gardiners, Ditchers and Gravemakers;
they hold up *Adam*'s profession.
2nd Gravedigger. Was he a Gentleman?
1st Gravedigger. He was the first that ever bore Armes.

62

– and here is as romantic and tragic a tale of two friends:

> O Bessie Bell and Mary Gray,
>   They war twa bonnie lasses;
> They biggit a bower on yon Burn-brae,
>   And theekit it o'er wi' rashes.
>
> They theekit it o'er wi' rashes green,
>   They theekit it o'er wi' heather;
> But the pest cam' frae the burrows-town,
>   And slew them baith thegither.
>
> They thought to lye in Methven kirkyard,
>   Amang their noble kin;
> But they maun lye in Stronach haugh,
>   To biek forenent the sin.
>
> O Bessie Bell and Mary Gray,
>   They war twa bonnie lasses;
> They biggit a bower on yon Burn-brae,
>   And theekit it o'er wi' rashes.

Biggit and *theekit* means builded and thatched; and the twelfth
line, to bask beneath the sun.

64

A tragic tale is hidden, rather than told, in this old Scottish ballad.
It resembles a half ruinous house in a desolate country, densely
green with briar and bramble, echoing with wild voices – its

memories gone. Mr Nahum's picture for it was of a figure in a woman's bright clothes and scarlet hood, but with what looked to me like the head of his own skeleton deep within the hood. And on a stone nearby sat a little winged boy.

66

'Her highborn kinsman'

... And there was a wind in the night as they fared onward, a wind in the mid-air, playing from out the clouds. And presently after, the twain descended into the valley, the one traveller's foot stumbling as he went, against the writhen roots that jutted from between the stones of the path they followed. And it seemed that the voice of one unseen cried, Lo! And the traveller looked up from out of the valley of his journey, and, behold, a wan moon gleamed between the ravelled clouds; and the face of his companion showed for that instant clear against the sky in the shadow of its cloak. And it was the face of a nobleman; renowned for his patience; courteous and cold; whose name is Death ...

'But our love ...'

A Gyges Ring they beare about them still,
To be, and not seen when and where they will.
They tread on clouds, and though they sometimes fall,
They fall like dew, but make no noise at all.
So silently they one to th'other come,
As colours steale into the Peare or Plum,
And Aire-like, leave no pression to be seen,
Where e're they met, or parting place has been.

ROBERT HERRICK

... Lord Thomas was buried without kirk-wa',
    Fair Annet within the quiere;
  And out o' the tane their grew a birk,
    The other a bonny briere.

And ay they grew, and ay they threw,
    As they wad faine be neare;
And by this ye may ken right weil,
    They were twa luvers deare.

68

This is yet another singing-game rhyme. When London was nothing but a cluster of beehive huts in the hill clearings of the great Forest of Middlesex above the marshes and the Thames, there can have been no bridge. There *may* have been a bridge, it seems, in A.D. 44, eighty-seven years after the death of Caesar; and for centuries there was certainly a ferry, Audery the Shipwright being one of its ferrymen, his oars the shape of shovels, and his boat like a young moon on her back.

The rhyme appears to refer to the wooden bridge built in 994 at Southwark, which was destroyed in 1008 by King Olaf, the Saint of Norway, to whose glory four London churches are dedicated. Olaf had become the ally of Ethelred (the Unready), and to defeat the Danes who had captured the city he first screened his fighting ships with frameworks of osier for the protection of his men, who then rowed them up to the Bridge against the tide. They wapped and bound huge ropes or hawsers round its timber piers, swept down with the slack with the tide, and so brought the bridge to ruin.

The first stone bridge, in building from 1196 to 1208, was partially destroyed by fire four years afterwards. A picture of the romantic re-built bridge of Elizabeth's time shows its chapel, its precipitous gabled houses, its haberdashers', goldsmiths', booksellers' and needle shops, its cut-waters or starlings and narrow arches, its gate-house with the spiked heads atop, its drawbridge and pillory, and that strange timber mansion, with not a nail in its wood, called None-such, where perhaps lived the Lord Mayor – all this may be gloated over in any old seventeenth-century map of London. (John Visscher's of 1616 shows a windmill in the Strand!) So narrow were its nineteen arches, and so vehemently flowed the tides beneath them, that at ebb it was mortally dangerous for a novice to shoot them in a boat. But between Windsor and Gravesend it is said there were forty thousand watermen and wherrymen in Shakespeare's day, yelling 'Eastward Ho!' or 'Westward Ho!' for passengers. The Bridge was the glory of London; as the Thames it spanned was its main thoroughfare. Fire was its chief enemy; the Great Fire in 1616 and that in 1633, after which it long continued to be used, though dark, dismal and dangerous. The present monster of granite, over which the people of London stream to and fro throughout the day, like ants at the flighting, was built thirty yards west of the old one and began to span the river in 1832.

70

'*This city*'

So these bygone all-welcoming Londoners spent their time, England being in effect, says Fuller, 'all a great *Cooke's-shop*, and no reason any should starve therein.'

London, thou art of townes *A per se* [1]
  Soveraign of cities, seemliest in sight,
Of high renoun, riches and royaltie;
    Of lordis, barons, and many a goodly knyght;
    Of most delectable lusty ladies bright;
Of famous prelatis, in habitis clericall;
    Of merchauntis full of substance and of myght;
London, thou art the flow'r of Cities all . . .

Above all ryvers thy Ryver hath renowne,
  Whose beryll stremys, pleasant and preclare,
Under thy lusty wallys renneth down,
    Where many a swanne does swymme with wyngis fare;
    Where many a barge doth sail and row with are,
Where many a ship doth rest with toppe-royall.
    O! towne of townes, patrone and not compare:
London, thou art the floure of Cities all . . .

        1. First and foremost

Strong be thy wallis that about thee standis;
  Wise be the people that within thee dwellis;
Fresh is thy ryver with his lusty strandis;
    Blith be thy chirches, wele sownyng be thy bellis;
    Rich be thy merchauntis in substaunce that excellis;
Fair be their wives, right lovesom, white and small;
  Clere be thy virgyns, lusty under kellis! [1]
London, thou art the flow'r of Cities all . . .

WILLIAM DUNBAR

Earth has not anything to show more fair:
Dull would he be of soul who could pass by
A sight so touching in its majesty:
This City now doth, like a garment, wear
The beauty of the morning; silent, bare,
Ships, towers, domes, theatres, and temples lie
Open unto the fields, and to the sky;
All bright and glittering in the smokeless air
Never did sun more beautifully steep
In his first splendour, valley, rock, or hill;
Ne'er saw I, never felt, a calm so deep!
The river glided at his own sweet will:
Dear God! the very houses seem asleep;
And all that mighty heart is lying still!

WILLIAM WORDSWORTH

But London awakes, and even in the seventeenth century we find
Abraham Cowley fretting at evils now endlessly multiplied.

Well then; I now do plainly see
This busy world and I shall ne'er agree;
The very honey of all earthly joy
Does of all meats the soonest cloy;

1. Cap-nets of silk or of gold

345

And they, methinks, deserve my pity,
Who for it can endure the stings,
The crowd, the buzz, the murmurings
Of this great hive, the city.

ABRAHAM COWLEY

71

'He opened house to all'

The subject being good victuals, here is the 'Bill of Fare at the Christening of Mr Constable's Child, Rector of Cockley Cley, in Norfolk, January 2, 1682.'

A whole hog's head souc'd with carrots in the mouth, and pendants in the ears, with guilded oranges thick sett.

2 Ox^s cheekes stewed with 6 marrow bones.

A leg of Veal larded with 6 pullets.

A leg of Mutton with 6 rabbits.

A chine of bief, chine of venison, chine of mutton, chine of veal, chine of pork, supported by 4 men.

A Venison Pasty.

A great minced pye, with 12 small ones about it.

A gelt fat turkey with 6 capons.

A bustard with 6 pluver.

A pheasant with 6 woodcock.

A great dish of tarts made all of sweetmeats.

A Westphalia hamm with 6 tongues.

A Jowle of Sturgeon.

A great charg^r of all sorts of sweetmeats with wine, and all sorts of liquors answerable.

And here is another from that inexhaustible Tom Tiddler's ground, *Rustic Speech and Folklore* for the 'funeral meats' of a farmer who died near Whitby in 1760: 'Besides what was distributed to 1,000 poor people who had 6d. each in money, there was consumed

> 110 dozen penny loaves,
> 9 large hams,
> 8 legs of veal,
> 20 stone of beef,
> 16 stone of mutton,
> 15 stone of Cheshire cheese, and
> 30 ankers of ale.'

But even such a feast as this is little more than a fast compared with that given by Philip, Duke of Burgundy, the father of Charles the Bold, on the 8th of February, 1454. It is described in the Memoirs of Olivier de la Marche, and I am indebted to G. G. and M. M. Stuart for permission to quote from their translation.

'The hall was a large one, hung with tapestry representing the life of Hercules. It was entered by five doors at which stood Archers in black and grey robes. Within were several Knights and Esquires superintending the banquet; the former were garbed in damascus cloth and the latter in satin of the same colours.' So multitudinous were the dishes that Olivier de la Marche was unable to relate them: 'But this much I remember – each course consisted of 48 varieties of food, and the vessels holding the roast meats were chariots of gold and azure.'

And here are five of the fifteen *entremets* which stood on three tables – one large, one middle-sized and the last small:

'A cunningly constructed cruciform church, with glass windows and a bell; inside were four choristers.'

'A beautiful fountain of glass and lead . . . round it were apricot trees of glass with leaves and flowers marvellously natural; the whole was enclosed in a little meadow surrounded by rocks of sapphire and other rare stones; in the centre stood a small figure of St Andrew, holding his cross before him; from one point thereof sprung a jet of water to the height of a foot, falling back onto the meadow where it disappeared so cunningly that none could guess what became of it.'

'A jester on a bear, among rocky mountains covered with ice most cunningly.'

There was also 'a great ship at anchor, laden with merchandise and manned by sailors; methinks that in the largest vessel in the world there could not be greater variety of sails and ropes than on this one,' while the longest table was ornamented with 'a huge pie, in which there were twenty-eight living musicians, who played in turn on divers instruments.'

While the noble company were eating and drinking they were entertained with various devices, one of which was as follows:

'By the door through which the other entremets had entered came a wonderfully large and beautiful white stag with golden antlers; its back covered with red silk, as well as I can remember. It was ridden by a fair boy twelve years of age, clad in a short crimson velvet robe, fine shoes and a black cap cut into many points. He held the stag's antlers with each hand, and, as soon as they were in the hall he began a song, in a loud, clear voice, to which the stag sang the tenor part, there being no other performers except him and the child. The name of the song they sang was "Naught have I ever seen like this".' And no wonder.

At the end of the feast Toison-d'Or, king of arms, brought in a living pheasant and the Duke of Burgundy rose from his chair and vowed a vow upon this 'noble bird':

'I swear firstly to God my Creator and to the glorious Virgin Mary, and secondly to the Ladies and the Pheasant, that if it please that most victorious and most Christian Prince, my King, to join a crusade and risk his life for the defence of the Christian faith and to oppose the damnable enterprise of the Grand Turk and the infidels, and unless I am prevented by some real bodily impediment, I will serve in person and with my army in that crusade, as faithfully as, by God's Grace, I may . . .'

But man is mortal, and limited always to the possible, except in his dreams. For which reason the Duke of Burgundy's four dozen dishes to a course is but a Town Mouse's crumb of Wedding Cake compared to Mac Conglinne's Vision in No. 73, which is from the Gaelic of A.D. 1100–1200, as translated by Kuno Meyer. *Bragget*, line 27, appears to have been a concoction or decoction of ale, honey, sugar and spice.

As for table-manners, they are always changing (for better or worse), as a few words from a minute volume – entitled *The Rules of Civility or Certain Ways of Deportment Observed amongst all Persons of Quality upon several Occasions* [1685] – will show:

' 'Tis not manners as soon as you are set at the Table to bawl out, "*I eat none of this, I eat none of that; I care for no Rabbit; I love nothing that tastes of Pepper, Nutmeg, Onyons, etc . . .*" It is better therefore to restrain, or at least conceal those repugnancies as much as we can; and to take all that is offer'd: If our disgust be invincible, we may let it lie upon our Plate, eat something else, and when we see our opportunity, give that away that we did not like.

'If we be to eat out of the dish, we must have a care of putting in our Spoons before our Superiors . . . much less are we to pick out the best pieces though we be the last that help ourselves . . . 'Tis uncivil to put your hand twice together into the Dish; much less are we to eat bit by bit out of the Dish with our Fork . . . Having served yourself with your Spoon, you must remember to wipe it, and indeed as oft as you use it, for some are so nice they will not eat Potage or anything of that Nature in which you put your Spoon unwiped, after you have put it into your Mouth.

'How hungry soever you be, it is indecent to eat hastily or raven-ously, as if you would choak yourself . . . You must not eat Por-ridge out of the Dish, but put it handsomely upon your Plate, and if it be too hot, you must not blow every Spoonful you eat, but have patience till it cools of itself. If you happen to burn your Mouth, you must endure it if possible, if not you must convey what you have in your Mouth privately upon your Plate, and give it away to the Footman; For though Civility obliges you to be neat, there is no necessity you should burn out your Guts.' Which is coarse but convincing.

' "What hour is't, Lollio?"
"Towards belly hour, sir."
"Dinner time? thou mean'st *twelve* o'clock."
"Yes, sir, for every part has his hour; we wake at six, and look

about us, that's eye-hour; at seven we should pray, that's knee-
hour; at eight walk, that's leg-hour; at nine gather flowers, and
pluck a rose, that's nose-hour; at ten we drink, that's mouth-hour;
at eleven, lay about us for victuals, that's hand-hour; at twelve go
to dinner, that's belly-hour." '

From The Changeling

72

'And bring us in good ale'

– really good ale, that is, before beer was made 'so mortal small'; a
hundred and thirty-three years before tea-leaves came from China
(to be boiled and the decoction stored in a barrel), and a hundred
and forty before the first coffee-house in London; and even, one
might be tempted to add, before milk came from the cow, for as
late as 1512 the two young sons of the fifth earl of Northumberland,
Lord Percy, aged eleven (who afterwards loved Anne Boleyn), and
his younger brother, Maister Thomas Percy, were allowed for
'braikfaste' even on 'Fysch', or Fast Days: 'Half a Loif of
houshold Brede, a Manchet, a Dysch of Butter, a Pece of Saltfish,
a Dysch of Sproits or iii White Herrynge,' and a Potell of Bere,
i.e. two quarts or eight mugfuls.

But once again good ale, like that which sustained Mother Redcap of Holloway:

Old Mother Redcap, according to her tale,
Lived twenty and a hundred years by drinking this good ale;
It was her meat, it was her drink, and medicine beside,
And if she still had drank this ale, she never would have died.

73

'I' sooth a Feast of Fats' (from the Irish of the twelfth century)
like that dream of the rats in the 'Pied Piper of Hamelin' as they
scuttled to their doom in the ice-cold Weser. For a feast of sweets
there is Porphyrio's in the 'Eve of St Agnes':

And still she slept an azure-lidded sleep,
In blanchèd linen, smooth, and lavendered,
While he from forth the closet brought a heap
Of candied apple, quince, and plum, and gourd;
With jellies soother than the creamy curd,
And lucent syrops, tinct with cinnamon;
Manna and dates, in argosy transferred
From Fez; and spicèd dainties, every one,
From silken Samarcand to cedared Lebanon.

These delicates he heaped with glowing hand
On golden dishes and in baskets bright
Of wreathèd silver: sumptuous they stand
In the retirèd quiet of the night,
Filling the chilly room with perfume light . . .

For a banquet of enchantment there is Lamia's, and of magical
fruits, poor Laura's in 'Goblin Market'; Romeo too went feasting,
with the Capulets – but only his eyes; so too Macbeth, but *his* eyes
betrayed him. Bottom in his ass's ears asked only for a munch of
your good dry oats, a handfull of pease, and a bottle of hay, then
fell asleep before even Queen Titania could magick them up for
him. As for the poor Babes, blackberries and dewberries were *their*
last supper. These are but a few scores of banqueting delights in
poetry – but to include them all would need such a larder as Jack
peeped into when he sat supping in the Giant's kitchen.

74

'Pigeon-holes . . . stool-ball . . . barley-break'

This fragment is a patchwork of the half-forgotten. 'Pigeon holes'
was a ball-game, played on the green, with wooden arches and little
chambers as in a dovecot – a kind of open-air bagatelle. 'Stool-ball'
was popular with Nancies and Franceses on Shrove Tuesday.
Barley-break was in Scotland a kind of 'I spy', played in a stack-
yard, and in England a sort of 'French and English', in three marked

spaces or compartments, the middle one of which was called hell. And here – while we are on the subject of old and gallant pastimes – is a brief and early exposition of our noble and National Game of Cricket. It comes from a book with the title, *A Nosegay for the Trouble of Culling; or, Sports of Childhood*:

'Cricket is a game universally played in England, not by boys only, for men of all ranks pique themselves on playing it with skill. In Mary-le-bone parish there is a celebrated cricket ground much frequented by noblemen and gentlemen.

'The wicket consists of two pieces of wood fixed upright and kept together by another piece which is laid across the top and is called a bail; if either of these pieces of wood be thrown down by the ball the person so hitting them becomes the winner.

'The ball used in this game is stuffed exceedingly hard. Many windows and valuable looking-glasses have been broken by playing cricket in a room.'

It was in a cricket match in the summer of 1775, when no less than three 'balls' had rolled in between a Mr Small's two stumps without stirring the bail, that it was decided to add stump iii.

But (primitive) Cricket was being played in England at least as far back as the year in which Chaucer was born, for on the border of a manuscript of the *Romance of Alexander* that was written and illuminated about 1340 and is now in the Bodleian Library, there are the liveliest coloured pictures showing children playing games – games that were then no doubt already centuries old, and are yet – as each new billow of children breaks on the world's shore – as new as ever. Shown in action are two kinds of Cricket, Bowls, Stilts, Hot-cockles, Whip-tops, Dice, Balancing, Blind-man's Bluff and Chess.

In full swing, apart from these, are Nine-men's Morris or Moreles, small boys Cock-fighting, Tilting, Quintain (a boy mounted on a kind of wheeled wooden horse without a head being dragged along towards the quintain, and holding for lance a stout pole), Punch and Judy, performing horses, and a performing bear (with a chain attached to its collar that would hold in curb a dinosaur). Instruments of music are also shown in play – mandore, harp, viol, psaltery, bagpipes, hurdy-gurdy, shawm, organ and drums.

As for 'tansey' (line 5), here is a recipe for it (to go with the sillabub, No. 22): 'Take 15 eggs, and 6 of the whites; beat them very well; then put in some sugar, and a little sack; beat them again, and put about a pint or a little more of cream; then beat them again; then put in the juice of spinage or of primrose leaves to make it green. Then put in some more sugar, if it be not sweet enough; then beat it again a little, and so let it stand till you fry it, when the first course is in. They fry it with a little sweet butter. It must be stirred and fryed very tender. When it is fryed enough, then put it in a dish, and strew some sugar upon it, and serve it in.'

75

'Mary's gone a-milking'

And, according to Sir Thomas Overbury (who dipped his pen in nectar as well as ink), 'A Fair and Happy Milk-maid,' is 'a Country Wench, that is so far from making herself beautiful by art, that one look of hers is able to put all face-physic out of countenance . . .

'She doth not, with lying long abed, spoil both her complexion and conditions, . . . she rises, therefore, with Chanticleer, her dame's cock, and at night makes the lamb her curfew. In milking a Cow, and straining the teats through her fingers, it seems that so sweet a milk-press makes the milk the whiter or sweeter; for never came almond glove or aromatic ointment on her palm to taint it . . . Her breath is her own which scents all the year long of June, like a new made haycock. She makes her hand hard with labour, and her heart soft with pity: and when winter evenings fall early (sitting at her merry wheel), she sings a defiance to the giddy wheel of Fortune. She doth all things with so sweet a grace, it seems *ignorance* will not suffer her to do ill, being her mind is to do well . . . She dares go alone and unfold sheep in the night, and fears no manner of ill, because she means none: yet to say truth, she is never alone, for she is still accompanied with old songs, honest thoughts, and prayers, but short ones . . .

'Thus lives she, and all her care is she may die in the springtime, to have store of flowers stuck upon her winding-sheet.'

76

'Cypresse black as ere was Crow'

Cypresse (according to a memorandum from one of Mr Nahum's books) is the fine cobweblike stuff we now call crape. Peaking-stickes, or poking-sticks, were gophering irons for frilling out linen, flounces, etc., etc., and not, as one might guess, curling tongs (since a pointed beard, and the V of hair on the forehead, used to be called peaks). A quoife or coif is a lady's head-dress, such as is still worn by nuns; while as for 'maskes for faces', fine ladies in Shakespeare's day customarily wore them (as old pictures show) when they went to see his plays. Masks were useful too in disguising the faces of his players, when – as was the custom in the London theatres up to 1629 – boys took women's parts; and in the streets eyes gleamed out of the holes in them, worn *then* for keeping the skin fair, untanned, and unfreckled, as Julia says of herself in Shakespeare's *Two Gentlemen of Verona:*

> But since she did neglect her looking-glasse,
> And threw her Sun-expelling masque away,
> The ayre hath starved the roses in her cheekes
> And pinched the lily-tincture of her face . . .

78

'Fairing'

In this – the earliest known letter of Shelley's – he too asks for a fairing – the kickshaws and gewgaws sold in the booths of a fair – and a toothsome one; though I haven't yet been able to discover what he meant by 'hunting nuts':

Monday, July 18, 1803.   (Horsham)

Dear Kate,
    We have proposed a day at the pond next Wednesday; and if

you will come to-morrow morning I would be much obliged to you; and if you could any how bring Tom over to stay all night, I would thank you. We are to have a cold dinner over at the pond, and come home to eat a bit of roast chicken and peas at about nine o'clock. Mama depends upon your bringing Tom over to-morrow, and if you don't we shall be very much disappointed.

Tell the bearer not to forget to bring me a fairing – which is some ginger-bread, sweetmeat, hunting-nuts, and a pocket book. Now I end.

I am *not*,
Your obedient servant,
P. B. SHELLEY

[Not only has my ignorance of hunting-nuts been now [1927] enlightened – what Shelley wanted being a long oval-shaped ginger-nut convenient for pocketing; not only has a recipe for making them been sent me by one kind informant, and the news that they are still to be bought at Nottingham Fair by another; but a third generously supplied me with positive specimens still almost hot from the oven.]

'Bonny brown hair'

And what could be more enchanting? But was it squirrel-brown, or chestnut, or hazelnut, or autumn-beech, or heather-brown, or walnut, or old hay colour, or undappled-fawn, or dark lichen, or velvet brown, or marigold or pansy or wallflower-brown – or yet another? – every one of which would look charming beneath the rim of a round blue-ribanded 'little straw hat'.

79

'My Dad and Mam they did agree'

Fifty years and three
Together in love lived we;
Angry both at once none ever did us see.

355

This was the fashion
God taught us, and not fear: –
When one was in a passion
The other could forbear.

80

To an eye looking down, the steeple of Widdecombe Church rises in the midst of Dartmoor like a lovely needle of ivory; and hidden beneath the turf around it lie, waiting, the bones of Tom Pearse, Bill Brewer . . . Old Uncle Tom Cobley and all.

83

'There were three gipsies'

– and they were of England (Somerset), though to judge from this old ballad they may have padded it down from the Highlands:

> There cam' Seven Egyptians on a day,
>   And wow, but they sang bonny!
> And they sang sae sweet, and sae very complete,
>   Down cam' Earl Cassilis' lady.
>
> She cam' tripping adown the stair,
>   And a' her maids before her;
> As soon as they saw her weel-faur'd face
>   They cast the glamourie owre her;
>
> They gave to her the nutmeg,
>   And they gave to her the ginger;
> And she gave to them a far better thing,
>   The seven gold rings off her finger.

There was a small black cobbled-up book entitled *Glamourie* in a red leather case in Thrae, but, alas, it was in a writing I could not

easily decipher. On the fly-leaf was scrawled 'H.B.', and beneath it
was the following:

> See, with eyes shut.
> Look seldom behind thee.
> In secret of selfship
> Free thee, not bind thee.
> Mark but a flower:
> 'Tis of Eden. A fly
> Shall sound thee a horn
> Wooing Paradise nigh.
> Think close. Unto love
> Give thy heart's steed the rein;
> So – course the world over.
> Then Homeward again.

84

'Whatever they find they take it'

> There was a robber met a robber
> On a rig of beans;
> Says a robber to a robber,
> 'Can a robber tell a robber
> What a robber means?'

And if not; why not? This inextricable and delectable scrap of
jingle I owe to Mr Ralph Hodgson. And the following version of
an old game rhyme (with its rare 'wood') first met my eye by the
kindness of another friend, Mrs Lyon:

> My Mother said that I never should
> Play with the gypsies in the wood,
> The wood was dark; the grass was green;
> In came Sally with a tambourine.

I went to the sea – no ship to get across;
I paid ten shillings for blind white horse;
I up on his back and was off in a crack,
Sally, tell my Mother I shall never come back.

86

This lament for matchless Robin Hood, who should shine in a far
better place than between 'Beggars' and 'Gilderoy', is the only
rhyme about him in this collection. The fact is, try as I might, I
could not make up my mind which to choose of the old greenwood
ballads. But they are all to be found in Professor Child's collection.
And if this neglect of the merry outlaw should induce anyone to
read *English and Scottish Ballads*, it will have been to good purpose.

87

A pretty song about a monstrously ugly scoundrel, though
handsome of feature. Gilderoy was a highwayman, sparing for his
prey neither man nor woman, and if there were 'roses' on his shoes,
they were blood-red. At last fifty armed avengers surrounded his
house at night and set on. He killed eight of them before he was
captured; which, if true, was bonnie fighting. Nevertheless, such a
villain he was that he was hanged, without trial, on a gibbet thirty
feet high, and the bones of him (despite the last stanza of the ballad)
dangled in chains forty feet above Leith Walk in Edinburgh for
fifty years afterwards.

Three things there be that prosper all apace,
    And flourish while they are asunder far;
But on a day they meet all in a place,
    And when they meet, they one another mar.

And they be these – the Wood, the Weed, the Wag; –
    The Wood is that that makes the gallows-tree;
The Weed is that that strings the hangman's bag;
    The Wag, my pretty knave, betokens *thee*.

Now mark, dear boy — while these assemble not,
   Green springs the tree, hemp grows, the wag is wild;
But when they meet, it makes the timber rot,
   It frets the halter, and it chokes the child.

SIR WALTER RALEIGH

Told How a Crew Was Cursed

   My name is Captain Kidd,
       Captain Kidd.
   My name is Captain Kidd,
       Captain Kidd.
   My name is Captain Kidd,
       And wickedly I did;
   God's laws I did forbid,
       As I sailed.

   My topsails they did shake
       As I sailed.
   My topsails they did shake
       As I sailed.
   My topsails they did shake,
       And the merchants they did quake,
   For many did I take
       As I sailed.

88

'And his name was Little Bingo'

In bounding health, it is said, a dog's nose and a woman's elbow
are always cold. The reason for which is explained in a legend (referred to in Mrs Wright's *Rustic Speech and Folklore*). It seems
that in the midst of its forty days' riding on the Flood, the Ark one
black night sprung a little leak. And Noah having forgotten to
bring his carpenter's bag on board, was at his wits' end to plug the

hole in its timbers. In the beam of his rushlight he looked and he looked and he looked; and still the water came rilling in and in. His dog, Shafet, was of course standing by, head on one side, carefully watching his master. And Noah, by good chance at last casting his eye in his direction, seized the faithful creature and, thrusting his nose into the leak, for a while stopped the flow. But Noah, a merciful man, and partial to animals, quickly perceived that in a few minutes poor Shafet would perish of suffocation, and as, by this time, his wife had descended into the fo'c'sle to see what he was about, he released his dog's nose, and, instead of it, stuffed in her charming elbow. Yet even that failed at last to plug the hole, so Ham was made to sit on it.

But not all dogs are 'good dogs' – as Launce in *The Two Gentlemen of Verona* knew:

'*Launce:* Nay, 'twill bee this howre ere I have done weeping. All the kinde of the *Launces*, have this very fault: I have received my proportion, like the prodigious Sonne, and am going with Sir *Protheus* to the Imperialls Court: I thinke *Crab* my dog, be the sowrest natured dogge that lives: My Mother weeping: my Father wayling: my Sister crying: our Maid howling: our Catte wringing her hands, and all our house in a great perplexitie, yet did not this cruel-hearted *Curre* shedde one teare: he is a stone, a very pibble stone, and has no more pitty in him then a dogge!'

And while dogges are about, here is a rhyme which if it be repeated twelve times a minute twelve times a day will keep the tongue supple and the wits clear:

> There was a man, and his name was Dob
> And he had a wife, and her name was Mob,
> And he had a dog, and he called it Cob
> And she had a cat called Chitterabob.
>
> Cob, says Dob,
> Chitterabob, says Mob.
> Cob was Dob's dog.
> Chitterabob Mob's cat.

90

'*Poor old horse*'

Sweet wind that up the climbing road
Fliest, where Summer, heated stands,
There drags the patient horse his load, –
O! bless him with thy flowing hands!
Wing o'er his dumb, distressèd face
And bathe his weeping brow with grace.

His sobs are mingled with thy sighs,
His taut lips meet eternal steel
Relentless as the goading cries
That scorn his plodding, grace appeal:
His parched tongue lolls, and yet he laves
Hourly his heart in Love's deep waves!

O! bless him, breeze, and shed him tears;
And when he mounts his last hill's crest
Thou, cherished by the labouring fears
Along his streaming mane, shalt rest
When he shall scan, with naked eyes
The rolling plains of Paradise.

M. M. JOHNSON

91

Messalina's monkey was, one would fancy, of the kind called a
marmoset, 'blacke and greene'. 'Their agilitie and manner of doing
is admirable, for that they seeme to have reason and discourse to
go upon trees, wherein they seeme to imitate birds.' There are so
few of these far fair cousins of ours in poetry that I am adding a
bevy of them from Sir John Maundeville's *Travels*.

'. . . From that City, (that is to say Cassay – the City of Heaven),
men go by Water, solacing and disporting themselves, till they come
to an Abbey of Monks – that is fast by – that be good religious men

after their Faith and Law. In that Abbey is a great Garden and a fair, where be many Trees of diverse manner of Fruits. And in this Garden, is a little Hill, full of delectable Trees. In that Hill and in that Garden be many divers Beasts, as of Apes, Marmosets, Baboons, and many other divers Beasts. And every day, when the Monks of this Abbey have eaten, the Almoner has the remnants carried forth into the Garden, and he smiteth on the Garden Gate with a Clicket of Silver that he holdeth in his hand, and anon all the Beasts of the Hill and of divers places of the Garden, come out, a 3000 or a 4000 of them; they approach as if they were poor men come a-begging; and the Almoner's servants give them the remnants, in fair Vessels of Silver, clean over gilt. And when they have eaten, the Monk smiteth eftsoons on the Garden Gate with the Clicket; and then anon all the Beasts return again to their places that they came from. And they say that these Beasts be Souls of worthy men, that resemble in likeness the Beasts that be fair: and therefore they give them meat for the love of God.'

'There is,' says Fuller, 'a sort of apes in India, caught by the natives thereof in this manner. They dress a little boy in his sight, undress him again – leaving the child's apparel behind them in the place, and then depart a competent distance. The Ape presently apparels himself in the same garments, till the child's cloathes become his Chains, putting off his Feet by putting on his Shoes, not able to run to any purpose, and so soon taken.'

92

'*O happy fly!*'

And here is another of these creatures – 'a sleepy fly that rubs its hands', in Thomas Hardy's words – William Blake's:

> Little Fly,
> Thy summer's play
> My thoughtless hand
> Has brushed away.

Am not I
A fly like thee?
Or art not thou
A man like me?

For I dance,
And drink, and sing,
Till some blind hand
Shall brush my wing.

If thought is life
And strength and breath,
And the want
Of thought is death;

Then am I
A happy fly
If I live
Or if I die.

But the Happy Fly is nowadays gone so dismally out of favour
that it would perhaps be prudent to draw attention from him to
Lovelace's 'Grasshopper':

O thou that swing'st upon the waving hair
  Of some well-fillèd oaten beard,
Drunk every night with a delicious tear
  Dropt thee from heaven, where thou wert reared!

The joys of earth and air are thine entire,
  That with thy feet and wings dost hop and fly;
And when thy poppy works, thou dost retire
  To thy carved acorn-bed to lie.

Up with the day, the Sun thou welcom'st then,
  Sport'st in the gilt plaits of his beams,
And all these merry days mak'st merry men,
  Thyself, and melancholy streams.

93

'Lo, the bright air alive with dragonflies'

There is an old dialect children's rhyme about these lightlike shimmering *stingless* insects:

> Snakestanger, snakestanger, vlee aal about the brooks;
> Sting aal the bad bwoys that vor the fish looks,
> Bút let the góod bwoys ketch aál the vish they can,
> And car'm away whóoam to vry 'em in a pan;
> Bread and butter they shall yeat at zupper wi' their vish
> While aal the littull bad bwoys shall only lick the dish.

But even littull bad bwoys want a light to light them to bed, and 'there is a kind of little animal of the size of prawnes,' says Champlain, 'which fly by night, and make such light in the air that one would say that they were so many little candles. If a man had three or four of these little creatures, which are not larger than a filbert, he could read as well at night as with a wax light.'

As indeed men used to in South America if we are to believe Du Bartas:

> New-Spain's *cucuio*, in his forehead brings
> Two burning lamps, two underneath his wings:
> Whose shining rayes serve oft, in darkest night,
> Th' imbroderer's hand in royall works to light:
> Th' ingenious turner, with a wakefull eye,
> To polish fair his purest ivory:
> The usurer to count his gistring treasures:
> The learned scribe to limn his golden measures.

95

'The Pet Lamb', by William Wordsworth, is of a more delicate light and colour and music than this poem. But it is much better known. And there is a secret something in the words of Mary Howitt's that wins one's heart for the writer of it.

'A thousand flocks were on the hills'

'... And so ... I walked upon the Downes, where a flock of sheep was; and the most pleasant and innocent sight that ever I saw in my life. We found a shepherd [and his dog] and his little boy reading ... the Bible to him; so I made the boy read to me, which he did, with the forced tone that children usually do read, that was mighty pretty, and then I did give him something, and went to the father, and talked with him ... He did content himself mightily in my liking his boy's reading, and did bless God for him, the most like one of the old patriarchs that ever I saw in my life, and it brought those thoughts of the old age of the world in my mind for two or three days after. We took notice of his woollen knit stockings of two colours mixed, and of his shoes shod with iron, both at the toe and heels, and with great nails in the soles of his feet, which was mighty pretty; and, taking notice of them, "Why," says the poor man, "the Downs, you see, are full of stones, and we are fain to shoe ourselves thus; and these," says he, "will make the stones fly till they ring before me."'

SAMUEL PEPYS (July 14, 1667)

97

... Poor Wat, far off upon a hill,
Stands on his hinder legs with listening ear,
To hearken if his foes pursue him still:
Anon their loud alarums he doth hear;
 And now his grief may be comparèd well
 To one sore sick that hears the passing-bell.

Then shalt thou see the dew-bedabbled wretch
Turn, and return, indenting with the way;
Each envious briar his weary legs doth scratch,
Each shadow makes him stop, each murmur stay:
 For misery is trodden on by many,
 And being low never reliev'd by any ...

Venus and Adonis

'As he was speaking, Harry, casting his eyes on one side, said, "See! see! there is the poor hare skulking along! I hope they will not be able to find her: and, if they ask me, I will never tell them which way she is gone."

'Presently, up came the dogs, who had now lost all scent of their game, and a gentleman mounted upon a fine horse, who asked Harry if he had seen the hare? Harry made no answer; but, upon the gentleman's repeating the question in a louder tone of voice, he answered that he had. "And which way is she gone?" said the gentleman.

' "Sir, I don't choose to tell you," answered Harry, after some hesitation.

' "Not choose!" said the gentleman, leaping off his horse, "but I'll make you choose in an instant": and coming up to Harry, who never moved from the place where he had been standing, began to lash him in a most unmerciful manner with his whip, continually repeating, "Now, you little rascal, do you choose to tell me now?" To which Harry made no other answer than this: "If I would not tell you before, I won't now, though you should kill me."

'But this fortitude of Harry, and the tears of Tommy, who cried in the bitterest manner to see the distress of his friend, made no impression on this barbarian, who continued his brutality till ... When they were gone, Tommy came up to Harry in the most affectionate manner, and asked him how he did? – "A little sore," said Harry, "but that does not signify ..." '

But see 'The Story of Cyrus' in the *History of Sandford and Merton.*

98

This is another translation by Kuno Meyer from the ancient Irish – only the bare bones, that is, of a poem that in its original tongue must have been many times more musical with internal rhyme and gentle echo and cadence; for the craft of Gaelic verse was an exceedingly delicate one.

I like it for the sake of its cat, its monk, and its age, but chiefly because it reminds me of my own far-away days at Thrae – brooding there as I used to in solitude and silence over Mr Nahum's books.

As for 'white Pangur' and his kind, 'it is needlesse,' says Topsell, 'to spend any time about [Puss's] loving nature to man, how she flattereth by rubbing her skinne against ones legges, how she whurleth with her voyce, having as many tunes as turnes; for she hath one voice to beg and to complain, another to testifie her delight and pleasure, another among her own kind by flattring, by hissing, by spitting, insomuch as some have thought that they have a peculiar intelligible language among themselves.' So also John de Trevisa, in 1387: 'The catte is a beaste of uncertain heare [hair] and colour; for some catte is white, some rede, some blacke, some skewed [piebald] and speckled in the fete and in the face and in the eares. He is a beste in youth, swyfte, plyaunte, and mery, and lepeth and reseth [rusheth] on all thynge that is tofore him; and is led by a strawe and playeth therwith. He is a right hevy beast in aege, and ful slepy, and lyeth slily in wait for myce. And he maketh a ruthefull noyse and gastfull, whan one proffreth to fyghte with another, and he falleth on his owne fete whan he falleth out of hye places.'

The writings of the ancient Egyptians show that, far from detesting to wet his paws, he would then *swim* in pursuit of fish. They painted a cat for the sound 'miaou' in their hieroglyphics; gazed into his changing moonlike eyes and revered him; and embalmed him when dead.

Having borrowed him from Egypt, the Romans brought him to Britain (though we already had a wilding of our own, *Felis Catus*), with the ass, the goat, the rabbit, the peacock, not to speak of the cherry, the walnut, the crocus, the tulip, the leek, the cucumber, etc. The Monk's Pangur, then, came of a long lineage.

So valuable were cats in *Wales* in the eleventh century (two or three hundred years after Pangur), that their price was fixed by law: for a blind kitten a penny; for a kitten with its eyes open, twopence; for a cat of one mouse, fourpence, and so on. And to kill one of the Prince's granary cats meant payment of a fine of as much wheat as would cover up its body when suspended by its tail. In Scotland (where the true wild ancient Caledonian cat is now steadily increasing) there has long been a complete Clan of Cats – apart from the

witches. As for the Cheshire Cat, he grins, I imagine, not because
he has nine lives, is said to be melancholy, may look at a king, and
has nothing to do with Catgut, Cat's cradle, and Cat-i'-the-pan,
but because he has read in a dictionary that Dick Whittington sailed
off to the Isle of Rats, not with a Cat, but with *acat* or *achat*,
meaning goods for trading – Coals! Long may he grin! How but
one country Gib or Tom may befriend the brightfaced heartsease
(so sturdy a little dear that it will bloom at burning noonday in a
gravel path) Charles Darwin tells in his *Origin of Species*.

'*Grimalkin*'s' 'loving nature' to creatures *other* than man and
the heartsease is hinted at in this old Scots nursery rhyme:

> There was a wee bit mousikie,
> That lived in Gilberaty, O,
> It couldna get a bite o' cheese,
> For cheetie-poussie-cattie, O.
>
> It said unto the cheesikie,
> 'Oh fain wad I be at ye, O,
> If 't were na for the cruel paws
> O' cheetie-poussie-cattie, O.'

and his powers, when of the right colour (though there's much to
be said for a calemanchos cat), in this:

> Wherever the cat of the house is black,
> Its lasses of lovers will have no lack.

99

'*On what wings dare he aspire?*'

The verb *dare* (I gather from Webster) was once used only in the
past tense, the preterite; for 'dare he' therefore in this poem we
should now write *dared he*.

100

Andrew Marvell has three rare charms – his poetry is wholly his own; it is as delightful as the sound of his name; and the face in his portrait is as enchanting as either.

101

'Of all the birds that I do know' should of course instantly conjure up 'Of all the girls that are so smart'; but 'Sallie' is known to the whole world 'by heart'. The 'Philip' of Nos. 101–2 is, I suppose, the hedge-sparrow or dunnock, that gentle and happy little cousin of the warblers – as light and lovely in voice as they are on the wing. As everyone knows, a bull-finch can be taught to whistle like a baker's boy, and will become so jealous of his mistress that he will hiss and ruff with rage at every stranger. Jackdaws and magpies, too, will become friends to a friend. But a lady whom I have the happiness to know has a nightingale that was hatched in captivity, and so has never shared either the delights or the dangers of the wild. So easy is he in her company, that he will perch on her pen-tip as she sits at table, and sing as if out of a garden in Damascus.

102

'*He would chirp*'

'... As she [St Douceline] sat at meat, if anyone brought her a flower, a bird, a fruit, or any other thing that gave her pleasure, then she fell straightway into an ecstasy, and was caught up to Him Who had made these fair creatures ... One day she heard a lonely sparrow sing, whereupon she said to her companions, "How lovely is the song of that bird!" and in the twinkling of an eye she was in an ecstasy, drawn up to God by the bird's voice ...'

The above is from *A Medieval Garner*, and this, from a Note to *A Saint's Tragedy*, by Margaret L. Woods: When the blessed

Elizabeth 'had been ill twelve days and more, one of her maids sitting by her bed heard in her throat a very sweet sound, ... and saying, "Oh, my mistress, how sweetly thou didst sing!" she answered, "I tell thee, I heard a little bird between me and the wall sing merrily; who with his sweet song so stirred me up that I could not but sing myself." '

> I have wished a bird would fly away
> And not sing by my house all day;
>
> Have clapped my hands at him from the door
> When it seemed as if I could bear no more.
>
> The fault may partly have been in me,
> The bird was not to blame for his key.
>
> And of course there must be something wrong
> In wanting to silence any song.

ROBERT FROST

'Loving red-breasts'

> My dear, do you know
>   How a long time ago,
>   Two poor little children,
> Whose names I don't know,
> Were stolen away
> On a fine summer's day,
>   And left in a wood,
> As I've heard people say.
>
> And when it was night,
> So sad was their plight,
>   The sun it went down,
> And the moon gave no light!
> They sobbed and they sighed,
> And they bitterly cried,
>   And the poor little things,
> They laid down and died.

And when they were dead,
The robins so red
   Brought strawberry leaves,
And over them spread;
And all the day long,
They sang them this song, –
Poor babes in the wood!
Poor babes in the wood!
   And don't you remember
The babes in the wood?

Wherefore (apart from other excellent reasons) –

   The robin of the red breast
   Ay, and the cutty wren –
   If e'er ye take 'em out of nest,
   Ye'll never thrive again.

   The robin of the red breast,
   Martin and swallow –
   If e'er ye steal one egg of theirs,
   Bad luck'll follow.

   For sure, the robin and the wren
   Are God Almighty's cock and hen.

105

' 'Tis a note of enchantment'

It was a note of enchantment such as this that haunted the memory of Edward Thomas when he was writing his poem called *The Unknown Bird*. I give only a few lines, but the rest of the beautiful thing may be found in his *Poems:*

Oftenest when I heard him I was alone,
Nor could I ever make another hear.
La-la-la! he called seeming far-off —
As if a cock crowed past the edge of the world,
As if the bird or I were in a dream . . .

. . . O wild-raving winds! if you ever do roar
   By the house and the elms from where I've a-come,
Breathe up at the window, or call at the door,
   And tell you've a-found me a-thinking of home.

WILLIAM BARNES

107

'*Like a lady bright*'

'They say,' says mad Ophelia, 'they say the owle was a Baker's daughter. Lord, we know what we are, but know not what we may be. God be at your Table.' And thus runs the story:

Our Saviour being footsore, weary and hungry, went one dark-ening evening into a baker's shop and asked for bread. The oven being then hot and all prepared for the baking, the mistress of the shop cut off a good-sized piece of the risen dough to bake for Him. At this her fair, greedy daughter, who sate watching what was forward from a little window, upbraided her mother for this wasting of profit on such an outcast, and snatching the platter out of her hands, she chopped the piece of dough into half, and half, and half again. Nevertheless when this mean small lump was put into the oven it presently began miraculously to rise and swell until it exceeded a full quartern of wheaten bread. In alarm at this strange sight the daughter — her round blue eyes largely eyeing the stranger in the dim light — turned on her mother, and cried out: 'O Mother, Mother, *Heugh, heugh, heugh!*'

'As thou hast spoken,' said our Saviour, 'so be thou: child of the Night.' Whereupon, the poor creature, feathered and in the likeness of an owl, fled forth in the dark towards the woodside.

109

'The white owl'

When night is o'er the wood
  And moon-scared watch-dogs howl,
Comes forth in search of food
  The snowy mystic owl.
His soft, white, ghostly wings
  Beat noiselessly the air
Like some lost soul that hopelessly
  Is mute in its despair.

But now his hollow note
  Rings cheerless through the glade
And o'er the silent moat
  He flits from shade to shade.
He hovers, swoops and glides
  O'er meadows, moors and streams;
He seems to be some fantasy –
  A ghostly bird of dreams.

Why dost thou haunt the night?
  Why dost thou love the moon
When other birds delight
  To sing their joy at noon?
Art thou then crazed with love,
  Or is't for some fell crime
That thus thou flittest covertly
  At this unhallowed time?

                    F. J. PATMORE

III

'Her small soul'

Smallest of all shrill souls among the English birds is the wren, but she has a remote relative that dwells in the dark, silent and enormous forests of South America, the Humming Bird, so swift and tiny a creature that it sucks a flower's nectar on the wing, its plumage being of a sheen lovelier than words can tell. There are two early descriptions of it; the first from Purchas's *Pilgrimes*, by Antonia Galvano of New Spain:

'There be certaine small birds named *vicmalim*, their bil is small and long. They live of the dew, and the juyce of flowers and roses. Their feathers bee small and of divers colours. They be greatly esteemed to worke gold with. They die or sleepe every yeere in the moneth of October, sitting upon a little bough in a warme and close place: they revive or wake againe in the moneth of April after that the flowers be sprung, and therefore they call them the revived birds – *Vicmalim.*'

The second is Gonzalo Ferdinando de Oviedo's – his very name a string of gems:

'. . . I have seene that one of these birds with her nest put into a paire of gold weights [scales] altogether, hath waide no more than a *tomini*, which are in poise 24 graines, with the feathers, without the which she would have waied somewhat less. And doubtlesse, when I consider the finenesse of the clawes and feete of these birds, I know not whereunto I may better liken them then to the little birds which the lymners of bookes are accustomed to paint on the margent of church bookes, and other bookes of divine service. Their feathers are of manie faire colours, as golden, yellow, and greene, beside other variable colours. Their beake is verie long for the proportion of their bodies, and as fine and subtile as a sowing needle. They are verie hardy [valiant], so that when they see a man clime the tree where they have their nests, they fly at his face, and strike him in the eyes, comming, going, and returning with such swiftnesse, that no man should lightly beleeve it that had not seene it . . .'

Nor this of bats, either, as related by W. H. Hudson. He was walking at dusk one summer's evening in a sunken lane frequented by these hooked, cowled, mouselike creatures, which pestered him by repeatedly darting at the light check cap he was wearing. To fend them off he raised a light flexible cane he was carrying into the aire and twirled it as rapidly as possible in a circle above his head – an inverted cone of motion. But this was not the slightest obstacle to his sharp-eyed, exquisite-skinned persecutors. They flew through it!

112

'It caught his image'

And Shelley:

> . . . I cannot tell my joy, when o'er a lake
> Upon a drooping bough with nightshade twined,
> I saw two azure halcyons clinging downward
> And thinning one bright bunch of amber berries,
> With quick long beaks, in the deep there lay
> Those lovely forms imaged as in a sky . . .

Anyone so happy as to be able to remember Mary Coleridge as a friend, will agree that to have seen her eyes is to have seen her own pool and Shelley's lake imaging such lovely flitting halcyons.

114

'King Pandion he is dead'

A wild and dreadful legend is hidden here – of a king who wronged his Queen and her sister, daughters of Pandion, and how they avenged themselves upon him, sacrificing his son to their hatred.

That Queen, goes this old tale, became a nightingale, her sister a
swallow (crimson still dying the feathers of her throat), the evil
king a hoopoe, and his firstborn was raised to life again a pheasant.

115

'*A sparhawk proud*'

– a little bird but of a noble family. Listen, at least, to Auceps, the
Faulkner or Falconer, in *The Compleat Angler*. '. . . And first, for
the Element that I use to trade in, which is the Air . . . It stops not
the high soaring of my noble generous *Falcon*; in it she ascends to
such an height, as the dull eyes of beasts and fish are not able to
reach to; their bodies are too gross for such high elevations . . .
But her mettle makes her careless of danger, for she then heeds
nothing, but makes her nimble Pinions cut the fluid air, and so
makes her high way over the steepest mountains and deepest rivers,
and in her glorious carere looks with contempt upon those high
Steeples and magnificent Palaces which we adore and wonder at;
from which height I can make her to descend by a word from my
mouth (which she both knows and obeys), to accept of meat from
my hand, to own me for her Master, to go home with me, and be
willing the next day to afford me the like recreation . . .'

In hawking (as in hunting) the novice had to learn the appro-
priate *terms* of his craft or art, and every company or flock or
flight of birds had its special word, such as: A siege of herons, a
spring of teals, a gaggle of geese, a badelynge (paddling) of ducks,
a muster of peacocks, a bevy of quails, a congregation of plovers,
a dule of turtle-doves, a walk of snipes, a fall of woodcocks, a
building of rooks, a murmuration of starlings, an exaltation of larks,
a watch of nightingales and a charm of goldfinches.

To every beast of the chase, too, was given a name for its foot-
prints, tail, age, droppings, and 'lodgement': to the hart its *harbour*,
the hare its *form*, the boar its *couch*, the marten its *tree*, the otter its
watch, the badger its *earth*, and the coney its *sit* or its *burrow*.

120

'Come wary one'

... Tak any brid,[1] and put it in a cage,
And do al thyn entente and thy corage
To fostre it tendrely with mete and drinke,
Of allĕ deyntees that thou canst bethinke,
And keep it al-so clenly as thou may;
Al-though his cape of gold be never so gay,
Yet hath this brid, by twenty thousand fold,
Lever in a forest, that is rude and cold,
Gon etĕ wormĕs and swich wrecchednesse.
For ever this brid wol doon his bisinesse
To escape out of his cagĕ, if he may;
His libertee this brid desireth ay ...

GEOFFREY CHAUCER

When I was a child of eight or nine I had a passion for sparrows, and used often to set traps for them; but even if I succeeded in taking one alive, which was not always, I could never persuade it to live in a cage above a day or two. However much I pampered it, it drooped and died. Then, like a young crocodile, I occasionally shed tears. One fine morning, I remember, I visited a distant trap and, as usual, all but stopped breathing at discovering that it was 'down'. Very cautiously edging in my fingers towards the captive, I was startled out of my wits by a sudden prodigious skirring of wings, and lo and behold, I had caught – and lost – a starling. He fled away twenty yards or so, and perched on a hillock. I see him now, his feathers glistening in the sun, and his sharp head turned towards me, his eyes looking back at me, as of foe at foe. And that reminds me of the Griffons – the guardians of the mines of the one-eyed Arimaspians.

'... From that land go men toward the land of Bacharie, where

1. Bird

be full evil folk and full cruel ... In that country be many griffounes, more plentiful than in any other country. Some men say that they have the body upward as an eagle, and beneath as a lion; and truly they say sooth that they be of that shape. But a griffoun hath the body more great, and is more strong, than eight lions, of such lions as be on this side of the world; and larger and stronger than an hundred eagles, such as we have amongst us. For a griffoun there will bear flying to his nest a great horse, if he may find him handy, or two oxen yoked together, as they go at the plough. For he hath his talons so long and so broad and great upon his feet, as though they were hornes of great oxen, or of bugles (bullocks), or of kine; so that men make cups of them, to drink out of. And of their ribs, and the quills of their wings, men make bows full strong, to shoot with arrows and bowbolts ...'

So, too, Marco Polo on the Rukh, or Roc – the bird to whose leg Sinbad bound himself in order to escape out of the precipitous valley of diamonds:

'By people of the island – that is the island of Madagascar, where ivory abounds, ambergris, and red sandal-wood – it is reported that at a certain season of the year, a ... bird, which they call a rukh, makes its appearance from the southern region. In form it is said to resemble the eagle, but it is incomparably greater in size; being so large and strong as to seize an elephant with its talons, and to lift it up into the air, from whence it lets it fall to the ground, in order that when dead it may prey upon the carcase ...

'The grand khan having heard this extraordinary relation, sent messengers to the island ... When they returned to the presence of his majesty, they brought with them (as I have heard) a feather of the rukh, positively affirmed to have measured ninety spans, and the quill part to have been two palms in circumference. This surprising exhibition afforded his majesty extreme pleasure, and upon those by whom it was presented he bestowed valuable gifts.'

But a griffoun is only a gigantic starling, so to speak; an it is a pity mine and I were enemies. 'If a sparrow come before my window,' wrote John Keats in one of his letters, 'I take part in its existence, and pick about the gravel.' Traps, gins, guns and birdlime are little help in this.

A Skylark wounded in the wing,
A Cherubim does cease to sing . . .

The wild Deer wandering here and there
Keeps the Human Soul from care . . .

The wanton Boy that kills the Fly
Shall feel the Spider's enmity . . .

Kill not the Moth nor Butterfly,
For the Last Judgment draweth nigh . . .

The Beggar's Dog and Widow's Cat,
Feed them, and thou wilt grow fat . . .

To see a World in a Grain of Sand,
And a Heaven in a Wild Flower,
Hold Infinity in the palm of your hand,
An eternity in an hour.

WILLIAM BLAKE

. . . What is heaven? a globe of dew,
Filling in the morning new
  Some eyed flower whose young leaves waken
On an unimagined world:
  Constellated suns unshaken,
Orbits measureless, are furled
  In that frail and fading sphere,
  With ten millions gathered there,
  To tremble, gleam, and disappear.

PERCY BYSSHE SHELLEY

The men who wrote these words, truly and solemnly meant them. They are not mere pretty flowers of the fancy, but the tough piercing roots of the tree of life that grew within their minds.

126

This poem and many others (but not all) I copied out of Mr Nahum's book in their original spelling. At first I found the reading of them tiring and troublesome. It was like looking at a dried-up flower or beetle. But there the things were; and after a good deal of trouble I not only began to read them more easily, but grew to like them thus for their own sake. First, because this was as they were actually written, before our English printers agreed to spell alike; and next, because the old words with their look of age became a pleasure to me in themselves. It was like watching the dried-up flower or beetle actually and as if by a magic of the mind coming to life. Besides, many of Shakespeare's shorter poems were already known to me. It touched them with newness to see them as they appeared (seven years after his death), in the pages of the famous folio volume of *Plays* that was printed in 1623 by Isaac Jaggard and Edward Blount.

Not only that; for it is curious too to see how in the old days English was constantly changing – its faded words falling like dead leaves from a tree, and new ones appearing. In a book which William Caxton printed as far back even as 1490, he says: 'And certainly our language now used varieth far from that which was used and spoken when I was born. For we Englishmen be born under the domination of the moon, which is never steadfast but ever wavering, waxing one season and waneth and decreaseth another season.'

Moreover, if the spelling of a word alters its effect on the eye, it must also affect the *mind* of the reader; and I must confess that 'my lovynge deare', looks to me to tell of somebody more lovable even than 'my loving dear'. And what of shoogarplummes, cleere greye eies, this murrkie fogghe, the moones enravysshyng?

'Even when,' says Mr. Havelock Ellis, in *The Dance of Life*, 'we leave out of consideration the great historical tradition of variety in this matter, it is doubtful . . . whether the advantages of encouraging everyone to spell like his fellows overbalance the advantages of encouraging everyone to spell unlike his fellows. When I was a teacher in the Australian Bush I derived far less enjoyment from the more or less "correctly" spelt exercises of my pupils than from the occasional notes I received from their parents, who, never having been taught to spell, were able to spell in the grand manner. We are wilfully throwing away an endless source of delight . . .'

A small niece of a friend of mine once wrote a little tale with the title, 'A Bqlir Chesterdrores' – a peculiar chest-of-drawers. Now that surely is spelling in the grand manner.

And John Aubrey would have agreed: 'A Gentlewoman,' he says in his *Miscellanies*, [1696], dreamt that 'a pultess of blew corants' would cure her sore throat; and it did so. 'She was a pious woman, and affirmed it to be true.' But would a mere *poultice of black currants* have had the same effect?

And surely a butcher's book looks a little more *sensitive* when its entries show like this:

				s.	d.
nec la	-	-	-	5	9
bf stk	-	-	-	3	6
kdy	-	-	-	1	0
Sho Mtt	-	-	-	11	3
P. saus	-	-	-	2	8
Bris	-	-	-	3	7

128

'Shee carries me above the skie'

... This palace standeth in the air,
By necromancy placèd there,
That it no tempest needs to fear,
   Which way soe'er it blow it;
And somewhat southward toward the noon,
Whence lies a way up to the moon,
And thence the Fairy can as soon
   Pass to the earth below it.

The walls of spiders' legs are made
Well mortisèd and finely laid;
He was the master of his trade
 It curiously that builded:
The windows of the eyes of cats,
And for the roof, instead of slats,
Is covered with the skins of bats,
 With moonshine that are gilded . . .

MICHAEL DRAYTON

129

To see the 'pretty elf': 'Gette a square christall in lenth three
inches. Lay the christall in the bloude of a white henne, 3 Wednes-
daies and 3 Frydaies. Take it out, wash it with Holy Aq. Take 3
hazle sticks an yeare groth, pill [peel] them fair and white. Write
the fayrie's name in bloud mix'd with inke. Write on eche stick.
Then burie themm under some hill whereat fayries haunte the
Wednesdaie before you call her. The Fridaie following, take them
uppe and call her at eight or three or tenn of the clock . . . but be
in clene life and turn thy face towards East. You may command thys
fayrie to the utmost.'

131

. . . Such a soft floating witchery of sound
 As twilight Elfins make, when they at eve
 Voyage on gentle gales from Fairy-Land,
 Where Melodies round honey-dropping flowers,
 Footless and wild, like birds of Paradise,
 Nor pause, nor perch, hovering on untamed wing! . . .

S. T. COLERIDGE

133

'For fear of little men'

'Terrestrial devils,' says Robert Burton, 'are those Lares, Genii, Fauns, Satyrs, Wood-nymphs, Foliots, Fairies, Robin Good-fellows, Trulli, etc., which as they are most conversant with men, so they do them most harm . . . These are they that dance on heaths and greens . . . and leave that green circle, which we commonly find in plain fields, which others hold to proceed from a meteor falling, or some accidental rankness of the ground, so nature sports herself; they are sometimes seen by old women and children . . . Paracelsus reckons up many places in Germany, where they do usually walk in little coats, some two foot long. A bigger kind there is of them called with us hobgoblins, and Robin Goodfellows, that would in those superstitious times grind corn for a mess of milk, cut wood, or do any manner of drudgery work . . . Dithmarus Bleskenius, in his description of Iceland, reports for a certainty, that almost in every family they have yet some such familiar spirits . . . Another sort of these there are, which frequent forlorn houses . . . They will make strange noises in the night, howl sometimes pitifully, and then laugh again, cause great flame and sudden lights, fling stones, rattle chains, shave men, open doors and shut them, fling down platters, stools, chests, sometimes appear in the likeness of hares, crows, black dogs, etc.' . . .

135

So too with Hazel Dorn, in the following poem by Mr Bernard Sleigh, who has very kindly allowed me to print it for the first time.

> They stole her from the well beside the wood.
> Ten years ago as village gossips tell;
> One Beltane-eve when trees were all a-bud
>   In copse and fell.

Ominous, vast, the moon rose full and red
Behind dim hills; no leaf stirred in the glen
That breathless eve, when she was pixy-led
      Beyond our ken.

For she had worn no rowan in her hair, –
Nor set the cream-bowl by the kitchen door, –
Nor whispered low the pagan faery prayer
      Of ancient lore;

But trod that daisied ring in hose and shoon,
To hear entranced, their elf-bells round her ring;
The wizard spells about her wail and croon
      With gathering ring.

Swiftly her arms they bound in gossamer,
With elvish lures they held her soul in thrall;
With wizard sorceries enveloped her
      Past cry or call.

A passing shepherd caught his breath to see
A golden mist of moving wings and lights
Swirl upwards past the red moon eeriely
      To starlit heights.

While far off carollings half drowned a cry,
Mournful, remote, of 'Mother, Mother dear,'
Floating across the drifting haze, – a sigh
      'Farewell, Farewell!'

In the small hours of Beltane or May Day, it was once the custom to light up great bonfires on the hills of the Highlands – a relic of sun-worship as old as the Druids. Mr Gilbert Sheldon tells me, indeed, that as late as 1899 he saw the hills round Glengariff ablaze with them. They must be kindled with what is called need-fire. And need-fire is made by nine men twisting a wimble of wood in a balk of oak until the friction makes sparks fly. With these they ignite dry agaric, a fungus that grows on birch-trees (which have a highly inflammable bark), and soon the blaze is reddening the complete countryside under the night-sky. Need-fire in a window-nook or carried in a lantern is – like iron – an invincible defence against witches and witchcraft. Beltane cakes – to be eaten whilst squatting on the hills, or dancing and watching the fire – are made out of a caudle of eggs, butter, oatmeal and milk.

'No rowan in her hair'

So potent is the flower or berry or wood of the rowan or witch-wood or quicken or whicken-tree or mountain ash against the wiles of the elf-folk, that dairymaids use it for cream-stirrers and cow-herds for a switch.

> Rowan-tree and red thread
> Gar the Witches tyne their speed.

136

'True Thomas'

There are four early copies in handwriting – two of them written about 1450 – of a rhymed romance telling how Thomas in his youth, while dreaming day-dreams under the Eildon Tree, was met and greeted by the Queen of fair Elfland. The ballad on p. 158 has been passed on from mouth to mouth.

Up to our own grandmothers' day, at least, this Thomas Rhymour of Ercildoune – a village not far distant from where the Leader joins the Tweed – was famous as a Wise One and a Seer (a See-er – with the inward eye). He lived seven centuries ago, between 1210 and 1297. Years after he had returned from Elfland – as the ballad tells – while he sat feasting in his Castle, news was brought to him that a hart and a hind, having issued out of the forest, were to be seen stepping fair and softly down the stony street of the town, to the marvel of the people. At this, Thomas at once arose from among his guests; left the feast; made down to the street; followed after these strange summoners: and was seen no more.

'Ilka tett', line 7, means every twist or plait; a 'fairlie', stanza 12, is a wonder, mystery, marvel; and the 'coat' in the last stanza, being of 'even cloth', was finer than the finest *napless* damask.

So, too, Young Tamlane, when a boy 'just turned of nine', was carried off by the Elfin Queen:

> Ae fatal morning I went out
>   Dreading nae injury,
> And thinking lang fell soun asleep
>   Beneath an apple tree.
>
> Then by it came the Elfin Queen
>   And laid her hand on me;
> And from that time since ever I mind
>   I've been in her companie . . .

He seems to have been an outlandish and unhuman creature – if this next rhyme tells of him truly (*gait*, meaning road; *pin* (?) knife [1]; *coft*, bought; *moss*, peat-bog; and *boonmost* – you can guess):

> Tam o' the linn came up the gait,
> Wi' twenty puddings on a plate,
> And every pudding had a pin,
> 'We'll eat them a',' quo' Tam o' the linn.
>
> Tam o' the linn had nae breeks to wear,
> He coft him a sheep's-skin to make him a pair,
> The fleshy side out, the woolly side in,
> 'It's fine summer cleeding,' quo' Tam o' the linn.

1. *Pin*, a friend tells me, here means, not a knife, but a peg or skcwer. ' I remember,' he writes, 'hearing my grandmother talk of the killing of the "Mert" – the cow killed at Martinmas for the family larder – and the making of black puddings from the blood. Each pudding was fastened with a *pin* . . . and all were hung on a pole, called, I think, the perk, and suspended from the kitchen ceiling, where they gleamed brown-black in the lamplight.'

Tam o' the linn he had three bairns,
They fell in the fire, in each others' arms;
'Oh,' quo' the boonmost, 'I've got a het skin';
'It's hetter below,' quo' Tam o' the linn.

Tam o' the linn gaed to the moss,
To seek a stable to his horse;
The moss was open, and Tam fell in,
'I've stabled mysel',' quo' Tam o' the linn.

137

'I made a garland for her head'

... Linen was her small camise,
White with ermine her pelisse,
    She had a silken gown.
Tiger lilies were her hose,
Flowers o' may her little shoes,
    Fitted tightly on.

For a girdle, tender leaves,
When the weather rained, grew green,
    Buttoned up with gold.
Cords of flowers swung above
Her wallet shapen all for love,
    And Love the giver bold.

On a mule she rode along,
And the mule was silver shod,
    Saddle gold inlaid;
On a crupper right behind
Three rose trees stood up in line
    For to give her shade.

She went riding through the mead;
All the knights who met her steed
   Bowed with courtly state.
'Lady fair, whence are you sped?'
'I am the boast of France,' she said,
   'Of renowned estate.

'My father is the nightingale
Who sings within the bosky dale
   On the tallest tree.
The mermaiden my mother is,
She who sings her melodies
   In the deep salt sea.'

'Lady, blessed was your birth,
Parentage of famous worth
   And renowned estate.
Would that God our Father dear
Gave you for to be my peer
   And my wedded mate.'

From the French, of the twelfth century; and translated by
Claude Colleer Abbot.

138

This song is from *Comus*, a masque written by Milton for the
entertainment of the Earl of Bridgewater, lord lieutenant of Wales,
at Ludlow Castle in 1634. That Castle's Hall is now open to the
sky – 'the lightning shines there; snow burdens the ivy.' From a
neighbouring room the two princes, Edward V and his brother,
went to their violent death in the Tower. Below the ruinous Castle
flow together the Teme and the Corve, on their way to the Severn
– of which 'fair' Sabrina, the daughter of Estrildis, is the Nymph,
she having been drowned in its waters by Guendolen, the jealous
queen of Locrine the son of Brut. Estrildis herself, the daughter of
King Humber, 'so farre excelled in bewtie, that none was then
lightly found unto her comparable, for her skin was so whyte that

scarcely the fynest kind of Ivorie that might be found, nor the snowe lately fallen downe from the Elament, nor the Lylles did passe the same.'

Milton's poems – *Lycidas*, for instance – are occasionally 'difficult' not so much because they are deep as because they refer to some ancient myth or legend. In the lines I have omitted from No. 138 are many such references awaiting the reader – one to the following tale of Glaucus, for example:

There is a secret herb which, if nibbled by fish already gasping to death in our air, gives them the power and cunning to slip back through the grasses into their waters again. Of this herb Glaucus tasted, and instantly his eyes dazzled in desire to share their green transparent deeps. Whereupon the laughing divinities of the rivers gave him sea-green hair sleeking the stream, fins and a fish's tail, and feasted him merrily. His story is told by Keats in the third book of his *Endymion*, while Leucothea's, another reference, is to be found in the fifth of the *Odyssey*. As for the Sirens, here is the counsel Circe gave Ulysses, the while his seamen lay asleep the night after they had returned in safety from Pluto's dismal mansions:

> . . . And then observe: They sit amidst a mead,
> And round about it runs a hedge or wall
> Of dead men's bones, their withered skins and all
> Hung all along upon it; and these men
> Were such as they had fawned into their fen,
>
> And then their skins hung on their hedge of bones.
> Sail by them therefore, thy companions
> Beforehand causing to stop every ear
> With sweet soft wax, so close that none may hear
> A note of all their charmings . . .

139

These songs are from the last act of *A Midsummer Night's Dream* – the Duke and his guests are retired, and now sleep far from Life's Play; and Puck and the fairies are abroad in his palace.

'I am sent with broome before'

When the cock begins to crow,
And the embers leave to glow,
And the owl crîes, Tu-whit – Tu-whoo,
  When crickets do sing
  And mice roam about,
  And midnight bells ring
  To call the devout:
When the lazy lie sleeping
And think it no harm,
Their zeal is so cold
And their beds are so warm.
When the long – long lazy slut
Has not made the parlour clean,
No water on the hearth is put,
But all things in disorder seem;
Then we trip it round the room
And make like bees a drowsy hum.
Be she Betty, Nan, or Sue,
We make her of another hue
  And pinch her black and blue.

But when the Puritans came in, the fairies (naturally) fled away.
And Richard Corbet bewailed their exile:

  'Farewell, rewards and fairies!'
    Good housewives now may say,
  For now foul sluts in dairies
    Do fare as well as they.
  And though they sweep their hearths no less
    Than maids were wont to do,
  Yet who of late, for cleanliness,
    Finds sixpence in her shoe? . . .

At morning and at evening both
   You merry were and glad;
So little care of sleep or sloth
   These pretty ladies had;
When Tom came home from labour,
   Or Ciss to milking rose,
Then merrily merrily went their tabour
   And nimbly went their toes.

Witness those rings and roundelays
   Of theirs, which yet remain,
Were footed in Queen Mary's days
   On many a grassy plain;
But since of late, Elizabeth,
And later, James came in,
They never danced on any heath
   As when the time hath been.

For times change, and with them changes the direction of man's imagination. He turns his questing thought now this way, now that; and though our learned dictionaries may maintain that fairy rings are but brighter circles in green grass formed by 'certain fungi, especially *marasmius oreades*' – who knows? –

He that sees blowing the wild wood tree,
And peewits circling their watery glass,
Dreams about Strangers that yet may be
   Dark to our eyes, Alas!

After all, Geoffrey Chaucer, even in *his* distant day, lamented that England was forsaken of the Silent Folk. Whisper, and they will return – bringing with them Prince Oberon, who 'is of heyght but of III fote, and crokyed shulderyd . . . And yf ye speke to hym, ye are lost for ever.'

140

Another mere fragment – from p. 182 of Mr C. M. Doughty's Play, entitled *The Cliffs*. For the supreme gifts bestowed on the

world by this great traveller and poet, the reader must seek out
not only this volume, but his *Arabia Deserta*, and his *Dawn in
Britain*.

'All in their watchet cloaks'

Nan Page (my daughter) and my little sonne,
And three or foure more of their growth, wee'l dress
Like Urchins, Ouphes, and Fairies, greene and white,
With rounds of waxen Tapers on their heads,
And rattles in their hands . . .

The Merry Wives of Windsor

141

In his book on English Poesy, Puttenham, who was born about
1520, says that a poet of the name of Gray won the esteem of
Henry VIII and the Duke of Somerset for 'making certeine merry
ballades, whereof one chiefly was, "the hunte is up, the hunte is
up."' Henry VIII, moreover, was himself a versifier, and a musician.
He 'did not only sing his part *sure*, but also composed services for
his Chappel of four, five, and six parts.' Here is the first stanza of
one of his poems:

As the holly groweth green,
And never changeth hue,
So I am, ever hath been
Unto my lady true . . .

which, with others equally surprising in sentiment, may be found in
full in that casket of antiquities, *Early English Lyrics*.

Queen Elizabeth inherited her father's pleasure in music and
poetry. She played 'excellently well' on the virginal – an oblong
quill-plucked instrument with a keyboard, like a diminutive piano-
forte or harpsicord, and of a tone 'small, but extraordinarily clear
and bright in quality'. She also made verses:

The doubt of future foes
    Exiles my present joy,
And wit me warnes to shun such snares,
    As threaten mine annoy.

For falsehood now doth flow,
    And subject faith doth ebbe,
Which would not be if reason rul'd,
    Or wisdome wev'd the webbe.

– and one cannot regret their brevity.

143

When John Peel, his hunting over, was carried at last to his grave, 'the old huntsmen gathered round it in a solid ring, each holding his dog by the slip.' And when the final *Ashes to ashes, dust to dust*, was pronounced, the whole company scattered 'their sprigs of rosemary over the coffin, then raising their heads, gave a simultaneous *Yo-ho! Tally-ho!* the sound of which became heightened by the dogs joining their voices, as they rung the last cry over their "earthed" companion.'

148

'A full fayre tyme'

What wonder May was welcome in medieval days – after the long winters and the black cold nights, when roads were all but impassable, and men, 'despisinge schetes' and nightgear, went to their naked beds with nought but the stars or a dip for candle and maybe their own bones and a scatter of straw for warmth? Is not 'Loud sing, Cuckoo!' our oldest song? Nevertheless, 'ne'er cast a clout . . .' for though

March will search ye;
    And April try;
May will tell ye
    Whether ye'll live, or die.

149

Only the sound remains
Of the old mill;
Gone is the wheel;
On the prone roof and walls the nettle reigns.

Water that toils no more
Dangles white locks
And, falling, mocks
The music of the mill-wheel's busy roar ...

Only the idle foam
Of water falling
Changelessly calling,
Where once men had a work-place and a home.

EDWARD THOMAS

150

'The ample heaven'

The unthrifty sun shot vital gold,
    A thousand pieces;
And heaven its azure did unfold
    Chequered with snowy fleeces;
    The air was all in spice,
        And every bush
A garland wore; thus fed my eyes,
    But all the earth lay hush.

Only a little fountain lent
    Some use for ears,
And on the dumb shades language spent –
    The music of her tears.

HENRY VAUGHAN

'*The time sa tranquil is and still*'

Clear had the day been from the dawn,
    All chequered was the sky,
Thin clouds, like scarves of cobweb lawn,
    Veiled heaven's most glorious eye.

The wind had no more strength than this,
    – That leisurely it blew –
To make one leaf the next to kiss
    That closely by it grew.

The rills, that on the pebbles played,
    Might now be heard at will;
This world the only music made,
    Else everything was still . . .

MICHAEL DRAYTON

153

Nor – says John Bunyan:

Nor let them fall under Discouragement
Who at their Horn-book stick, and time hath spent
Upon (their) A, B, C while others do
Into their Primer, or their Psalter go.
Some boys with difficulty do begin
Who in the end, the Bays, and Lawrel win.

On the other hand:

> Some Boys have Wit enough to sport and play,
> Who at their Books are Block-heads day by day.
> Some men are arch enough at any Vice,
> But Dunces in the way to Paradise.

Blockhead one may be, and in some respects almost certainly *is*, but to add books to one's 'sport and play' is to add an interest and delight whose wellspring will never fail. In this too we are incalculably better off than were our great-grandfathers when *they* were young. Ballads, chapbooks and broadsides, even for multitudes of those who could read, were once almost the only literature available. And as late as the early years of the nineteenth century the companion pieces that follow were the kind of reading their elders considered proper for children. The first comes from 'The Half Holiday Task Book or Mirror of Mind':

'A Gentleman met a little Girl in the street selling watercresses; and although he did not just then want any cresses he was so pleased with her neat, clean and modest appearance that he kindly gave her a penny; which of course greatly delighted her, so she went along full of gratitude crying "Water-cresses! Water-cresses!" and she soon sold all her stock. Now when she went home, her mother thought she had been asking more for her cresses than she ought because she had so much money; but the little girl told the truth, for

> *'Tis a sin, to cheat one's mother,*
> *As great as cheating any other.'*

The second has a less happy but not less edifying ending; its title being, 'Of the Boy and his Mother'.

'A Boy having stollen his School-fellows Horn-book at School, brought it to his Mother: By whom being not chastised, he played the Thief daily more and more. In process of time, he began to steal great things; at last being apprehended of the Magistrate, was led to execution: But his Mother following and crying out, he entreated the Serjeants that they would permit him to whisper in her Ear, who permitting him, the Mother hastening laid her Ear to her

Son's Mouth, he bites off a piece of his Mother's Ear with his Teeth.

'When his Mother and the rest rated at him, not only as being a Thief but also ungracious towards his own Mother, he said, "She is the cause of my undoing, for if she had punished me for stealing the Horn-book, I had not proceeded to greater things, nor been led to my Execution." '

Maybe. Still, the action *was* ungracious, and a boy who could steal a horn-book which was not only a lesson book but only worth about a ha'penny, was hardly a promising lad. Nowadays that stolen horn-book would be worth its weight in gold – they are so rare: though many millions of them must have been sold and used between 1450 and the beginning of the nineteenth century. They were usually made of wood but sometimes of cardboard or leather or metal or ivory. There is still in existence a delicate little horn-book of filigree silver, which was used by Queen Elizabeth. In shape they resembled a small oblong hand-glass – with a hole through the handle. A piece of string was passed through the hole, and the horn-book was tied round its owner's waist.

> He was never free
> From his A-B-C,
> A doleful thing for a child to be!

Fixed and fitted to one side of it was an oblong strip of parchment, card, or paper, containing the Criss-cross-row (the alphabet with a cross before A), a few digraphs, *ab*, *ba*, and so on, 'In the name of the Father ... ,' and the Lord's Prayer. This strip was protected from grubby fingers by a piece of transparent horn. Hence the name. Apart from horn-books, the alphabet was also stamped out in gilded gingerbread; so having learned your alphabet, you digested it.

After the horn-book followed the battledore, and 'slates' came in when battledores were going out; the reference to them, at any rate, in the following extract from a little paper-bound book entitled *Henry* of 1817 suggests a novelty:

'Henry was a little boy about five years old; and one day, whilst his mother was busy at work, he stood by her side, and amused himself with trying to write upon a pretty little slate, that had been given to him for being a good boy; it had a red leather frame, and at the top was a little hole through which a string was put, with a slate pencil tied to the end of it, for Henry to write with; and there was another bit of string put through the same hole, with a little piece of sponge tied to it, that Henry might rub out those letters he made badly: and after he had written on his slate till he was tired, he left off, and stood still a little time, and then he said to his mother, "Mother, I am just thinking that I wish I knew where all the things in the world come from, and what is the use of them": and his mother said, "I believe there are very few people that know so much as that, my dear; but you may, by paying attention, learn the use of a great many . . ."'

There we must leave him – on the Royal Road to Learning. The one thing, however, the vast majority of these bygone tales suggest is that their authors considered children to be little better than half-witted. Any stuffing, they thought (provided it was indigestible) was good enough for goslings; and a glance at some of the children's books of to-day will prove that this hideous falsity is not yet extinct. If every writer of learning or imagination made it his happy privilege to write but one book for the young on his own beloved subject, and put his *whole mind* into it, just as Faraday wrote his *History of a Candle* – what joy there would be in store for the children yet unborn.

Little articles, like horn-books, rattles, mugs, intended for work-a-day human use, at first crude and simple in workmanship (see Robinson Crusoe's entries in his Diary for January of the third year of his becoming a castaway), are apt as time goes by, to become more and more delicate and curious. As long, that is, as they are made by hand (so that a man can put his pleasure as well as his labour into them) and are not turned out by the thousand from a machine, which may have beauty and unfailing skill, but is senseless.

In any case they remain lively little reminders of their own day and fashion and are well worth a close examination when found – antiquated needle-cases, old keys (great and small), seals, thimbles, bobbins, bodkins, penknives, scissors, watch-keys, perfume bottles,

shoe-buckles, snuffers, patch-boxes; even old kitchen utensils –
candlesticks, gridirons, tinder boxes, roasting jacks, warming pans,
skillets, chafing dishes. Indeed there was a large and exciting volume
published a few years ago on the subject of *Pins and Pin-Cushions*
alone. Whatever concerns one's childhood, too, becomes enriched
and endeared in memory, and even the most trivial objects that
have passed out of common use and have become old-fashioned or
antiquated, seem to belong to the childhood of humanity itself.
Who would not treasure a fragment of Noah's Ark, a lock of
Absalom's hair, Prester John's thumb-ring, Scheherezade's night-
lamp, a glove of Caesar's or one of King Alfred's burnt cakes?

But to come back to the reader in his shadie nooke:

> Tales of my Nursery! shall that still loved spot,
> That window corner, ever be forgot,
> Where through the woodbine – when with upward ray
> Gleamed the last shadow of departing day –
> Still did I sit, and with unwearied eye,
> Read while I wept, and scarcely paused to sigh!
> In that gay drawer, with fairy fictions stored,
> When some new tale was added to my hoard,
> While o'er each page my eager glance was flung,
> 'Twas but to learn what female fate was sung;
> If no sad maid the castle shut from light,
> I heeded not the giant and the knight.
>   Sweet Cinderella, even before the ball,
> How did I love thee – ashes, rags, and all!
> What bliss I deemed it to have stood beside,
> On every virgin when thy shoe was tried!
> How longed to see thy shape the slipper suit!
> But, dearer than the slipper, loved the foot.

'Or the Streete cryes all about'

A friend whose judgment in such matters it would be mere vanity
to question assures me that this rhyme 'O for a Booke' is nothing

but a 'modern imposture', and its spelling all sham. So be it: and yet even at that there is a warm breath of Summer in it and a green and shady tree, while the street cries it refers to are at any rate as old as Babylon.

According to *London Lickpenny* the cries most audible in his time—the fifteenth century—were 'Hot Pease!' 'Hot fine Oatcakes!' 'Whiting, maids, whitings!' 'Hot codlings!' 'Maribones! Maribones!' 'Have you any Old Boots?' 'Buy a Mat!'—with a general hullabaloo of 'What d'ye lack? What d'ye lack?' and an occasional bawling of 'Clubs!' to summon the tag, rag and bobtail to a row.

Many of the old cries were in rhyme.

Screens:

> I have Screenes, if you desier
> To keepe your Butey from the fire.

Oranges:

> Fine Sevil oranges! Fine lemmons, fine!
> Round, sound, and tender, inside and rine.
> One pin's prick will their vertue show;
> Tell their liquor by their weight, as anyone may
> know.

Cherries:

> Round and sound,
> Two-pence a pound,
> Cherries, rare ripe cherries!

Cherries dangling on a stick:

> Cherries a ha'penny a stick:
> Come and pick! Come and pick!
> Cherries big as plums! Who comes, who comes?

There were three rhymed cries for Hot Cross Buns alone:

> One a penny, poker,
> Two a penny, tongs,
> Three a penny, fire-irons,
> Hot Cross Buns!

One a penny, two a penny,
　　Hot Cross Buns,
Sugar 'em and butter 'em,
　　And stick 'em in your muns [mouths].

One-a-penny, two-a-penny, hot-cross-buns
If your daughters will not eat 'em, why, then, give 'em to your
　　sons;
But you haven't any of these pretty little elves,
You can't do no better than to eat 'em up yourselves.
　　One-a-penny, two-a-penny, hot-cross-buns:
　　All hot, hot, hot, all hot.

Of singing cries, nowadays we may still hear in the sunny summer London streets the sweet and doleful strains of 'Won't you
buy my sweet blooming lavender: Sixteen branches a penny!' And
in the dusk of November the muffin-man's bell. Besides these, we
have 'Rag-a'-bone!' 'Milk-o!' 'Any scissors to grind?' 'Clo'
props!' 'Water-cresses!' and, as I remember years ago,

　　Young lambs to sell, white lambs to sell;
　　If I'd as much money as I could tell
　　I wouldn't be crying, Young lambs to sell!

154

　　Who liveth so merry in all this land
　　As doth the poor widdow that selleth the sand?
　　And ever she singeth as I can guesse,
　　Will you buy any sand, any sand, mistress?

　　The broom-man maketh his living most sweet,
　　With carrying of brooms from street to street;
　　Who would desire a pleasanter thing,
　　Than all the day long to doe nothing but sing?

> The chimney-sweeper all the long day,
> He singeth and sweepeth the soote away;
> Yet when he comes home, altho' he be weary,
> With his sweet wife he maketh full merry . . .

– which carries with it a faint, a very faint, rumour of William Blake.

155

'*With hey! with how! with hoy!*'

In *Rustic Speech and Folklore* Mrs Wright gives the decoys with which the country people all over England beguile their beasts and poultry into 'shippon, sty, or pen'; or holla them on their way, but much, I have found, depends on him who hollas!

For *Cows*: Coop! Cush, cush! – While the milkmaid calls – Hoaf! Hobe! Mull! Proo! Proochy! Prut!

For *Calves*: Moodie! Mog, mog, mog! Pui-ho! Sook, sook!

For *Sheep*: Co-hobe! Ovey!

For *Pigs*: Check-check! Cheat! Dack, dack! Giss! or Gissy! Lix! Ric-sic! Shug, shug, shug! Tantassa, tantassa pig, tow a row, a row! Tig, tig, tig!

For *Turkeys*: Cobbler! Peet, peet, peet! Pen! Pur, pur, pur!

For *Geese*: Fly-laig! Gag, gag, gag! Ob-ee! White-hoddy!

For *Ducks*: Bid, bid, bid! Diddle! Dill, dill! Wid! Wheetie!

For *Pigeons:* Pees! Pod!

And for *Rabbits*: Map!

> On Winter mornings when the air is still
> The Ploughman's cries come floating down the hill,
> Ge-e-e-e Up! Ge-e-ee Whoa
> The selfsame sharp and throaty cries are they –
> The teamsters used in Julius Caesar's day –
> Ge-e-e-e Up! Ge-e-e-e Whoa!

Nothing is changed, since tillage first began
The same brown earth has yielded food to man.

Nothing is changed – save ploughman, team and share:
A thousand furrows have been made just there;

And every time, with cautious sidelong looks,
Have followed, close behind, the hungry rooks.

And every time the team was kept in hand
By those two potent phrases of command –
   Ge-e-e-e Up! Ge-e-e-e Whoa!
Which every horse on earth can understand
From Christiana to Van Dieman's Land,
   Ge-e-e-e Up! Ge-e-e-e Whoa!

E. V. LUCAS

'Yea, and I do vow unto thee,' cried the voice out of the rock; 'call unto them but in their own names and language, and the strong and delicate creatures of the countries of the mind will flock into the living field of thy vision, and above the waters will befall the secret singing of birds, and thou shalt be a pilgrim. Mark how intense a shadow dwells upon this stone! Therein too lurk marvels to be seen.' The voice ceased, and I heard nothing but the tapping of a fragment of dry lichen which in the draught of the hot air caused by the burning sunlight stirred between rock and sand. And I cried, 'O unfortunate one, I thirst!'

156

'A poor thing,' as Audrey says, but homely and melodious and once *some*body's own: such a somebody as inscribed on the walls of Burford Church:

> . . . Love made me Poet
> And this I writt,
> My harte did do yt
> And not my witt.

It must be confessed however [in 1928], that it was not Audrey who said in the play what she was made to say here, but Touchstone; and that he did not say: 'A *poor* thing' but an *ill-favoured*!

> O Memory, thou strange deceiver!
> Who can trust her? How believe her?
> While she keeps in one same pack
> Dream and real upon her back.
> When I call her, want her most,
> She's gone wandering and is lost.
> She's capricious as the wind,
> Yet what sweets she leaves behind.
> Where – without her – I? for lo,
> When she's gone I too must go!

159

'*There is a Garden in her face*'

Thomas Campion was 'borne upon Ash Weddensday being the twelft day of February. An. Rg. Eliz. nono' – 1567. He had one sister, Rose. He was educated at Peterhouse, Cambridge, and this was his yearly allowance of clothes: 'A gowne, a cap, a hat, ii dubletes, ii payres of hose, iiii payres of netherstockes, vi payre of shoes, ii shirts, and two bandes.' He was allowed also one quire of paper every quarter; and a half a pound of candles every fortnight from Michaelmas to Lady Day. He studied law, may for a time have fought as a soldier in France, and became a physician. He died on March 1, 1620, and was buried on the same day at St Dunstan's in the West, Fleet Street, the entry in the register under that date being 'Thomas Campion, doctor of Phisicke, was buried.'

I have taken these particulars from Mr S. P. Vivian's edition of his poems, because it is pleasant to share even this of the little that is known of a man who was not only a fine and original poet and 'a most curious metrist' – though for two centuries a forgotten one – but also because he was one of the chief songwriters in the great age of English Music. Like all good craftsmen, he endeavoured to do his work 'well, surely, cleanly, workmanly, substantially, curiously, and sufficiently,' as did the glaziers of King's College Chapel, which is distant but a kingfisher's flight over a strip of lovely water from his own serene Peterhouse. It seems a little curious that being himself a lover of music he should have at first detested rhyming in verse. But he lived none the less to write such delicate rhymed poems as this.

In the preface to his *Book of Ayres*, he says, 'I have chiefly aymed to couple my Words and Notes *lovingly* together, which will be much for him to doe that hath not power over both.'

161

I see His blood upon the rose
And in the stars the glory of His eyes,
His body gleams amid eternal snows,
His tears fall from the skies.

I see His face in every flower;
The thunder and the singing of the birds
Are but His voice – and carven by His power
Rocks are His written words.

All pathways by His feet are worn,
His strong heart stirs the ever-beating sea,
His crown of thorns is twined with every thorn,
His cross is every tree.

JOSEPH PLUNKETT

163

'These flowers, as in their causes, sleep'

– while, also flowers may themselves be the *causes* of poems, as, in a degree, a rain-bow'd dewdrop in a buttercup is of the buttercup's causing.

In May, when sea-winds pierced our solitudes,
I found the fresh Rhodora in the woods,
Spreading its leafless blooms in a damp nook,
To please the desert and the sluggish brook.
The purple petals, fallen in the pool,
Made the black water with their beauty gay;
Here might the red-bird come his plumes to cool,
And court the flower that cheapens his array.
Rhodora! Let the sages ask thee why
This charm is fasted on the earth and sky . . .
Why thou wert there, O rival of the rose!
I never thought to ask, I never knew;
But, in my simple ignorance, suppose
The self-same Power that brought me there brought you . . .

RALPH WALDO EMERSON

And here anemone and cyclamen – in an enchanting little poem
of but the day before yesterday:

Long ago I went to Rome
    As pilgrims go in Spring,
Journeying through the happy hills
    Where nightingales sing,
And where the blue anemones
    Drift among the pines
Until the woods creep down into
    A wilderness of vines.

Now every year I go to Rome
    As lovers go in dreams,
To pick the fragrant cyclamen,
    To bathe in Sabine streams,
And come at nightfall to the city
    Across the shadowy plain,
And hear through all the dusty streets
    The waterfalls again.

MARGARET CECILIA FURSE

406

'The Phœnix builds her spicy nest'

The Phœnix, in faith rather than by sight, is thus described by Pliny: 'She is as big as an eagle, in colour yellow, and bright as gold, namely all about the neck, the rest of the bodie a deep red purple; the taile azure blue, intermingled with feathers among of rose carnation colour: and the head bravely adorned with a crest and pennache finely wrought, having a tuft and plume thereupon right faire and goodly to be seene.'

Her life is but three hundred and nine years less in duration than that of the many-centuried patriarch Methuselah. When the lassitude of age begins to creep upon her, she wings across sea and land to the sole Arabian Tree. There she builds a nest of aromatic twigs, cassia and frankincense, and enkindling it with her own dying ardour she is consumed to ashes. And yet – while still they are of a heat beyond the tempering of the sun that shines down on them from the heavens, they magically stir, take form and re-awaken; and she arises to life renewed – in her gold, her rose carnation, her purple and azure blue.

The Phœnix

O blest unfabled Incense-Tree,
That burns in glorious Araby,
With red scent chalicing the air
Till earth-life grow Elysian there!

Half buried to her flaming breast
In this bright tree, she makes her nest,
Hundred-sunned Phœnix! when she must
Crumble at length to hoary dust!

Her gorgeous death-bed! her rich pyre
Burnt up with aromatic fire!
Her urn, sight-high from spoiler men!
Her birthplace when self-born again!

The mountainless green wilds among,
Here ends she her unechoing song!
With amber trees and odorous sighs
Mourned by the desert where she dies! . . .

GEORGE DARLEY

164

This and No. 348 are but the merest fragments of the *Faerie Queene*; but they reveal what an echoing mutable melody are its words. And were ever light and colour so living, natural and crystal clear? Reading this verse, hearing its sounds and sharing its vision in the imagination, you cannot think Thomas Nash was too fantastical when he wrote: 'Poetry is the Honey of all Flowers, the Quintessence of all Sciences, the Marrow of Art and the very Phrase of Angels.' Indeed, as Spenser's epitaph in Westminster Abbey says of him, he was the Prince of Poets of his time, and poet of poets he has always remained. John Keats, when he was a boy, used to sit in a little summer-house at Enfield with his schoolfellow, Cowden Clarke, drinking in his honeyed verse, and laying up store of purest English for his own brief life's matchless work. So, too, Abraham Cowley:

'How this love [for poetry] came to be produced in me so early is a hard question. I believe I can tell the particular little chance that filled my head first with such chimes of verse as have never since left ringing there. For I remember when I began to read, and to take some pleasure in it, there was wont to lie in my mother's parlour (I know not by what accident, for she herself never in her life read any book but of devotion), but there was wont to lie Spenser's works; this I happened to fall upon, and was infinitely delighted with the stories of the knights and giants and monsters and brave houses which I found everywhere there (though my understanding had little to do with all this); and by degrees with the tinkling of the rhyme and dance of the numbers, so that I think I had read him all over before I was twelve years old . . .'

167
'The busy woodpecker'

The birds of England have few country names by comparison
with her wild flowers; and in this the green Woodpecker and the
Long-tailed Tit are easily first. But no wonder. For the woodpecker
– plumage, laughter, and 'habits' – is a captivating creature; and
to anybody who cares to watch a living nimble delightful thing at
all, even a glimpse of a Long-tailed Tit is an event. To see *one*,
indeed, is usually to see a complete family. You hear their small
shrill calling, look up, and lo! – scattering from tree to tree they
flit, with their loose, grey, ruffish feathers, small hooked beaks,
and long slim tails, searching for caterpillars and tiny beetles,
clinging to spray or twig wrong-side-up and upside-down, noisy,
merry, alert. And then – all gone, vanished, fled! Into some other
green garden – as momentary as a rainbow.

Among the green woodpecker's country names are Sprite,
Hickway, Woodspite, Popinjay, Yaffle, Highhoe, Rindtabberer,
Yaffingale, Green peck, Yuckel, Cutbill, Rain Pie, Nickerpecker,
and Woodweele; while the long-tailed Tit, who is cousin to the
Blue or Tom, Cole, Marsh, Great Ox-eyed, and Crested Tits, and
known (to the ornithologist) as *Acredula Caudata*, of the family
Paridae, is also called Millithrums, Hedgejug, Long-tailed Mufflin
or Capon or Mag or Pie or Pod; Huck-muck, Mum-ruffin, Juffit,
Poke-pudding, Bum barrel and Bottle-Tom.

Wild birds of course *derive* their names – varying from county
to county – from their songs, colours, customs, nests and haunts.
But it is curious how capricious the choice has been. For while
some of the most familiar birds – robin, sparrow, thrush, nightingale, blackbird – have few names; others hardly less familiar have
many, like the Sand-piper, who is known to his friends all over the
country either as Watery pleeps, or Killie-leepsie, or Willy-wicket,
or Dickie-di-dee, or Sandie, or Water junket, or Skittery deacon,
or Bundie, or Steenie Pouter; or like the Barn Owl, who is also
Church Owl, Roarer, Billy Wix, Pudge, Cherubim, Outlet and

Povey. Yet the Kingfisher is merely the Dipper, though– to make up this – there is a pleasant little story about it in connection with Noah.

Then again, though the Wheat-ear's 'haunts' – old ruins, grave-yards, cairns – 'has gotten it a bad name', there seems little to grumble at in Wittol, Chock, Clodhopper, Jobbler, and Coney chuck: the Goldfinch is also King Harry, Speckled Dick, Fools-coat, and Sweet William; the long-tailed Duck is Coal-and-Candle-light or Caloo; the small-songed clumsy-toed but dainty-coloured Chaffinch is Pink-twink, Shell-apple, Chaffy, and Charbob; while that remarkably officious, multitudinous, pugnacious and amusing bird the starling is nothing much more than Jacob or Gyp.

Sea birds commonly have as many names as royal princesses, and fishermen keep an eye on them, both for luck and the weather. But there is no more room – except for a legend that Nature when she had finished the Great Northern Diver discovered that she had left out its legs, and then in a pet flung any sort of a pair after it; while on the other hand it is said that when the song thrush reaches its teens it sheds its old legs and grows new ones.

'*A spirit interfused around,*
A thrilling, silent life'

'The afternoon sunshine flooded the wide plain, and as he walked through it he seemed to be walking through a kind of sea that was dancing with millions and millions of little golden sparks of light. The grasshoppers shrilled like birds; all the soft din that filled his ears came from insects; it was as if the world had been abandoned by everything else. Sometimes, where there was a flat stone or a bare patch of sandy soil, a lizard or a snake glittered in ecstatic trance. They never moved, even when he passed close by them. And Demophon suddenly knew that he and the snakes and the lizards and the grasshoppers and the butterflies and even the earth over which he walked, were one. And he knew at the same time that what united them was just this spirit which had guarded him by the pool. It was in this they all drew their breath and had their common life. It was the spirit of love – but hatred and fear were death. It was not a very clear thought doubtless; perhaps it was not even a thought at all; and yet it lit up his mind, and something else that was not his mind. His very body was lost in its happiness, so that he passed swiftly across the round ground, as he had seen birds sliding down the air on motionless wide wings.

What was it – this something that was not his mind, that was even closer to him than his mind? It dwelt in him: it was the sadness which rose and mingled with the beauty that flowed in through his eyes from the summer fields, and through his ears from the wind and the sea: it was his longing for his lost playmate, his love for those spotted snakes, his friendship with this tiny flying beetle that had settled on his hand. It dwelt in him; but might it not be truer to say that it *was* Demophon? His home really was, then, in those far-off islands in the West; and he was not setting out on a journey, but going back, going home. A sudden mist gathered in his eyes, and he shook his head half angrily. How foolish he was getting, and how babyish! And looking up he saw that the dark, wooded slopes of Helikon were close at hand.'

From *Demophon* by FORREST REID

168

'*If I were as wise as they,*
I would stray apart and brood'

'Twas at the season when the Earth upsprings
From slumber; as a spherèd angel's child,
Shadowing its eyes with green and golden wings,
    Stands up before its mother bright and mild,
Of whose soft voice the air expectant seems –
So stood before the sun, which shone and smiled
    To see it rise thus joyous from its dreams,

The fresh and radiant Earth. The hoary grove
Waxed green, and flowers burst forth like starry beams;
    The grass in the warm sun did start and move,
And many sea-buds burst under the waves serene.
How many a one, though none be near to love,
    Loves then the shade of his own soul, half seen
In any mirror – or the spring's young minions,
The wingèd leaves amid the copses green:
    How many a spirit then puts on the pinions
Of fancy, and outstrips the lagging blast,
And his own steps, and over wide dominions
    Sweeps in his dream-drawn chariot, far and fast,
More fleet than storms . . .

PERCY BYSSHE SHELLEY

170

The poems of Robert Herrick and of Thomas Campion, though well known in their own day, remained for many years practically unread and forgotten. Thomas Traherne's (who died in 1674) had an even more curious fate, for they were discovered in manuscript and by chance on a bookstall so lately as 1896, and were first taken to be the work of Henry Vaughan. Here is a passage in prose from his *Centuries of Meditation:*

'The corn was orient and immortal wheat which never should be reaped nor was ever sown. I thought it had stood from ever-lasting to everlasting. The dust and stones of the street were as precious as gold; the gates were at first the end of the world. The green trees when I saw them first through one of the gates transported and ravished me; their sweetness and unusual beauty made my heart to leap, and almost mad with ecstasy, they were such strange and wonderful things. The men! oh, what venerable and reverend creatures did the aged seem! Immortal cherubims! And young men glittering and sparkling angels! and maids strange seraphic pieces of life and beauty! Boys and girls tumbling in the

412

street were moving jewels: I knew not that they were born or should die. But all things abided eternally as they were in their proper places. Eternity was manifest in the light of the day, and something infinite behind everything appeared, which talked with my expectation and moved my desire . . .'

172

'But silly we'

This poem, I think, carries with it the thought that in study of that great book, that fair volume, called the World, there is no full stop, no limit, pause, conclusion. Like bees, with their nectar and honeycomb, man stores up his knowledge and experience in books. These and his houses outlast him; the things he makes; and here and there a famous or happy or tragic name is for a while remembered. Else, we are given our brief chequered busy lives – then vanish away, seeming but restless phantoms in Time's panoramic dream. So far at least as this world is concerned. And generations of men – as of the grasses and flowers – follow one upon another.

> Oh, yes, my dear, you have a Mother,
> And she, when young, was loved by another,
> And in that mother's nursery
> Played *her* mamma, like you and me.
> When that mamma was tiny as you
> She had a happy mother too:
> On, on . . . Yes, presto! Puff! Pee-fee! –
> And Grandam Eve and the apple-tree.
> O, into distance, smalling, dimming,
> Think of that endless row of women,
> Like beads, like posts, like lamps, they seem –
> Grey-green willows, and life a stream –
> Laughing and sighing and lovely; and, Oh,
> You to be next in that long row!

And yet, 'But silly we' is true of most of us and of most of our time on earth. As Coventry Patmore says:

> An idle Poet, here and there,
>   Looks round him, but, for all the rest,
> The world, unfathomably fair,
>   Is duller than a witling's jest.
> Love wakes men, once a life-time each;
>   They lift their heavy lids, and look;
> And, lo, what one sweet page can teach
>   They read with joy, then shut the book:
> And some give thanks, and some blaspheme,
>   And most forget; but, either way,
> That and the Child's unheeded dream
>   Is all the light of all their day.

Or again, in the words of Sir John Davies – long since dead:

> ... I know my Soul hath power to know all things,
>   Yet is she blind and ignorant in all:
> I know I am one of Nature's little kings,
>   Yet to the least and vilest things am thrall.
> I know my life's a pain and but a span,
>   I know my sense is mocked with everything;
> And, to conclude, I know myself a man
>   Which is a proud and yet a wretched thing.

175

From an old book entitled *A Posie of Gilloflowers, eche differing from other in Colour and Odour, yet all sweete*. There were memorable and sonorous names for collections of poems in the days of Humfrey Gifford (of whom nothing is known but that he made this Posie) – such as *Wits Commonwealth; The Banket of Sapience; The Paradise of Dainty Devices; A Gorgeous Gallery of Gallant Inventions; A Handfull of Pleasant Delights.*

'Ye buds of Brutus' land'

– sons of those, that is, who, according to the ancient myth were descended from Brut or Brute, the Trojan, lineally descended from 'the demy god Eneas, the sonne of Venus', daughter of Jupiter, the conqueror of Albion and the founder of London, from whose name comes *Britain* and *British*. He landed at Totnes (then in Cornwall) in B.C. in 1136, and was a Jack nonpareil in his dealings with giants; three of his victims being Geomagog, Hastripoldius and Rascalbundy.

'Soldiers are prest'

– that is, seized by the King's men, the press-gangs, and carried away by force to fight in the wars.

'Your Queen'

'To the Most High, Mightie and Magnificent Empresse Renowmed for Pietie, Vertue, and all Gratious Government Elizabeth by the Grace of God Queene of England Fraunce and Ireland and of Virginia.' So runs Spenser's dedication of *The Faerie Queene*, while in *The Shepheardes Calender* for April are the lines:

> See, where she sits upon the grassie greene,
> (O seemely sight)
> Yclad in Scarlot like a mayden Queene,
> And Ermines white.
> Upon her head a Cremosin coronet,
> With Damaske roses and Daffadilles set:
> Bayleaves betweene,
> And Primroses greene
> Embellish the sweete Violet.

At her christening, wrote Edward Hall in his *Chronicles*, she was 'yclad', not in 'scarlot', but in purple:

'The seventh day of September being Sunday, between three and four of the Clock at afternoon, the Queen was delivered of a fair Lady. The Mayor and his brethren, and forty of the chief of the citizens, were commanded to be at the Christening the Wednesday following, upon the which day the Mayor, sir Stephen Pecocke, in a gowne of Crimson Velvet, with his collar of S.S. and all the Aldermen in Scarlet, with collars and chains, and all the council of the city with them, took their barge after dinner, at one of the clock . . . and so rowed to Greenwich, where were many lords, knights, and gentlemen assembled. All the walls between the King's place and the Friers, were hanged with Arras, and all the way strawed with green Rushes: the Friers' Church was also hanged with Arras.

'The Font was of silver, and stood in the midst of the Church, three steps high, which was covered with a fine cloth, and divers gentlemen with aprons, and towels about their necks, gave attendance about it. That no filth should come into the Font, over it hung a square Canopy of crimson Satin, fringed with gold. About it was a rail covered with red silk. Between the choir and the body of the Church, was a close place with a pan of fire, to make the child ready in. When all these things were ordered, the child was brought to the hall, and then every man set forward: First the citizens two and two, then gentlemen, Esquires and Chaplains, next after them the Aldermen, and the Mayor alone; next the Mayor the king's council, the king's Chaplain in copes; then Barons, Bishops, Earls. Then came the Earl of Essex, bearing the covered basins gilt; after him the Marquis of Exeter with the taper of virgin wax; next him the Marquis Dorset, bearing the salt; and behind him the lady Mary of Norfolk, bearing the chrysom which was very rich of pearl and stone.

'The old Duchess of Norfolk bare the child in a Mantle of purple velvet with a long train furred with Ermine. The Duke of Norfolk, with his Marshal's rod went on the right hand of the said Duchess, and the Duke of Suffolk on the left hand, and before them went the officers of arms. The Countess of Kent bare the long train of the child's mantle, and between the Countess of Kent and the child went the Earl of Wiltshire on the right hand and the Earl of Derby on the left hand, supporting the said train. In the midst over the said child was borne a Canopy . . .

'The Godfather was the lord Archbishop of Canterbury: the Godmothers were the old Duchess of Norfolk, and the old Marchioness of Dorset, widows. And the child was named Elizabeth . . . And then the trumpets blew. Then the child was brought up to the altar, and the Gospel said over it: and after that immediately the Archbishop of Canterbury confirmed it, the Marchioness of Exeter being Godmother. Then the Archbishop of Canterbury gave to the Princess a standing cup of gold, fretted with pearl: the Marchioness of Dorset gave three gilt bowls pounced with a cover: the Duchess of Norfolk gave to her a standing cup of gold: and the Marchioness of Exeter gave three standing bowls graven, all gilt with a cover.

'Then was brought in Wafers, Comfits, and Ypocras in such plenty that every man had as much as he would desire. Then they set forwards, the trumpets going before in the same order, toward the king's place as they did when they came thitherward, saving that the gifts that the Godfather and the Godmothers gave were borne before the child . . . And all the one side as they went was full of staff torches to the number of five hundred, borne by the guard and other of the king's servants . . . In this order they brought the princess to the Queen's chamber, and the Mayor and the Aldermen tarried there awhile.

'And at the last the Dukes of Norfok and Suffolk came out from the King, thanking them heartily, and said the King commanded them to give them thanks in his name: and from thence they were had to the cellar to drink, and so went to their Barges . . .'

No other English princess has ever kindled so many poets to her praises. There is a book (now in the Bodleian Library) which was written by her at the age of eleven for a New Year's gift to her step-mother, Queen Katherine Parr. The embroidered binding has 'K-P' in the centre, and this is surrounded by a diamond-shaped design with four flowers of hearts-ease embroidered at the corners. If this work is Elizabeth's, there was reason for her choice of this particular flower. For Queen Katherine, soon after Henry's death in January 1547 (and she had been forced to marry him) returned to her old love, Sir Thomas Seymour, and about April of the same year they were secretly married. He was brutally unkind to her three step-children, Edward, Elizabeth, and Mary, but she herself did her utmost to protect them. She died September 5th, 1548, aged only 36.

A few months before his marriage with her, Sir Thomas (now Lord Admiral) Seymour received the following letter from the Princess Elizabeth herself – then in her fourteenth year. Two years afterwards he was executed for treason.

February 27, 1547.

My Lord Admiral,

The letter you have written to me is the most obliging, and, at the same time, the most eloquent in the world. And as I do not feel myself competent to reply to so many courteous expressions, I shall content myself with unfolding to you, in few words, my real sentiments. I confess to you that your letter, all eloquent as it is, has very much surprised me; for, besides that neither my age nor my inclinations allows me to think of marriage, I never could have believed that any one would have spoken to me of nuptials at a time when I ought to think of nothing but sorrow for the death of my father. And to him I owe so much, that I must have two years at least to mourn for his loss. And how can I make up my mind to become a wife before I shall have enjoyed for some years my virgin state, and arrived at years of discretion . . . Let your highness be well persuaded that though I decline the happiness of becoming your wife I shall never cease to interest myself in all that can crown your merit with glory, and shall ever feel the greatest pleasure in being your servant and good friend.

ELIZABETH

With a slight twist of that kaleidoscope, the imagination, these few historical 'facts' might even now be transmuted into an entrancing folk-tale. But where are the folk?

In *A Midsummer Night's Dream*, Oberon tells Puck how he saw that 'Faire Vestall' again in danger of Love's sharp arrows – and 'The Imperiall Votresse passèd on In maiden meditation, fancy free.' But Shakespeare, if positively invited to Court, it is said, 'was in paine'.

Not so Francis Bacon. 'He gave marks very early of a pregnant and happy disposition, far above his years ... Queen Elizabeth took a particular delight in trying him with questions; and received so much satisfaction from the good sense of his answers that she was wont to call him, in mirth, her young Lord Keeper.' While he was still a boy, she once asked him his age. 'He answered ... that he was just two years younger than her happy reign.'

It was a ready, pretty, yet considered grace-note, and the small sharp light it throws upon his young mind and character pierces clean through his life and work – work as far outside of Shakespeare's imaginative orbit as *Twelfth Night*, *The Tempest*, and *Macbeth* – or merely 'Full fathom five' – were beyond his own. 'He was immeasurably a less wise man than Shakespeare, and not a wiser writer.'

And so with many other early sayings and doings, for a child is the beginning of a man, precisely as a sapling is the beginning of an oak. Both change, not in kind, but in degree.

176

The writer of this magnificent Battle Hymn died in 1910, at the age of ninety-one. If only the writer of our own 'National Anthem', had realised how much and how often his fellow countrymen were to be fated to use his words, he would have perhaps have taken a little more trouble with them (as much, at any rate, as Shelley and Flecker took in *their* versions of it), and would have found a pleasanter rhyme than 'over us' for 'glorious', and than 'voice' for 'cause'. If, on the other hand, he had read the following *Grace* which Ben Jonson made at the moment's call before James the First, he might perhaps have refrained from rhyming altogether, and so, by sheer modesty, would have missed being immortalized:

> Our King and Queen the Lord God Blesse,
> The Paltzgrave, and the Lady Besse.
> And God blesse every living thing
> That lives, and breathes, and loves the King.

God Bless the Counsell of Estate,
And Buckingham the fortunate.
God blesse them all, and keep them safe,
And God blesse me, and God blesse Raph.

'The king,' says John Aubrey, 'was mighty enquisitive to know who this Raph was. Ben told him 'twas the drawer at the *Swanne* taverne, by Charing-crosse, who drew him good canarie. For this drollery his majestie gave Ben an hundred poundes . . .'

177

'To those,' it is said, 'who have resided a long time by the falls of Niagara, the lowest whisper is distinctly audible.' Their hearing accustoms itself to that unending and enormous roar, and becomes more exquisite. This is untrue of those whose finer sense is lulled by the roar of war: they become deafened, and cannot hear the voice of the soldier 'out in the sun-dried veldt alone' – of which mere human fractions of 'units' every army is composed. And so war may poison and defile even when its intention and its cause are honour and faith. In this particular poem (No. 177), the soldier is one of those who fought in the Transvaal in the years 1899–1901.

180

Rupert Brooke, Wilfred Owen, Edward Thomas, Julian Grenfell, Charles Sorley, Francis Ledwidge, Alan Seeger, Joyce Kilmer – these are the names of but a few of the men, none of them old, many of them in the heyday of their youth and promise, who besides proving themselves soldiers in the Great War had also proved themselves poets. Within his powers, every true poet lives in his country's service. These in that service died.

'. . . Old stairs wind upwards to a long corridor, the distant ends of which are unseen. A few candles gutter in the draughts. The shadows leap. The place is so still that I can hear the antique timbers talking. But something is without which is not the noise of the wind. I listen, and hear it again, the darkness throbbing; the badly adjusted horizon of outer night thudding on the earth – the incessant guns of the great war.

'And I come, for this night at least, to my room. On the wall is a tiny silver Christ on a crucifix; and above that the portrait of a child, who fixes me in the surprise of innocence, questioning and loveable, the very look of warm April and timid but confiding light. I sleep with the knowledge of that over me, an assurance greater than that of all the guns of all the hosts. It is a promise. I may wake to the earth I used to know in the morning.'

H. M. TOMLINSON

184

The reader may speculate how it is that while room has been found here for this entrancing rhyme, none has been made for Macaulay's longer Lays, Browning's Cavalier Songs, and a host of poems equally gallant and spirited. Perhaps he will forgive their absence if he will consider what is said on page 20, and if he will also remember that every chooser is bound to make his choice.

There is, too, the little fable of the Woodcutter's son. This fuzz-headed boy, called Dick or Dickon, while playing on an elder pipe the tune of 'Over the Hills' one dappled sunshine morning in the woods, happening to squinny his eye sidelong as he blew, perceived a crooked and dwarf old man standing beside him where before was only a solitary bearded thistle. This old man, the twist of whose countenance showed him to be one with an ear for woodland music, invited the Woodcutter's son to descend with him into the orchards of the Gnomes – and to help himself. This he did, and marvellously he fared. On turning out his pockets that night – the next day being a Sunday – his Mother found (apart from the wondrous smouldering heap of fruits – amethyst, emerald, rubies and the topaz, which he had given her) two or three strange unpolished stones, and these also from the Old Man's orchards. And she climbed up with her candle, he being abed, and asked him why he had burdened himself with such worthless, common-looking things when he might have carried off their weight in diamonds big as dumplings. 'Well, you see, mother,' he drowsily replied, 'I chose of the best and brightest till my eyes dazzled; and then there was a bird that called, Dick! Dick! Dick! Dick! and those pebbles were among her eggs.'

185

'*We be the King's men*'

The song of Soldiers from Act I, Scene 1, Part i of that mighty play, *The Dynasts*. 'The time is a fine day in March, 1805. A highway crosses the ridge, which is near the sea, and the south coast is seen bounding the landscape below, the open Channel extending beyond.'

'*One Buonaparty*'

'Full of eager expectation,' wrote Amelia Opie in a letter from Paris to a friend in England [in 1802], 'I stationed myself where I could command the white marble stairs of the palace – those steps once stained with the blood of the faithful Swiss Guards, and on which I now expected to behold the "Pacificator", as he was called by the people and his friends – the hero of Lodi. Just before the review was expected to begin, we saw several officers in gorgeous uniforms ascend the stairs, one of whom, whose helmet seemed entirely of gold, was, as I was told, Eugène de Beauharnais. A few minutes afterwards there was a rush of officers down the stairs, and amongst them I saw a short, pale man, with his hat in his hand ... but, though my friend said in a whisper, "*C'est lui*," I did not comprehend that I beheld Buonaparte, till I saw him stand alone at the gate.

'In another moment he was on his horse, and rode slowly past the window; while I ... gazed on him intently; endeavouring to commit each expressive, sharply chiselled feature to memory; contrasting also ... his small, simple hat, adorned with nothing but a little tri-coloured cockade, and his blue coat, guiltless of gold embroidery, with the splendid head adornings and dresses of the officers who followed him . . .

'At length the review ended; too soon for me. The Consul sprang from his horse – we threw open our door again, and, as he slowly reascended the stairs, we saw him very near us, and in full face again, while his bright, restless, expressive, and, as we fancied, dark blue eyes, beaming from under long black eyelashes, glowed over us with a scrutinising but complacent look . . .

'I could not speak; I had worked myself up to all my former enthusiasm for Buonaparte; and my frame still shook with the excitement I had undergone . . .'

As regards that 'dark blue eye' 'which one could no more look into than one can look into the sun,' Amelia Opie was right in using the word 'fancied', as there seems to be little doubt that Napoleon's eyes were a light blue grey – '*gris bleu*'. But eyes vary in colour not only according to the light dwelling upon them, but also to the colour they happen to neighbour, blue especially echoing blue. When that blue is tinged with lilac the owner of the eyes is, in this respect at least, rarely endowed. It is the eye-lid, however, with its exquisitely fine lines, curves and contours, and the set of the eye beneath the brow that gives most of its meaning and expression to the glassy pupil. But not all, perhaps, for sailors' eyes not only have a hint of distance in them, like the sea-birds', but seem to have been sea-washed. Nor do landsmen's eyes always remain the same colour throughout life. Age can curiously change a bright brown or amber into a hue with a distinct suggestion of green in it; though wholly *green* eyes are even more uncommon than the green light in the sunset which Coleridge saw (and which we therefore now see often) – a feat which much amused some of his contemporaries.

In short you cannot look too much at eyes, from Shelley's in the Gallery of the Bodleian, to Coventry Patmore's in the National Portrait Gallery; from the tiny bright shrewd bit of glass stuck in a pig's head to the giraffe's dark deep lustrous crystal; in which strange, living mirror you may be able to detect the reflection of your own tinied image.

186

From *The Dynasts*, Act II, Scene I, Part iii – the song sung in Camp on the Plain of Vittoria by Sergeant Young (of Sturminster Newton) of the Fifteenth (King's) Hussars on the eve of the longest day in the year 1813 and of Wellington's victory.

187

From *The Dynasts*, Act V, Scene vii, Part i. Boatmen and burghers with their pipes and mugs are sitting on settles round the fire in the taproom of the *Old Rooms* Inn at Weymouth. The body of Nelson on board his battered *Victory* has lately been brought to England to be buried in St Paul's; and this is the Song the Second Boatman sings.

'Nelson's mother died in 1767, leaving eight, out of eleven children ... Three years afterwards, when Horatio was only twelve years of age, being at home during the Christmas holidays, he read in the county newspaper that his uncle [Maurice] was appointed to the *Raisonnable*, of 64 guns. "Do, William," said he to a brother who was a year and a half older than himself, "write to my father, and tell him that I should like to go to sea with Uncle Maurice." Mr Nelson was then at Bath, whither he had gone for the recovery of his health: his circumstances were straitened, and he had no prospect of ever seeing them bettered: he knew that it was the wish of providing for himself by which Horatio was chiefly actuated, and did not oppose his resolution; he understood also the boy's character, and had always said, that in whatever station he might be placed, he would climb, if possible, to the very top of the tree. Accordingly Captain Suckling was written to.

' "What," said he in his answer, "has poor Horatio done, who is so weak, that he, above all the rest, should be sent to rough it out at sea? But let him come, and the first time we go into action a cannonball may knock off his head, and provide for him at once ..." '

ROBERT SOUTHEY

'We knew not what the day had done
for us at Trafalgár'

'Once, amidst his sufferings, Nelson had expressed a wish that
he were dead; but immediately the spirit subdued the pains of
death, and he wished to live a little longer; doubtless that he might
hear the completion of the victory which he had seen so gloriously
begun. That consolation – that joy – that triumph was afforded him.
He lived to know that the victory was decisive; and the last guns
which were fired at the flying enemy were heard a minute or two
before he expired.'

The 'Nothe' (line 8) is the promontory that divides for Weymouth, where lived Nelson's Captain Hardy, its harbour or back-
sea on the north, and the Portland Roads, its front-sea on the south;
'Roads', meaning protected seas where ships may *ride* at anchor.
On this tempestuous and fateful night, October 21, 1805, the
breakers were sweeping clean across the spit of land called the
Narrows. On the further side runs for a round ten miles that enormous wall of pebbles – Chesil Beach, whose stones the tides sort
out so precisely, the least in size towards Lyme Regis, that a native
can tell even in a thick mist where he has landed on the beach merely
by measuring them with his eye. About ten miles up this water
swim in Spring the swans of the Swannery of Abbotsbury with
their cygnets, each mother-bird striving to decoy as many of her
rivals' fledgelings into her train as she can. So deals a proud and
powerful nation with the lesser kingdoms of the earth; though
stepmothers are not always welcome.

About four years and a half before Trafalgar, on April 2nd,
1801, Nelson and Parker had won the Battle of the Baltic – as
Thomas Campbell (who was then twenty-four), in his now-famous
poem tells:

> . . . Like leviathans afloat
> Lay their bulwarks on the brine;
> While the sign of battle flew
> On the lofty British line:

It was ten of April morn by the chime:
As they drifted on their path,
There was silence deep as death;
And the boldest held his breath,
For a time . . .

So accustomed, indeed, are we mere landsmen to the exploits of
the Navy on the High Seas that we easily forget it was once to our
forefathers a novelty and a wonder – such a wonder as might be
compared with the fabulous Castles in Spain or the Gardens of
Babylon, as the old nameless poet of the following lines recounts:

Cease now the talke of wonders! nothing rare
Of floateing ilandes, castles in the aire!
Of wooden walls, graves walkeing, flieing steedes,
Or Trojan horse! The present truth exceeds
Those ancient fables; floating iles great store,
Sent from the British Ile, now guard her shore,
And castles strong without foundations stande
More safe on waters pavement then on lande . . .

189

' *The Sailors* '

Here is one of them – come home to his sweetheart, and she (until
stanza 6) not recognizing him:

As I walked out one night, it being dark all over,
The moon did show no light I could discover,
Down by a river side where ships were sailing,
A lonely maid I spied, weeping and bewailing.

I boldly stept up to her, and asked her what grieved her,
She made me this reply, 'None could relieve her,
For my love is pressed, 'she cried,' to cross the ocean,
My mind is like the Sea, always in motion.'

He said, 'My pretty fair maid, mark well my story,
For your true love and I fought for England's glory,
By one unlucky shot we both got parted,
And by the wounds he got, I'm broken hearted.

'He told me before he died his heart was broken,
He gave me this gold ring, take it for a token, –
"Take this unto my dear, there is no one fairer,
Tell her to be kind and love the bearer." '

Soon as these words he spoke she ran distracted,
Not knowing what she did, nor how she acted,
She run ashore, her hair showing her anger,
'Young man, you've come too late, for I'll wed no stranger.'

Soon as these words she spoke, her love grew stronger,
He flew into her arms, he could wait no longer,
They both sat down and sung, but she sung clearest,
Like a Nightingale in spring, 'Welcome home, my dearest.'

He sang, 'God bless the wind that blew him over.'
She sang, 'God bless the ship that brought him over,'
They both sat down and sung, but she sung clearest,
Like a Nightingale in spring, 'Welcome home, my dearest.'

To get any rhythm into this doggerel is like persuading a donkey
to gallop. And yet how clearly one sees the dark night, the disguised
sailor and his sweetheart talking together on the river strand, and
the ships on its bosom in the gloom; while the wistful, deceitful
tale he tells her is as old as Romance. Once get cantering, too; how
pleasing is the motion!

'Token of all brave captains'

The captain stood on the carronade: 'First lieutenant,' says he,
'Send all my merry men aft here, for they must list to me;
I haven't the gift of the gab, my sons – because I'm bred to the
    sea;
That ship there is a Frenchman, who means to fight with we.
    For odds bobs, hammer and tongs, long as I've been to sea,
    I've fought 'gainst every odds – but I've gained the
    victory!'

'That ship there is a Frenchman, and if we don't take she,
'Tis a thousand bullets to one, that she will capture we;
I haven't the gift of gab, my boys, so each man to his gun;
If she's not mine in half an hour, I'll flog each mother's son.
    For odds bobs, hammer and tongs, long as I've been to sea,
    I've fought 'gainst every odds – and I've gained the
    victory!'

We fought for twenty minutes, when the Frenchman had
    enough;
'I little thought,' said he, 'that your men were of such stuff;'
Our captain took the Frenchman's sword, a low bow made to he;
'I haven't the gift of the gab, monsieur, but polite I wish to be.
    And odds bobs, hammer and tongs, long as I've been to sea,
    I've fought 'gainst every odds – and I've gained the
    victory!'

Our captain sent for all of us: 'My merry men,' said he,
'I haven't the gift of the gab, my lads, but yet I thankful be:
You've done your duty handsomely, each man stood to his gun;
If you hadn't, you villains, sure as day, I'd have flogged each
    mother's son,
    For odds bobs, hammer and tongs, as long as I'm at sea,
    I'll fight 'gainst every odds – and I'll gain the victory!'

FREDERICK MARRYAT

191

'The green grass is growing abune their grave'

... O thou, whom chance leads to this nameless stone,
From that proud country which was once my own,
By those white cliffs I never more must see,
By that dear language which I spake like thee,
Forget all feuds, and shed one English tear
O'er English dust. A broken heart lies here.

LORD MACAULAY

192

From his childhood, which was spent in a little shop in Dublin, Mangan had a dark and troubled life. But always a passionate love for his country, Ireland – his Dark Rosaleen – burned on in his imagination as it is revealed in the wild and haunting music of this poem.

197

There are so many words in this poem strange to an English ear that it seems better to explain them here rather than interrupt the actual reading of it too much. After all, the little that is not plain speaks in its music, and that is a very large part of what we call its 'meaning'. For the meaning of a poem is *all* the experience, thought, vision, insight, music, happiness that we can get out of it – it is all that it *does* to us.

Stanza (1) 'loaning' is a green path in the fields, and 'ilka' means every; 'wede' means faded or vanished. (2) 'bught' is a sheep-fold; 'scorning' I suppose means cracking jokes at one another; 'dowie' means sad and drooping; 'daffing' and 'gabbing' is larking and gossiping; a 'leglin' is a milkpail. (3) 'hairst' means harvest; 'bandsters', sheaf-binders; 'lyart' is faded with age; 'runkled' wrinkled; 'fleeching' is wheedling or coaxing or flirting. (4) 'swankies' means the blithe lads of stanza 2; 'bogle' means goblin or bogey – an evening game like 'I spy', I should think. (5) 'Dool and wae' means sorrow or grief and woe.

199

Robert Hayman, a Merchant of Bristol at the age of twenty-five, was a nephew of Sir Walter Raleigh's. He became Governor of a Plantation called *The British Hope* in Newfoundland. In 1628 he settled in Guiana (of whose gilded and barbaric Amazonian princesses his uncle tells in Hakluyt's *Voyages*). He made his will in 1633, and nothing more was afterwards heard of him – at least by the people of Bristol.

Poetry shines out of his stumbling verses like the setting sun through a thicket of thorns. Their 'Totnes' is an exceedingly old town, mainly consisting of that 'long street' where, when a boy, he met 'godly Drake'. At its East-Gate is the Brutus-stone – for here Brut of Troy is said first to have trodden English soil, having landed from the Dart. Twenty miles distant to westward of the town lies on its rivers Plymouth – the Spaniards' wasps' nest – its Francis Drake now gazing out to sea from the Hoe. Twenty miles to the east on the coast is Hayes Barton, where Raleigh was born about 1552. And seven miles down the Dart is the village of Greenway, the home of his half-brother, Sir Humphrey Gilbert, the discoverer of Newfoundland, who was in that year a boy of about sixteen. Here amidstream juts up the Anchor Rock upon which, runs the story, the discoverer of tobacco and of the potato used to sit and smoke his pipe. In 1587 Gilbert and Raleigh sailed together in search of the as yet Unfoundland but on that voyage in vain.

200

'For Hally now is dead'

Hally was Henry, Prince of Wales, the eldest son of James I, Queen Elizabeth's godson, and a beloved patron of the arts and poetry to whom Sir Walter Raleigh looked for happy favours. He was little of body and quick of spirit, and, like Alexander, delighted 'to witch the World with noble horsemanship'. He died when he was nineteen. In Windsor Castle may be seen a suit of armour made for this young prince when he was a boy – a suit which for grace and craftsmanship is said to be one of the most beautiful things of its kind in the world.

201

'Ease after warre'

Soldier, rest! thy warfare o'er,
  Sleep the sleep that knows not breaking;
Dream of battled fields no more,
  Days of danger, nights of waking.
In our isle's enchanted hall,
  Hands unseen thy couch are strewing,
Fairy strains of music fall,
  Every sense in slumber dewing.
Soldier, rest! thy warfare o'er,
Dream of fighting fields no more:
Sleep the sleep that knows not breaking –
Morn of toil, nor night of waking . . .

SIR WALTER SCOTT

202

Here, again, the verse of this ancient fragment jolts, jars, and moves cumbrously as a cannon over rocky ground. But how wide and moving a picture it presents, and how noble is its utterance.

203

'The ambition and desire he [Alexander] had of honour,' says Plutarch, 'showed a greatness of mind and noble courage, passing his years. . . . For when he was asked one day (because he was swift of foot) whether he would assay to run for victory at the Olympian Games, "I could be content" (said he), "so I might run with Kings." ' When, too, 'they brought him news that his Father had taken some famous city, or had won some great battle, he was nothing glad to hear it, but would say to his playfellows: "Sirs, my Father will have all: I shall have nothing left me to conquer with you that shall be aught worth" . . .'

'Is it even so?' said my lady.
'Even so!' said my lord.

205

'*And the kings asleep*'

. . . Not a stone-cast from the summit of the hill where the snow was now parched and thinned away, stood a cairn of boulders and thereon sate three Eagles whose eyes surveyed the kingdoms of the world, its seas, and Man's lost possessions. And the Eagle that was eastwards of the three, a little rimpled her wings and cried: 'Where now? where now?' And the Eagle that shook upon her plumes the dazzle of the dying sun stretched out her corded neck and yelped: 'Man! Man!' And the mid-most Eagle stooped low her golden head and champed between her talons with her beak upon the boulder: 'The Earth founders,' she mewed. And a stillness lay over the hill as though of a myriad watching eyes.

As a huge stone is sometimes seen to lie
Couch'd on the bald top of an eminence;
Wonder to all who do the same espy,
By what means it could thither come, and whence;
So that it seems a thing endued with sense;
Like a sea-beast crawled forth, that on a shelf
Of rock or sand reposeth, there to sun itself . . .

WILLIAM WORDSWORTH

207

'Dance sedately'

– and here are two old rhymes for the dancing to. One for a Morris
Dance:

> Skip it and trip it nimbly, nimbly,
>   Tickle it, tickle it lustily;
> Strike up the tabour for the wenches' favour,
>   Tickle it, tickle it lustily.

> Let us be seene in Hygate Freene,
>   To dance for the honour of Holloway.
> Since we are come hither, let us spare for no leather
>   To dance for the honour of Holloway.

And this for a Flower Dance:

> Where's my lovely parsley, say?
> My violets, roses, where are they?
> My parsley, roses, violets fair,
> Where are my flowers? Tell me where?

And yet another for one's Lonesome Low:

> The king's young dochter was sitting in her window,
>   Sewing at her silken seam;
> She lookt out o' the bow-window,
>   And she saw the leaves growing green,
>   My luve;
> And she saw the leaves growing green.

She stuck her needle into her sleeve,
   Her seam down by her tae,
And she is awa' to the merrie greenwood,
   To pu' the nit and the slae,
     My luve;
   To pu' the nit and the slae.

'Dochter' is, of course, daughter, 'nit' is nut, and 'slae' sloe.

209

Pause an instant on the fifth word in the third stanza and you can actually *hear* the birds laughing – yaffle, blackcap, bullfinch and jay, and the droning and the whistling and the whir-r-r.

210

Scattered through this volume are many songs, a few of them – both words and music – exceedingly ancient. Mr Nahum had a cofferful of old hand-written music (square crotchets and quavers and handsome clefs); and many outlandish instruments were hung up in the dust and silence in one of his cupboards. I remember some small living thing set a string jangling when for the first time the door admitted me to a sight of their queer shapes and appearances. In an old book of 1548, *The Complaynt of Scotland*, there is a list of names, not only of folk-tales such as 'The tayl of the wolfe of the varldes end'; and 'The tayl of the giantes that eit quyk men,' but of song and dances that had long been in common love and knowledge even in those days. Here are a few of the songs:

Good You, Good Day, Wild Boy.
Broom, Broom on Hill.
Trolly lolly leman, dow.
All musing of Marvels, amiss have I gone.
O Mine Heart, hey, this is my Song.

Shall I go with You to Rumblelow Fair?
That Day, that Day, that Gentle Day.
Alas, that Samyn Sweet Face!
In ane Mirthful Morrow.

And here some of the dances:

> All Christian Men's Dance.
> Long Flat Foot of Garioch.
> The Lamb's Wind.
> Leaves Green.
> The Bace of Voragon.
> The Loch of Slene.
> The Bee.
> Shake a Trot, and
> The Vod and the Val.

The tunes to these were played at that time on four kinds of bagpipe (including a drone bagpipe), a trump, a recorder, a 'fiddell', and a 'quhissil' – which is the pleasantest way of spelling *whistle* I have yet seen. The melodies and words of most of them are, apparently, now forgotten.

None the less folk-dancing has taken new life again and many of the old dances have not only been retrieved but are being danced *now* [1928] all over England, Scotland and Wales: among them

> Bonnets so Blue.
> None so Pretty.
> Jenny Pluck Pears.
> Rufty Tufty.
> Trunkles.
> Dargason.
> Lull me Beyond Thee.
> Halfe Hannikin.
> Hey diddle dis!

Laudnum Bunches.
Swaggering Boney.
Bonny Green Garters, and
Lumps of Plum Pudding.

'Fa la la' (No. 210) is not of this kind – a folk-song – but one of hundreds of madrigals, 'ayres' and ballets of which both the words and the music were written in England in the first twenty years or so of the seventeenth century. Apart from the psalm-singing which the Flemish weavers had brought over with them in the previous century, the English had always been musical by nature. But now that natural gift broke into full flower, and English music, such as William Byrd's, John Dowland's, John Wilby's, Philip Rossiter's, Thomas Weelkes' and many others' – became as famous in Europe as English poetry is to-day. It was the advent of foreign music and musicians to England – the Italian, and Handel and Mendelssohn – that put it for a while ungratefully out of mind. But why should one excellent thing oust another?

About the beginning of this century the madrigals (like the carols) were triumphantly rediscovered. They are being not only read but sung again; and Dr Fellowes has lately published a volume containing the words of hundreds of these lively, nimble and heart-entrancing rhymes – intended by their writers to carry with them a double charm – not only their own verbal melody, grace and beauty, but also their music's.

My own technical knowledge of music is scanty indeed, but this may be said: a madrigal is intended to be sung, unaccompanied with instruments, by voices only – three to five, six, or seven, it may be, and men's and women's or boys', coursing, echoing, interweaving, responding and rilling together like the countless runnels and wavelets of a brook over its stones, or a wood full of singing birds at evening. An ayre is different. It is for the voice – singing its melody to the accompaniment of lute, viol or virginal, as a nightingale may sing at dusk above the murmur of a softly-brawling brook. A ballet, the most ancient of all three, went hand in hand and foot to foot with a dance.

All I wish to make clear is that the printed words of such jingles as No. 210 and 212 can give only a fraction of the pleasure their makers intended, who in writing had always the singing voice and often the twangling string in mind. Their very age to my fancy gives them an enticing strangeness, grace, and freshness. For in their company the imagination returns to the days when first they rang out in the taverns and parlours and palaces and streets of a London that from every steeple and tower was within sight of green fields; a noble city of only three hundred thousand inhabitants (including children) wherein you might any day find William Shakespeare, Ben Jonson, Chapman and the rest talking together in its taverns, the *Mermaid* or the *Triple Tun*, while that ill-fortuned traveller and statesman, Sir Walter Raleigh, fallen upon evil days, sat mewed up in the Tower of London, engrossed in his *History of the World*.

As for the taverns, they were as numerous as their signs were enticing. An inquisitive observer in the reign of James I left behind him a list he had himself scribbled down solely of those between Whitehall, Charing Cross and the Tower.

'On the way from Whitehall to Charing Cross we pass,' says he, 'the White Hart, the Red Lion, the Mairmade, [the] iij Tuns, [the] Salutation, the Graihound, the Bell, the Golden Lyon.

'In sight of Charing Cross: the Garter, the Crown, the Bear and Ragged Staffe, the Angel, the King Harry Head.

'Then from Charing Cross towards ye cittie: another White Hart, the Eagle and Child, the Helmet, the Swan, the Bell, King Harry Head, the Flower-de-luce, Angel, the Holy Lambe, the Bear and Harroe, the Plough, the Shippe, the Black Bell, another King Harry Head, the Bull Head, the Golden Bull, "a sixpenny ordinary", another Flower-de-luce, the Red Lyon, the Horns, the White Hors, the Prince's Arms, Bell Savadge's In, the S. John the Baptist, the Talbot, the Shipp of War, the S. Dunstan, the Hercules or the Owld Man Tavern, the Mitar, another iij. Tunnes Inn, and a iij. Tunnes Tavern, and a Graihound, another Mitar, another King Harry Head, [the] iij Tunnes and the iij. Cranes.'

His 'Mairmade' does not appear to have been *the* Mermaid (where Raleigh in his heyday presided at 'those *Lyrick* Feasts') for that, according to *A Life of Shakespeare*, was in Bread Street,

Cheapside, but he noted no less than three *Triple Tuns*, and all of them in the City.

Not only in the Taverns and Inns, too, but in every barber's shop lively music abounded, and a gentleman was scarcely a *gentleman* if he had no skill at all with voice, lute or viol. 'My Lord [Sandwich],' Pepys confided to his Diary on June 5th, 1660, 'called for the lieutenant's cittern, and with two candlesticks, with money in them for cymbals, we made barber's music, with which my Lord was well pleased.' And while a stray customer quilled the cittern, the barber barbered: 'How, sir, will you be trimmed? will you have your beard like a spade or a bodkin, a pent-hous on your upper lip, or an ally on your chin? a low curle on your head like a bull, or dangling lockes like a spaniell? your mustachoes sharpe at the ends, like shomaker's aules, or hanging down to your moth like goates flakes? your love-lockes wreathed with a silken twist, or shaggie to fall on your shoulders?'

In these early days the Booksellers also hung out their signs. In 1582 there were above sixty of them in the neighbourhood of Old St Paul's alone, including the *Bible*, the *Gun*, the *Parrot*, the *Brazen Serpent*, the *Green Dragon*, the *Golden Anchor*, the *Cradle* and the *Swan*.

Fewer then than they are now were the human beings who remain deaf to the magic both of words and music. 'I know very well,' wrote Sir William Temple, 'that many, who pretend to be wise by the forms of being grave, are apt to despise both poetry and music as toys and trifles too light for the use or entertainment of serious men. But whoever find themselves wholly insensible to these charms, would I think do well to keep their own counsel, for ... while this world lasts, I doubt not but the pleasure and request of these two entertainments will do so too; and happy those that content themselves with these, or any other so easy and so innocent; and do not trouble the world or other men, because they cannot be quite themselves, though nobody hurts them!

'When all is done, Human Life is, at the greatest and the best, but like a forward Child, that must be played with and humoured a little to keep it quiet till it falls asleep, and then the Care is over.'

211

'*The onely pretty ring time*'

Amo, amas,
I love a lass,
As cedar tall and slender;
Sweet cowslip's face
Is her nominative case,
And she's of the feminine gender.
Horum quorum,
Sunt divorum,
Harum, scarum, Divo;
Tag rag, merry derry, periwig and hatband,
Hic – hoc – hârum, genitivo.

JOHN O'KEEFE

There was a mayde came out of Kent,
Deintie love, deintie love;
There was a mayde cam out of Kent,
Daungerous be:
There was a mayde cam out of Kent,
Fáyre, propre, small and gent,
As ever upon the grounde went,
For so should it be . . .

When you speake (Sweet)
I'ld have you do it ever. When you sing,
I'ld have you buy and sell so: so give Almes,
Pray so: and for the ord'ring your Affayres,
To sing them too. When you do dance, I wish you
A wave o' the sea, that you might ever do
Nothing but that: move still, still so:
And owne no other function . . .
My prettiest Perdita.

The Winter's Tale

As for Kent and the 'deintie love' that came out of it – (and see also Note 220) an old saying runs: 'There could be nothing better – neither in *Kent* nor Christendom.' In other words, Kent 'has the first cut, and all the loaf besides'. How else? – when, as far back as the year 55 B.C. Caesar realized that it was the most civilized region of England and it has ever since been her 'garden'. Its sea-cliffs named her – Albion; its time is the World's. Yet another old wayside rhyme runs:

> A knight of Cales, and a gentleman of Wales,
> And a Laird of the north country –
> A yeoman of Kent with his yearly rent
> Could buy them out – all Three.

Health, Wealth, and Happiness! Still no doubt even the minor counties have their charms; and each, too, boasts its own scenery, tradition, accent and wares. An interesting old list of the last, *i.e.*, their 'natural commodities' – is given by Thomas Fuller in his *Worthies* [1672]. Here is a selection:

Cumberland	Pearls, Black-lead and Copper.
Hampshire	Red Deer, Honey, Wax and Hogs.
Cambridgeshire	Eeels, Hares, Saffron and Willows.
Cornwall	Diamonds, Ambergris, ('sweetest of gums'), Garlic ('most stinking of roots'), Pilchards, Slate and Tin.
Lincolnshire	Pikes, Wild-fowl, Feathers and Pippins.
Somerset	Lead, Cheese, Mastiffs, Woad ('a deep black tincture' – with which our British ancestors blued themselves), 'and that *Lapis Calaminaris* which, added to copper, makes brass.'
Surrey	Fuller's Earth, Walnuts and Box.
Warwickshire	Sheep, Ash and Coal.
Sussex	Iron, Wheatears, Carps and Talc.

Worcestershire	Lampreys, Perry and Salt.
Yorkshire	Geat [Jet], Alum, Lime and Horses.
Northamptonshire	Saltpetre and Pigeons.
Nottinghamshire	Liquorice.
Staffordshire	Nails.
Wiltshire	Wool.

And last, but still first, beloved *Kent*, with her Morello Cherries, her Flaze, Saint Foine, Madder and Trouts.

> And though myn English be sympill to myn entent,
> Hold me excusid, for I was borne in Kent.

The Wheatear (of Sussex), a bird not much larger than a nightingale, was (and may still be) a glutton's delicacy. I myself have seen poulterers' shops (in 'Stupidity St.') festooned with skylarks as if with holly at Christmas. Apart from their singing and their beauty, none but a gourmandizer, surely, hungers after *little* birds (e.g., wagtails!). Four wheatears on a glutton's dish is a horrid sight; four hungry men sitting round a table with a fat roast goose in the middle is less so. A sense of proportion seems to be the umpire – though possibly not in relation to sprats or white-bait. When we read in *Gulliver's Travels* that the Queen of the Brobdignagians, who was sixty-six feet in height and upwards of six tons in weight, was seen by Gulliver to 'craunch the Wing of a Lark, Bones and all, between her Teeth, although it was nine times as large as that of a full grown Turkey; and put a bit of Bread in her Mouth as big as twelve penny loaves' – we are intent chiefly on seeing as plainly as we can her Majesty at her meal, and are not in the least shocked by that gigantic lark.

The Lamprey (of Worcestershire), is chiefly famous for having been the death of Henry I. It is to be captured at its best on the western sea-sands, at midnight of harvest full-moon. It is a mottled, slimy, eel-like fish . . . 'being so full of holes,' says Fuller, 'that it would appear Nature intended it rather for an instrument of music than for man's food'. The best manner of dressing it, he counsels, is to drown it in malmsey, then 'close the mouth thereof with a nutmegg, the holes with so many cloves ... When it is rolled up round, put in thereto a filbard-nut, kernells stamped, crums of bread, oil, spices, etc.'

> Such pretie things would soon be gon
> If we should not so them remembre.

212

There *might* be an instant's check or faltering at the eighth line, but make it 'when the WINDS BLOW and the SEAS FLOW' – the great flood of air and water banking up as it were into the words as does the Atlantic in a gale at the Spring Equinox – and all's well.

213

'And the fleas that tease in the High Pyrenees'

'The flee is a lyttell worme, and greveth men mooste; and scapeth and voideth peril with lepynge and not with runnynge, and wexeth slowe and fayleth in colde tyme, and in somer tyme it wexeth quiver and swyft; and spareth not kynges.'

> Great fleas have little fleas upon their back to bite 'em,
> And little fleas have lesser fleas, and so *ad infinitum*.
> The great fleas themselves in turn have greater fleas to go on,
> While these again have greater still, and greater still, and so on.

Now, the marvel of the Cuckoo, says Pliny, is that if anyone on hearing her two Springtime notes for the first time in the year takes up the earth lying within the compass of his *right* footprint, it will prove a sovran remedy against fleas.

214

George Wither, says Aubrey, could make verses as fast as he could write them. So, too, could Shakespeare. 'What he thought,' said his editors, 'he uttered with that easiness that we have scarse received from him a blot in his papers.'

Still: – 'So, So-a! fair and softly!' said the old Shropshire farmer to Job his plough-horse when he kicked up his heels as if to break into a gallop; 'So, So-a! When thou'rt a steeplechaser, my dear, or born a high-blood Arab, there'll be time enough for that. *Some goes their best slow.*'

'*The fives did fit her shoe*'

... Her feet beneath her petticoat
Like little mice stole in and out,
   As if they feared the light;
But oh, she dances such a way!
No sun upon an Easter-day
   Is half so fine a sight.

Her cheeks so rare a white was on,
No daisy makes comparison;
   Who sees them is undone;
For streaks of red were mingled there,
Such as are on a Catharine pear,
   The side that's next the sun.

Her lips were red; and one was thin
Compared to that was next her chin
   (Some bee had stung it newly);
But, Dick, her eyes so guard her face,
I durst no more upon them gaze,
   Than on the sun in Júly ...

SIR JOHN SUCKLING

Why Júly ceased to be so pronounced (and what the first Caesar would have thought of it) I cannot say. Until then (with April) it was the prettiest month-name in the calendar, which, in most respects, is an anomalous litter of relics. *A Student's Pastime* gives the Anglo-Saxon names and the author's – W. W. Skeat's – translation of them. What is delightful in them is that they are homely and country, not alien, names, and as close to nature as its fur is to a mole. Both December and January were called after *Yule*. June and July were both called by a word meaning mild or warm. February was Mire-month; March, Fierce-month; April, Easter-month; August, Weed-month; September, Holy-month; and October was (?) Windy or 'storm felling' month. November was the month of Sacrifice, and May was Three-milkings-month, because then the cows could be milked thrice daily.

' I still did scorn to stint her
From sugar, sack, or fire'

The subject being lasses, sack and sugar, here is an extract taken from a rare little book entitled *The Journal of a Young Lady of Virginia* which I owe to the kindness of a friend, Mrs Arthur Kinsolving. The year is 1782 – six years after the end of the War of Independence. The Mr Washington mentioned is not the great general George but a kinsman; the 'young lady' is writing to her friend, Polly; and what a gay, light-hearted, romantic, nutritious experience it all is:

'*October* 26. I have but one moment to tell you we are just going to set out for Bushfield. Mr Turberville's Coach is waiting for us at the road.

'*October* 27. When we got here we found the House pretty full. Nancy was here. I had to dress in a great hurry for dinner. We spent the evening very agreeably in chatting. Milly Washington is a thousand times prettyer than I thought her at first, and very agreeable. About sunset, Nancy, Milly, and myself took a walk in the Garden (it is a most butifull place). We were mighty busy cutting thistles to try our sweethearts, when Mr Washington caught us; and you can't conceive how he plagued us – chased us all over the Garden, and was quite impertinent.

'I must tell you of our frolic after we went in our room. We took it into our heads to want to eat; well, we had a large dish of bacon and beaf; after that, a bowl of Sago cream; and after that, an apple pye. While we were eating the apple pye in bed – God bless you! making a great noise – in came Mr Washington, dressed in Hannah's short gown and peticoat, and sezed me and kissed me twenty times, in spite of all the resistance I could make; and then Cousin Molly. Hannah soon followed, dress'd in his Coat. They joined us in eating the apple pye, and then went out. After this we took it in our heads to want to eat oysters. We got up, put on our rappers, and went down in the Seller to get them: do you think Mr Washington did not follow us and scear us just to death! We went up tho, and eat our oysters. We slept in the old Lady's room too, and she sat laughing fit to kill herself at us. She is a charming old lady – you would be delighted with her. I forgot to tell, Mr Beal attended us here. I have been makeing Milly play on the fortipianer for me; she plays very well. I am more and more delighted with her. She has just returned from the Fredericksburg races, and has given me a full account of them.

'I have been filling out tea, and after that we took a walk to the river by Moonlight. The garden extends to the river. Nancy observed walking by moonlight, she thought, reminded us of our absent Friends. I joined her in thinking so, and my thoughts were at that instant with my Polly. We returned in the house, and I prevailed on Milly to entertain us an hour or two on the fortipianer. We wanted very much to sleep in a room by ourselves to-night and try the *dum cake*, but could not persuade Nancy – she was afraid. . . . Adieu, my ever dear Polly . . . Farewell.'

216

'*A shining night*'

A Mole-Catcher am I, and that is my trade,
I potters about wi' my spunt and my spade,
   On a moonshiny night, O 'tis my delight
     A-catching o' moles.

The traps that I set for the mole in his run,
There's never a night, sirs, but I catches one
   On a moonshiny night . . .

Along of the lanes as by night time I go,
There's things, that I see, as the folks don't know
   On a moonshiny night . . .

There's frolic and lark in the field and the park,
For others than moles will be out in the dark
   On a moonshiny night . . .

There's many a sight and there's many a sound
What maketh me laugh as I'm making my round
   On a moonshiny night . . .

But nothing I says, for I'm mum as a bell,
You certainly know that no tales will I tell,
   On a moonshiny night, O 'tis my delight
     A-catching o' moles . . .

218

'Up in the morning early'

One man shall mow my meadow,
Two men shall gather it together,
Two men, one man, and one more
Shall shear my lambs and ewes and rams
And gather my gold together.

Two men shall mow . . .

And so, in the next stanza, to *three*, then *four* and *ad inf*.

'And St John's bell rings for matins'

June 24 is not only the birthday of St John the Baptist, but also the year's Sun Day, for about this day, following through the night but a little way beneath the horizon, he rises at dawn furthest North of East on his annual journey. As on May-day so on St John's it was once the custom, all England over, to set huge bonfires blazing on the hilltops, around which the country people danced and sang. The dairy-maid who had the breath and was fleet enough of foot to ring around, between dusk and daybreak nine such merry bonfires before they were burnt out, assured her heart of a happy marriage within the year.

219

'It's dabbling in the dew makes the milkmaids fair!'

The aïr to gi'e your cheäks a hue
O' rwosy red, so feaïr to view,
Is what do sheäke the grass-bleädes grae
At breäke o' dae, in mornén dew;
Vor vo'k that will be rathe abroad,
Will meet wi' health upon their road.

447

But biden up till dead o' night,
When han's o' clocks do stan' upright,
By candlelight, do soon consume
The feäce's bloom, an' turn it white.
An' moon-beäms cast vrom midnight skies
Do blunt the sparklen ov the eyes.

Vor health do weäke from nightly dreams
Below the mornen's eärly beams,
An' leäve the dead-aïr'd houses' eaves,
Vor quiv'ren leaves, an' bubblen streams,
A-glitt'ren brightly to the view,
Below a sky o' cloudless blue.

WILLIAM BARNES

The words in this poem are spelt as they are spoken in Dorset-shire. 'Rathe' means early; and 'below' beneath. The stanzas echo and re-echo with half-hidden rhymes.

220

... She ware a frock of frolicke green,
Might well beseeme a mayden queene,
    Which seemly was to see;
A hood to that so neat and fine,
In colour like the columbine,
    Y-wrought full featously.

Her features all as fresh above,
As is the grasse that growes by Dove;
    And lyth as lasse of Kent.
Her skin as soft as Lemster wooll,
As white as snow on Peakish Hull,
    Or swanne that swims in Trent ...

223

' Music, when soft voices die,
Vibrates in the memory'

There is sweet music here that softer falls
Than petals from blown roses on the grass,
Or night-dews on still waters between walls
Of shadowy granite, in a gleaming pass;
Music that gentlier on the spirit lies,
Than tir'd eyelids upon tir'd eyes;
Music that brings sweet sleep down from the blissful skies.

ALFRED, LORD TENNYSON

225

This 'Country Rhime', with Nos. 121 and 434, is taken from *A Book for Boys and Girls*, written by John Bunyan. It came into the world on May 12th, 1686, two years before Bunyan died on Snow Hill in London; and two years after the publication of the Second Part of *The Pilgrim's Progress*, 'wherein is set forth the manner of the setting out of Christian's Wife and Children, their dangerous journey, and safe arrival at the Desired Country.'

When Bunyan was young — though he afterwards repented of it — he exulted in ringing the bells with the ringers in the steeple of the village church of Elstow, where he was born, and where his grandfather, Thomas Bunyan, was 'a common baker of human bread'.

All these 'Homely rhimes' are followed in this particular *Book for Boys and Girls* by 'comparisons'; as here: first the bells; then a lesson about them. They are parables. But in Mr Nahum's copying many of the lessons were omitted; perhaps because he preferred to think out his own. Not that the poetry that is intended to teach, to praise virtue, and to instil wisdom in the heart and mind of its readers is any the less poetry for this reason. Nevertheless, *every* beautiful thing in this world – the hyssop in the wall and the cedar of Lebanon, Solomon in all his glory and the ring on his finger, carries with it joy and wonder of the life that is ours, and gratitude to the Maker of all. And poets who, when writing, are too intent upon teaching, are apt to forfeit their rarest poetry.

It is hard to believe that Bunyan was accused of having stolen his great book. But so it was; and in 'An Advertisement to the Reader' he sturdily refutes the charge – laughs at it:

> Some say the *Pilgrim's Progress* is not mine,
> Insinuating as if I would shine
> In name and fame by the worth of another,
> Like some made rich by robbing of their Brother . . .
>   It came from mine own heart, so to my head,
> And thence into my fingers trickled [trickle-èd] . . .
>   Manner and matter too was all mine own,
> Nor was it unto any mortal known,
> 'Till I had done it. Nor did any then
> By books, by wits, by tongues, or hand, or pen,
> Add five words to it, or wrote half a line
> Thereof: the whole, and every whit is mine . . .
> Witness my name, if anagram'd to thee,
> The letters make, *Nu hony in a B.*

JOHN BUNYAN

226

'*As if the tower in all its stones awoke*'

In foreign countries, says Fuller, England was once called the 'ringing Island', being famous for having 'greater, more, and more tuneable bells than any one country in Christendom, Italy itself not excepted.' 'The Art of Ringing, moreover, requires a Thoughtful and Ingenious Headpiece' – inasmuch as a *maximus* (or peal of twelve bells) 'will afford more changes than there have been hours since the Creation.'

But long before bells were pealed or volleyed they were dinged or sounded singly, and for different purposes, and it was not only customary to give them names, but to inscribe their names in their metal. The bells that once sounded over the Lincolnshire fens from the Benedictine Abbey of Croyland, for example, were named Pega, Bega, Tatwin, Turketyl, Bettelin, Bartholomew and Guthlac; while in the thirteenth century the bells at Osney were named Auclaire, Doucement, Austin, Marie, Gabriel and John. The oldest known dated bell is that which hangs in St Chad's Church, Claughton: it is inscribed *Anno Dni MCC No. VI* (A.D. 1296).

The most famous bells now heard in England are Great or Mighty Tom of Oxford, Great Peter of York, Old Gabriel of Lewes, Old Kate of St Mark's Lincoln, Bell Harry and St Dunstan of Canterbury, Black Tom of Dewsbury, Great Peter of Gloucester, and Great Peter and Grandison of Exeter; and the tolling of Tom Lincoln is said to turn the milk sour for miles around. Great Paul, however, though of no great age, is England's prince of bells, his girth being such that he is beaten, not rung. His note is E Flat; his weight exceeds that of over two hundred grown men, and cut into his side are the words '*Vae mihi si non evangelisavero!*' – 'Woe, woe, unto me if I proclaim not the Gospel!'

Like Great Paul, the earliest bells bear inscriptions in Latin, *e.g.*, '*Maria Mater Dei est nomen meum: Sum Rosa pulsata mundi Maria vocata: Tu Petre pulsatus perversos mitiga flatus,*' – 'Do thou, O Peter, with thy kneeling, assuage the angry storms,' the last words referring to the belief that the ringing of bells has the effect described in the second couplet of this 'old monkish rhyme'.

> Men's death I tell
> By doleful knell.

> Lightning and thunder
> I break asunder.

> On Sabbath all
> To church I call.

The sleepy head
I raise from bed.

The winds so fierce
I doe disperse.

Man's cruel rage
I doe asswage.

Alas, an incalculable number of ancient bells were melted down at the Reformation and in Puritan days, or had their angel heads and lettering ruthlessly defaced.

Later inscriptions are in English, the earliest of these being often doggerel, but good doggerel; the later – of the Georges and afterwards – still doggerel, but bad. Here are a few examples:

Be not over busie.   (Early sixteenth century)

Jesus be our speed.   (1595)

Gev God the Glory   (1606)

Come when I call
To serve God all.   (1633)

When you die
Aloud I cry   (1687)

I ring to sermon with lusty boom,
That all may come and none stay at home   (1657)

To speak a parting soul is given to me:
Be trimmed thy lamp as if I tolled for thee.

All men that hear my mournful sound
Repent before you lye in ground.   (1602)

My roaring sounde doth warning geve
That men can not heare always lyve

Jesu, for Thy modir's sake,
Save all the souls that me gart make.
                                        Amen.

231

Now gaze the stags upon the glassy brooks,
    Then slowly through their leafy walks retire,
The huntsman from his close-shut casement looks,
    And heaps new wood upon his blazing fire;
The lowing kine, from out the flow'ry meads,
    Now pale and frozen, under shelter stand,
The ox within his stall contented feeds,
    And plough and wain are idle on the land;
The hind within the house his labour plies,
    The dreaming hound upon the hearth is laid,
The flapping sea-gull from the coastward flies,
    And robin now can perch on axe and spade:
This, this is Autumn, when the freezing sky,
And mournful air proclaim the Winter nigh.

                              LORD THURLOW

232

Dorothy was William Wordsworth's only sister and his friend
Coleridge's close friend. What she squandered on these two poets—
her self, her talk, her imagination, her love – only they could tell.
'She gave me eyes, she gave me ears,' once wrote her brother; she
shared his visionary happiness. With Coleridge she used to walk
and talk so nearly and dearly that again and again in her *Journal*
she uses all but the very words – that 'thin gray cloud', the line on
Spring, or on the one red leaf, for instance – which are so magically
his own in 'Christabel' (No. 345).

233

I read this—perhaps the loveliest of John Keats's odes, many times
before I realised that the whole of it is addressed to the musing
apparition or phantasm of Autumn whom in its second stanza he
describes as if she were in image there before him. This, perhaps,
was partly because the poem is usually printed with a full stop after
'clammy cells', and partly because of my own stupidity.

Even those who care most for poetry may differ in their choice
and appreciation of it. To Alice Meynell the 'Ode to the Nightingale' seemed to be the 'most imaginative', the 'Grecian Urn' the
finest ('for never was fancy more exquisite'), 'To Autumn' 'not
in so high a rank but lovely and perfect'. The 'Psyche' and 'Melancholy' she loved least, and yet what an unforgettable last two lines
has the 'Melancholy's' last stanza!

> I saw old Autumn in the misty morn
> Stand shadowless like Silence, listening
> To silence, for no lonely bird would sing
> Into his hollow ear from woods forlorn,
> Nor lowly hedge nor solitary thorn;
> Shaking his languid locks all dewy bright
> With tangled gossamer that fell by night,
>   Pearling his coronet of golden corn. . . .
>
> The squirrel gloats on his accomplished hoard,
> The ants have brimmed their garners with ripe grain,
>   And honey bees have stored
> The sweets of Summer in their luscious cells;
> The swallows all have winged across the main;
> But here the Autumn melancholy dwells,
>   And sighs her tearful spells
> Amongst the sunless shadows of the plain.

THOMAS HOOD

This is Touchstone the Fool's last song in *As You Like It:* and if they could continue so to sing, it is a thousand pities (professional) fools have gone out of fashion. Their wit, though raw at times, might keep things sweeter. Moreover, Touchstone was of ancient lineage, as is proved by this letter written by King John (and quoted in *Readings in English Social History*).

'To William Piculf, and Geoffry, his son.

John, by the grace of God, etc. Know ye, that we have given, and by the present charter have confirmed to William Piculf, our fool, Fonte-Ossanne with all its appurtenances, to have and to hold for himself, and his heirs, on condition of doing henceforward annually for ourselves the service of fool, as long as he shall live; and after his decease, his heirs shall hold the same land from us, by the service of one pair of gilded spurs, to be rendered to us annually.

Wherefore, we will and positively command that the foresaid Piculf and his heirs shall have and hold for ever, fairly and in peace, freely and in quiet, the foresaid land, with all its appurtenances, by virtue of the aforesaid service.'

'*A foolish thing*'

I thee advise
If thou be wise
To keep thy wit
Though it be small:
'Tis rare to get,
And far to fet,
'Twas ever yet
Dear'st ware of all.

GEORGE TURBERVILLE

'Far to fetch' it certainly is; but here is a little counsel to this end from the old Irish *Instructions of King Cormac* (of the ninth

century). Of Carbery I know no more, but doubtless there is much
to hear:

'O Cormac, grandson of Conn,' said Carbery, 'what is the
worst for the body of man?'

'Not hard to tell,' said Cormac. 'Sitting too long, lying too long,
long standing, lifting heavy things, exerting oneself beyond one's
strength, running too much, leaping too much, frequent falls,
sleeping with one's leg over the bed-rail, gazing at glowing embers,
wax, biestings [very new milk], new ale, bull-flesh, curdles, dry
food, bog-water, rising too early, cold, sun, hunger, drinking too
much, eating too much, sleeping too much, sinning too much,
grief, running up a height, shouting against the wind, drying
oneself by a fire, summer-dew, winter-dew, beating ashes, swimming on a full stomach, sleeping on one's back, foolish romping.' . . .

'O Cormac, grandson of Conn,' said Carbery, 'I desire to know
how I shall behave among the wise and the foolish, among friends
and strangers, among the old and the young, among the innocent
and the wicked.'

'Not hard to tell,' said Cormac.

> 'Be not too wise, nor too foolish,
> Be not too conceited, nor too diffident,
> Be not too haughty, nor too humble,
> Be not too talkative, nor too silent,
> Be not too hard, nor too feeble.
> If you be too wise, men will expect too much of you;
> If you be too foolish, you will be deceived;
> If you be too conceited, you will be thought vexatious;
> If you be too humble, you will be without honour;
> If you be too talkative, you will not be heeded;
> If you be too silent, you will not be regarded;
> If you be too hard, you will be broken;
> If you be too feeble, you will be crushed.'

'Our Play is done'

– after which, in Elizabeth's day, 'the characters (one or more) were wont to kneel down upon the stage and to offer a solemn prayer for the sovereign, or other patron':

'My tongue is wearie; when my Legs are too, I will bid you good night; and so kneele down before you: But (indeed) to pray for the Queene.'   *Henry IV.*

238

'The thistle now is older, . . .
His head is white as snow.'

... There was a day, ere yet the autumn closed,
When, ere her wintry wars, the earth reposed,
When from the yellow weed the feathery crown,
Light as the curling smoke, fell slowly down;
When the winged insect settled in our sight,
And waited wind to recommence her flight;
When the wide river was a silver sheet,
And on the ocean slept th' unanchor'd fleet;
When from our garden, as we look'd above,
There was no cloud, and nothing seem'd to move ...

GEORGE CRABBE

242

'The sea-blooms and the oozy woods'

In the ever mutable loveliness of air, sky and particularly of water Shelley found endless delight and bewitchment. In reference to the third stanza of this transfiguring ode he wrote: 'The vegetation at the bottom of the sea, of rivers, and of lakes, sympathizes with that of the land in the change of the seasons, and is consequently

457

influenced by the winds which announce it.' And, in a letter to his friend Thomas Love Peacock, describing the beauty of this Bay of Baiae, he tells him, 'The sea was so translucent that you could see the caverns clothed with the glaucous sea-moss and the leaves and branches of those delicate weeds that pave the bottom of the water.'

This is the Sea. In these uneven walls
    A wave lies prisoned. Far and far away
Outward to ocean, as the slow tide falls,
    Her sisters, through the capes that hold the bay,
Dancing in lovely liberty recede.
    But lovely in captivity she lies,
Filled with soft colours, where the waving weed
    Moves gently, and discloses to our eyes

Blurred shining veins of rock, and lucent shells
    Under the light-shot water, and here repose
Small quiet fish, and dimly-glowing bells
    Of sleeping sea-anemones that close
Their tender fronds and will not now awake
Till on these rocks the waves returning break.

EDWARD SHANKS

245

'Passèd joy'

I know that all beneath the moon decays,
And what by mortals in this world is brought
In Time's great periods shall return to nought;
That fairest states have fatal nights and days;

I know how all the Muse's heavenly lays,
With toil of spright which is so dearly bought,
As idle sounds, of few or none are sought;
And that nought lighter is than airy praise.

I know frail beauty's like the purple flower,
To which one morn oft birth and death affords;
That love a jarring is of minds' accords,
Where sense and will invassall reason's power.

Know what I list, this all can not me move,
But that – O me! I both must write and love!

WILLIAM DRUMMOND

246

'No crane talks'

I hear the crane, if I mistake not, cry
Who in the clouds forming the forkèd Y,
By the brave orders practized under her,
Instructeth souldiers in the art of war.
For when her troops of wandring cranes forsake
Frost-firmèd Strymon, and (in autumn) take
Truce with the northern dwarfs, to seek adventure
In southern climates for a milder winter;
A-front each band a forward captain flies,
Whose pointed bills cuts passage through the skies,
Two skilful sergeants keep the ranks aright,
And with their voyce hasten their tardy flight;

And when the honey of care-charming sleep
Sweetly begins through all their veines to creep
One keeps the watch, and ever carefull-most,
Walks many a round about the sleeping hoast,
Still holding in his claw a stony clod,
Whose fall may wake him if he hap to nod.
Another doth as much, a third, a fourth,
Untill, by turns the night be turnèd forth.

So also, according to travellers, talk, argue as if in conference
together, camp, sleep, and keep watch the wandering tribes of the
gaudy-dyed Baboons.

247

The North wind doth blow,
And we shall have snow,
And what will Cock Robin do then, poor thing?

He'll sit in a barn
And keep himself warm,
And hide his head under his wing, poor thing!

249

If this poem is read heedfully, pausingly, without haste, the very
words themselves will seem like snowflakes, floating into the mind;
and then, the beauty and the wonder.

251

Here again, as in music, there are 'rests' in the second, fourth
and fifth lines of each stanza. And is there any magic to compare
with the solemn unearthly radiance of the world when it is masked
with snow; then the very sparkling of the mind is like hoar-frost
on the bark of a tree.

253

'The wild woods'

Allan Cunningham's in Scotland, and these – Mr Robert Frost's
– in Vermont, U.S.A.:

Whose Woods these are I think I know,
His house is in the village though;
He will not see me stopping here
To watch his woods fill up with snow.

My little horse must think it queer,
To stop without a farmhouse near
Between the woods and frozen lake
The darkest evening of the year.

He gives his harness bells a shake
To ask if there is some mistake,
The only other sound's the sweep
Of easy wind and downy flake.

The woods are lovely dark and deep;
But I have promises to keep
And miles to go before I sleep:
And miles to go before I sleep.

255

There may be a few small verbal puzzles in this fifteenth-century carol – otherwise as clear, sharp and shining as a winter moon.

Kechoun is kitchen, and Stephen (who waited on the King at bed and board) stepped out of it into the hall, 'boar's head on hand'. *Kyst*, means cast; *eylyt*, aileth; *wod*, mad; and *brede* (?), to have wild fancies. '*Be to and al be on*' means like one man.

In later times a clay or eathenware box made all of a piece, with a slit in it, was carried by apprentices through the streets on the Feast of St Stephen, for money. Hence this day is now called 'Boxing Day'.

In the Isle of Man, however, the Christmas Box was called the Wren Box, and for this reason: There dwelt of old a Lorelei, siren or sea-elf, in the emerald-green creeks and caves of a solitary precipitous island. She was as lovely as she was cruel, and her shrill sweet voice rose amid the roaring and soughing of the waves in her steep rocky habitation as shines a poisonous flower in a dark forest. Thus she would at daybreak enchant to their doom sailors following their craft on the sea. Leaning to listen to this music creeping by them on the waters, they would draw in to her haunts. Of their bones were coral made; while she lived on; sang on. She was hunted down at last in her sea-grottoes by those who, like Ulysses, had sealed their ears against her incantations. Brought finally to bay, her beauty and bright hair suddenly dwindled and dimmed, and she escaped in the shape of – Jenny Wren. Alas, for Jenny Wren! condemned ever after for the woes of this siren to be pursued with sticks and stones by young loons, cullions and Jerry Sneaks, on every St Stephen's Day. As goes the rhyme:

'Oh, where are you going?' says Milder to Melder;
'Oh, where are you going?' says the younger to the elder.
'Oh, I cannot tell,' says Festel to Fose;
   'We're going to the woods,' says John the Red Nose.

'Oh, what will you do there?' says Milder to Melder;
'Oh, what will you do there?' says the younger to the elder.
'Oh, I do not know,' says Festel to Fose;
   'To shoot the cutty wren,' says John the Red Nose.

'How will you get him?' etc., etc.

These gentry have different names in different parts, *e.g.*, Robin the Bobbin, Richard the Robin, and Jackey the Land; Fozie Mozie, Johnnie Rednosie, and Foslin 'Ene; and a sinister company they look, especially 'Milder'!

In Ireland a totally different story was trumped up to excuse this dismal amusement: A party of Protestants, says John Aubrey, would have been surprised in sleep by the Popish Irish were it not for several wrens that 'wakened them by dancing and pecking on the drums as the enemy were approaching. For this reason the wild Irish mortally hate these birds, to this day, calling them the Devil's servants, and killing them wherever they catch them; they teach their children to thrust them full of thorns; you will sometimes on holidays see a whole parish running like mad from hedge to hedge a-wren-hunting' – the wren! – the neatest, nattiest, nimblest bird in all these islands, with more sheer joy of life to the square inch as his shrill 'shattering' voice declares – than most humans seem to have to the square acre.

257

Lullay, lullay, thou lytil child,
  Sleep and be well still;
The King of bliss thy father is,
  As it was his will.

The other night I saw a sight,
  A mayd a cradle keep:
'Lullay,' she sung, and said among,
  'Lie still, my child, and sleep.'

'How should I sleep? I may not for weep,
  So sore am I begone:
Sleep I would; I may not for cold,
  And clothes have I none.

'For Adam's guilt mankind is spilt
  And that me rueth sore;
For Adam and Eve here shall I live
  Thirty winter and more.'

258

'*Wolcum twelthe-day*'

And here is a rhyme (entitled Jolagiafir) for a memory-game that
used once to be played on Twelfth Night after the bean and pea or
silver-penny had been discovered in the Twelfth Cake, and the
Wassail Bowl had gone round with the Mince Pies:

  On the first day of Christmas, my true love sent to me
  A partridge in a pear-tree.

On the second day of Christmas, my true love sent to me
Two turtle doves and a partridge in a pear-tree.

On the third day of Christmas, my true love sent to me
Three French hens, two turtle doves and
A partridge in a pear-tree.

And so on to –

On the twelfth day of Christmas, my true love sent to me
Twelve lords a-leaping, eleven ladies dancing,
Ten pipers piping, nine drummers drumming,
Eight maids a-milking, seven swans a-swimming,
Six geese a-laying, five gold rings,
Four colly birds, three French hens,
Two turtle doves, and
A partridge in a pear-tree.

Here's a 'Twelve' from Scotland:

What will be our twelve, boys?
What will be our twelve, boys?
Twelve's the Twelve Apostles;
Eleven's maidens in a dance;
Ten's the Ten Commandments;
Nine's the Muses o' Parnassus;
Eight's the table rangers;
Seven's the stars of heaven;
Six the echoing waters;
Five's the hymnlers o' my bower;
Four's the gospel-makers;
Three's the three thrivers;
Twa's the lily and the rose,
That shine baith red and green, boys.
My only ane, she walks alane,
And evermair has dune, boys.

An English version of this begins:

> 'I'll sing you one, O!
>   Green grow the rushes, O!
>   One and one is all alone
>   And evermore shall be, O!'

For eleven, it has 'the eleven that went up to heaven'; for nine, 'the bright shiners'?); for eight, 'the bold rangers'; for five, 'the symbol at your door' (the magic pentacle); for three, 'the rivals' and for two, 'the lilly-white boys, clothèd all in green, Oh!'

And this is the rudiments of yet another, which was sent me by a lady who tells me she remembers it from her childhood, and remarks that the refrain seems 'very nonsensical' – like an ancient inscription on a stone which has been eroded by decay and rain and frost, and enringed by lichen:

> I have three presents from over the sea!
>   *Perry merry dixie Domine!*
> The first was a book which no man could read:
>   *Petrum patrum paradise temple.*
>   *Perry merry dixie Domine!*
> The second was a blanket without a thread:
>   *Perry merry dixie Domine!*
> The third was a cherry without a stone:
>   *Petrum patrum,* etc.

'*Wolcum alle and mak good cher*'

An old lady (Mrs Samuel Chandler) of Warwickshire, aged 88, was presented on Christmas Eve, 1844, with a little diary – and much else besides – by her son Richard. She used it, not to record the present, but the past; and the following extract is its first entry. It appears in *The Folk Lore Journal:*

'Beginning with Christmas Eve in the year 1759 (my third year) I perfectly remember on that day being carried by Thomas, an old Man-servant, to my Grandmother's – living in the Village of

Wootton Wawen, a mile and half from the Park, my Birthplace. Now as Pride is one of our earliest enemys, I date it to his agency that I certainly recollect on that eventful Day that I was wrap'd round by a scarlet broadcloth Cloak of my Mother's, bordered with white Fur.

'The object of my visit on that particular day was to see the Yule Block drawn into the house by a Horse, as a foundation for the Fire on Christmas Day, and according to the superstition of those times for the twelve days following, as the said Block was not to be entirely reduc'd to ashes till that time had passed by. On this subject being named in after years my good Father said [that] as they were of opinion that such an absurd practice would not be of long continuance, they sent me to see it to give me a chance at that early age of remembering that I had witness'd such a foolish ceremony; and the impression was so firmly stamp'd that even now in my 88th year it appears as visible to my mind's Eye as tho' it had been the transaction upon Christmas Eve now six weeks since.

'But the close of the day's tale remains still to be told. When I had been carried round the Kitchen several times, and told much more than I could then understand, my good Grandmother took me into her little Parlour and set me on her knees by a good fire, and without doubt gave me something very nice to eat, but this I do not retain, as my object seemed to be gratified by their strange sights; but I well remember old Thomas having orders to tap the Christmas Barrel of old Stingo, and bringing up a very large glass to shew the beauty of its appearance, and to drink to the health of good old Mistress and little Miss Sally [herself].

'Whilst this ceremony was performing, Carol Singers were heard at the Door. On its being opened, two tall Women entered, bearing between them a large Wassal Bowl, finely dress'd on the outside with Holly, Misseltoe, Ribbons, Laurustinus, and what other flowers could be had at that season. But what most delighted me was a pretty silver Cup, with a handle on each side slung in the middle withinside, and movd about as it was carried round. They sang a long Carol, with a chorus after each verse, repeating the word *Mirth*, etc., which I could not understand, and I well remember I was sadly puzzled to know the meaning, and ask'd my poor brother when I return'd home, who immediately sang the whole of it to me, explaining this great difficulty, and asking me why I did not enquire of Grandma or old Thomas . . .'

259

It looks as if this carol – of Henry VI's reign – was once a singing game: On the one side in the blaze of the Yule Log the Holly men with gilded and garlanded pole; and on the other Ivy with her maidens; each side taunting the other, and maybe tugging for prisoners. 'Ivy-girls', too, used to be burned by companies of boys, and Holly-boys by girls – all yawping and jodelling at the sport.

'Poppynguy' may perhaps be the jay, but it would be pleasanter company for the lark, if here it means the green woodpecker. He drills out his holes in the small hours of the morning, his slender barb-tipped tongue busy with what stirs within. He drums for his lady-love and *yaffles* or laughs out, glassy and clear in the sunny green tops of the woods.

260

'*When Isicles hang by the wall*'

> . . . The winter falls, the frozen rut
> Is bound with silver bars;
> The snowdrift heaps against the hut,
> And night is pierced with stars.

COVENTRY PATMORE

There is a peculiar magic (which may perhaps be less apparent to the Greenlanders) in icicles. Nor are its effects unknown to the fourfooted. In certain remote regions of Siberia there is said to be a singular little animal called the Ice-wolf. He has prick-ears, is a fierce feeder, and wears a winter coat so wondrous close and dense that three or four of our English moles' skins laid one over another would yet fall short of its match. But he seldom attains to a ripe age, and for this reason. As soon as he is freed from his dam's snow-burrow, he hastens off to the dwellings of the men of those parts, snuffing their fried seal-steaks and blubber, being a most incorrigible thief and very wary. And such is his craft that he mocks at gins, traps and pitfalls. But he has a habit which may prove his undoing. It is in this wise: The heat of these hovels is apt to melt a little of the snow upon them, its water trickling and coursing softly down till long, keen icicles are formed, upon which, whether hungry or fed, taking up his station in a plumb line beneath them, he will squat and gloat for an hour together, by reason of his pleasure in their clear glasslike colours. Hearing his breathing or faint snuffing, any human who wakes within will of a sudden violently shake the wall between. This dislodges the pendent icicles, and the squatting Ice-wolf is pierced to his death as with a sword.

Winter indeed makes crystal even of ink and has the power of enchanting every imagination; particularly Coleridge's:

> Therefore all seasons shall be sweet to thee,
> Whether the summer clothe the general earth
> With greenness, or the redbreast sit and sing
> Betwixt the tufts of snow on the bare branch
> Of mossy apple-tree, while the night thatch
> Smokes in the sun-thaw; whether the eave-drops fall
> Heard only in the trances of the blast,
> Or if the secret ministry of frost
> Shall hang them up in silent icicles,
> Quietly shining to the quiet Moon . . .

' *And Dicke the shepheard* '

The foddering boy along the crumping snows
With straw-band-belted legs and folded arm
Hastens, and on the blast that keenly blows
Oft turns for breath, and beats his fingers warm,

And shakes the lodging snows from off his clothes,
Buttoning his doublet closer from the storm
And slouching his brown beaver o'er his nose –
Then faces it agen, and seeks the stack
Within its circling fence where hungry lows
Expecting cattle, making many a track
About the snow, impatient for the sound
When in huge forkfulls trailing at his back
He litters the sweet hay about the ground
And brawls to call the staring cattle round.

JOHN CLARE

261

The wind blows cold, the weather's raw
The beggars now do skulk in straw,
Whilst those whose means are somewhat higher,
Do warm their noses by a fire.
Sack, *Hippocras*, now, and burnt brandy
Are drinks as warm and good as can be,
But if thy purse won't reach so high,
With ale and beer that want supply.

(1696)

'To make *Hypocras* the best way. Take 5 ounces of aqua vitae, 2 ounces of pepper, and 2 of ginger, of cloves and grains of paradice each 2 ounces, ambergrease three grains, and of musk two grains, infuse them 24 hours in a glass bottle on pretty warm embers and when your occasion requires to use it, put a pound of sugar into a quart of wine or cyder; dissolve it well, and then drop 3 or 4 drops of the infusion, and they will make it taste richly.'

For the purposes of transposing Walter de la Mare's great work into a paperback edition we were obliged to make two volumes out of the original book. These have been provided with a special slipcase to keep them together, but for any reader who may come across this first volume on its own we should like to point out that it is only half of the delights which Walter de la Mare collected.

Volume II of *Come Hither* contains 464 pages and the opening poem is No. 262 in the Collection – *Spring Quiet* by Christina Rossetti. (It also contains an Index of Authors and Poems.)